SEARCH FOR SECURITY

NORTHWESTERN UNIVERSITY African Studies

Number Five

Search for Security

An ethno-psychiatric study of Rural Ghana

M. J. FIELD

NORTHWESTERN UNIVERSITY
PRESS

CONTENTS

AUTHOR'S PREFACE

The romantic figure of the Noble Savage—gloriously glowing in rude but radiant physical health—was quickly banished into the realm of myth when Physical Medicine revealed that it was hardly possible to find in a primitive community any healthy person. Malaria, yaws, deficiency diseases, worms and other parasites were the basic burden which virtually every rural African had to learn to carry before he shouldered the additional economic and social demands of life. Egyptian peasants, for instance, regard the haematuria of bilharziasis as a sign of puberty.

But there still lingers the idea that mental stress and mental illness are the prerogative of "over-civilised" societies: that the simple savage may have Ancylostomiasis but cannot have Anxiety: that he may, in his innocence, believe his neighbour to be making bad magic against him, but he still sleeps like a top.

Nothing could be further from the truth. Whether the rural African has *more* mental illness than in the past—as he has, in the physical sphere, more venereal disease and more influenza—is another question. But mental illness, and plenty of it, is rooted in ancient tradition, though traditional habits of thought have other concepts for it.

In the nineteen-thirties, when I was carrying out various assignments of ethnographical field-work on behalf of the Gold Coast Government, I became aware of a widespread new movement, mainly in the forest-country. This was the springing up, like a crop of mushrooms, of new shrines, all designed to give supernatural protection and help to people increasingly preoccupied with a sense of insecurity. Among the pilgrim supplicants seen at those shrines were many who, even to the untutored eye, were mentally ill. Some were deluded, some hallucinated, some in morbid fear, others in exaggerated anxiety and so on. Some believed themselves bewitched, some felt themselves being changed into witches, others thought themselves already witches, mysteriously disseminating destruction. Their compatriots, invited by them to share their beliefs, readily did so: mental illness was not recognised as such, for it wore the garments of traditional ideology.

It became clear that the key to an understanding, not only of witchcraft but of many other preoccupations of unsophisticated people, was Clinical Psychiatry.

13

Then came the Second World War, and after it I was absent from West Africa for ten years. On returning in December 1955 (having meanwhile obtained a medical degree and some experience in Clinical Psychiatry), I found that the shrines, particularly in Ashanti, were still multiplying, and that they were still the first resort of people who had become in any way mentally ill, whether trivially or gravely.

I therefore made the shrines my source of rural cases of mental illness of recent onset. Though I worked at Ashanti shrines, the patients came from far and wide, thus offering a fair sample of all the Akan peoples of Ghana.

The chronic cases were Ashanti people, justly deemed "mad". These were not found at shrines: I sought them out in their own homes with the co-operation of various chiefs, village headmen and elders around my Ashanti base.

The picture of mental illness seen by the rural field-worker must be essentially different from that seen by the Mental Hospital Psychiatrist. The rural patient is never taken to the mental hospital, not because of any associated stigma, but because the illness is regarded as supernaturally determined and hence outside the province of hospitals. The only rural mental patients I have ever known to enter hospital were sent there by the Police Magistrate after homicidal assaults.

Of the treatment of patients at shrines I was only an observer. Through the courtesy of the priests I was permitted to witness the proceedings and to talk to patients and their relatives. Only in a very few cases where the patients were unable to co-operate in shrine treatment, or when such treatment had failed, did the relatives ever consult me. When, for instance, a mute patient could not confess his sins at the shrine, the priest would wash his hands of the case and the relatives would then sometimes ask me for "medicine to make him talk". The few sodium-amytal abreactions recorded among my case-histories were obtained under these conditions.

I have turned a deaf ear to those of my English friends who demand a chapter on Self-Government. They should know that rural people the world over—in Ghana no less than in England—know little and care less about any political upheaval short of military invasion or direct interference with their farms. Drought and blight concern them, but the birth of nations goes unnoticed.

Acknowledgments

My gratitude is due to the Medical Research Council for the grant which enabled the work to be carried out.

Author's Preface

To my Psychiatric mentor, Dr. E. H. Hare of the Maudsley Hospital, I render warm thanks, not only for his patient perusal of manuscript but for his broad-minded encouragement. But despite his kind and helpful criticisms the responsibility for the opinions expressed (many of which he would not endorse) is my own.

To the Chiefs of Badu, Nkyiraa, Offuman, Techiman and Wenchi (in alphabetical order) I am indebted for introductions to the priests of the shrines in their districts. From the priests and their elders I received not only help but repeated kindnesses and pleasant friendship.

In recording the previous histories of patients who had received hospital treatment for physical illnesses I had occasion to write to various hospitals and received painstaking and helpful replies from the Mission Hospitals at Agogo, Berekum, Hwediem, Techiman and Wenchi, and also from the Government Trypanosomiasis Unit at Kintampo. The Mission Hospital at Techiman is especially to be congratulated on the importance which it attaches to the keeping of records which may ultimately be used for research.

Dr. Auguste of Koforidna and Dr. Busby of Suhum also kindly gave me information concerning patients' previous physical illnesses.

When patients urgently in need of skilled physical treatment were willing to accept it, I always received most generous co-operation and help from either of the Mission Hospitals at Techiman or Wenchi.

For gifts of drugs administered to needy people—mostly children—in and around Mframaso I am indebted to the generosity of Wenchi Hospital, the Friends of Tarkwa Children, Mr. John Hall and Mr. Brian Brehaut.

To Dr. and Mrs. George Busby, who made me welcome to regard their home at Suhum as my own home, my warmest thanks are due.

I am also indebted for kind hospitality to the Rev. Robert and Mrs. Figures of the North Ashanti Mission.

My cheerful and indefatigable field-assistant, Mr. Emmanuel Okuampah, helped me in a great variety of ways—organising the building of a house, dispensing at the weekly clinic, recording routine "sheep" at formal *abisa*, extricating me from entanglements of Brong dialect, washing the Land Rover in rivers, smelling out new shrines and never losing our way in the forest. He made my interests his own, and I owe much to his active loyalty.

M. J. Field

Dulverton
Nov. 1958

EXPLANATORY GLOSSARY

(a) *Vernacular Terms*

abisa. Noun. Session before the shrine when supplicants make their requests and propound their problems (*bisa,* to ask).

Akan. Adjective. Those peoples of Ghana and the French Ivory Coast who speak various dialects of Twi and follow a matrilineal system of descent. They include most of the Ashanti, the Fante, Nzima, Akim, Kwahu and part of the Akwapim.

basa-basa. Adjective. Confused, disorganised, disorderly. To "talk *basa-basa*" is to talk deliriously or irrationally.

dunsini. Noun. Medicine-man who is not an *okomfo* but does divining with various apparatus, makes good *suman* and other reputable medicines and magics and is also a herbalist and physician.

gbeshi. Noun. Ga word denoting a spiritual entity, which abides in a person and determines his good or bad luck.

gwantoahene. Noun. Chief implorer operating at some shrines.

honhom. Noun. Generic term for spiritual beings, including all *abosom* and the Holy Ghost.

Kra. Noun. Usually translated "soul", but physical life depends on its presence and health on its intactness. Witches are thought to steal and feast on it, or on bits of it, causing the victim to die, become sick, barren, impotent, etc.

Kramu. Adjective used as noun. Moslem. *Kramu* medicine-men make both good and bad medicines by copying out bits of the Koran and giving the client the dissolved paper to drink. They also use all the indigenous methods.

Krontinhene. Noun. An auxiliary town chief.

mmoetia. Noun (singular *aboetia*). Mythical forest dwarfs, sometimes friendly familiars of certain people.

mpese-mpese. Noun used as adjective. Tassels of uncut, matted hair worn by an *okomfo, obosomfo* and *obrafohene* and by infants born after petition to an *obosom.*

17

nkotoba. Noun. Wooden clubs forming part of an *obosom brafo's* shrine insignia.

obayi. Noun. The evil spirit believed to abide in or about a witch, imparting power to do evil, fly by night, etc.

obayifo. Noun. Person having an *obayi.* I translate this word as "witch" from Anglo-Saxon *wicce* (feminine), *wicca* (masculine), originally from Gothic *veihan* (German *weihen*), to perform (rites).

obofohene. Noun. Head of the hunters.

obosom. Noun (plural *abosom*). Lesser deity. There are scores of these. All are believed sons and deputies of Onyame.

obosombrafo. Noun. An *obosom* who can be relied upon to punish sin by sickness or death.

obosomfo. Noun. Priest of an *obosom*. He may or may not be also an *okomfo*.

obrafohene. Noun. Chief executive officer of a shrine.

okomfo. Noun. Any person habitually or occasionally "possessed" by an *obosom* or *honhom* during which state of possession his utterances are taken as those of the *obosom*. Such possession is dissociation of personality.

Okyeame. Noun. Official spokesman of priest or chief.

Omanhene. Noun. Paramount chief.

Onyame. Noun. Sky-god, supreme God, almighty God.

sasa bonsam. Noun. Mythical forest monster.

sinkwafo. Noun. Shrine attendants, drummers, etc.

suman. Noun. Talisman, amulet or apparatus containing magical "medicine" or operative power. It may be for the prophylaxis and cure of disease, protection from enemies, help in hunting, etc., but may also be a bad *suman* supplied by a bad medicine-man for killing enemies.

sunsum. Noun. Mind, personality, intellect. This can absent itself in dreams or mind-wandering.

(b) *Technical Terms*

Coven. Archaic English word meaning a company or society of witches. From the same root: covey, covenant, Coventry.

Cross-cousins. Children of oppositely sexed siblings.

Delusion. A fixed, false belief of morbid origin, often absurd, unshakeable by argument or demonstration of its falsity or absurdity.

Depression. An illness of every degree of severity, characterised by low spirits, diminished mental and physical activity and feelings of worthlessness. Reactive depression is the result of external provocation (e.g., bereavement): endogenous depression has no obvious cause.

Dissociation. Mental mechanism whereby a split-off part of the personality temporarily possesses the entire field of consciousness and behaviour.

E.C.T. Electrical shock therapy.

Family. Strictly a bilateral kin group, but ethnologists should note that throughout this book I use the word not technically but loosely and popularly.

Hallucination. False subjective sense-impression (e.g., visions and voices) having no basis in the external world.

Ideas of Reference. The patient feels himself to be the topic of other people's conversation and the object of their disapproving observation.

Manic-depressive illness. Severe depression alternating with ill-judged overactivity and boisterous elation.

Misinterpretation. Sense-impression faultily interpreted (e.g., white cow, dimly seen at night, taken as a ghost).

N.a.d. Nil of note.

Neurosis. Illness of protean manifestations and all degrees of severity ultimately referable to faulty relations with other people. Appreciation of external reality is unaffected.

Obsessive-compulsive illness. The patient feels impelled against his will to carry out some unnecessary act such as repeated hand-washing, checking and re-checking, ruminating upon one idea or fear, etc. Some complain of sudden impulses, invariably successfully resisted, to make use of potential weapons, e.g. to use string for strangling. The pre-morbid personality is usually conscientious, meticulous, rigid, unadaptable and unready with decisions.

Projection. The attribution of subjective impressions to external causes.

Psychosis. Mental illness in which the whole personality becomes changed and the patient's appreciation of reality is impaired.

19

Schizophrenia. This does not mean split mind in the sense popularly supposed. It is a psychosis which if not arrested may progress to complete disintegration of the personality.

Sib. Clan; unilateral exogamous kinship group claiming descent from a common progenitor.

Siblings. Children of the same couple regardless of sex.

Part 1
THE BACKGROUND

I

THE SOCIAL, ECONOMIC
AND DOMESTIC BACKGROUND

§ 1. PREFACE

The purpose of this chapter is firstly to give the foreign reader, unfamiliar with standard West African works, a rough idea of what patients and supplicants are talking about when they refer to their towns, villages, homes, kinsmen and stools, and to their social, domestic and financial embarrassments; and secondly to exhibit some of the factors which may be supposed to determine the nature of mental ailments. All generalisations look foolish at the edges, and other observers will be able to quote exceptions to every one of the following statements—as indeed I abundantly could myself.

§ 2. TOWN AND VILLAGE

Apart from the few big cosmopolitan urban centres, the country is mainly agricultural and there are two kinds of life which farmers live. One is in the country-town and the other is in what is called the "village" (*akrowa, akura*).

Most country-towns are ancient, and till lately each was a democratic gerontocracy governed by a council of elders, each elder the head of a kinship group and holder of a small kinship "stool". The town "chief", with his own stool, was the chairman of this council, and he in turn was a member of a higher council of which the paramount chief of a federation* of country-towns was the chairman and organiser. Most country-towns had their own local gods, priests and religious festivals.

The country-towns were—and are—seldom urban in aspect. Farming was, and still is, carried on from the country-town on "stool land", the farmers having to trudge daily perhaps a few miles to the farms they

* *Oman*, usually translated "native state", but in its inception essentially a military federation.

had made by clearing forest. Some farms, though still on stool land, were so far out that it was convenient to make camps and return home only for festivals, funerals, family business and other occasions of social intercourse; such a permanent camp is called a "village". A man speaks of "my town" and "my village". When you go to look for a man in the place where he says he lives, you are frequently told, "He has gone to his village", and you may have to walk for some hours along forest footpaths till you find him. On the way, you will pass through several other "villages", each consisting of perhaps half a dozen small, rough mud-and-thatch buildings, where the people, who seldom have a visitor, will be delighted to see you and will shower kindly courtesies upon you.

When the land-hungry Adangmes and Akwapims—eager and indefatigable farmers—first took up cocoa-farming, they started the practice of buying distant tracts of land from other native states and making "villages" or groups of villages, scores or even hundreds of miles from their home-towns.* Such migrants usually returned home only for their annual religious festivals and for funerals.

Domestically, the important difference between the "home-town" and the "village" is that only in a village is one likely to find a household consisting only of man, wife and children.

In the home-towns of the Akan peoples (who are matrilineal), households are very large. Each consists, traditionally and usually in practice, of a man who is the head of the house, his younger brothers and sisters by one mother and the children of the sisters and of the sisters' daughters. The point to bear in mind is that men do not live with their wives. When a man marries, both he and his bride stay with their own mothers and maternal uncles and aunts. The wife goes to her husband at night. She cooks for him, on her own personal fireplace, in her own ancestral home, and takes or sends by a child the cooked meals to his home. A man provides for his wife and children: the number of fireplaces in a large compound shows the number of such economic units. Architecturally, the household is a central courtyard entirely surrounded by

---

* Sometimes migrants clustered closely in their new colonial area and built what superficially looked like a large new country-town. The huge cocoa-centre of Suhum in Akim was (till the death of the cocoa) really an enormous "village" built by migrant Akwapims who considered themselves as merely camping. Suhum never had a chief—only an *odikro* or headman—and the Suhum people had —and have—their "home-towns" and kinship ties in Akwapim.

The bloodless conquest of Akim by Akwapim and Adangme migrant farmers has been the most impressive social spectacle for the last fifty years, but not being amenable to study by the intensive method has been entirely overlooked by orthodox anthropologists.

rooms opening into it. A married man has a lock-up room of his own. The rooms are seldom entered except at night and everyone lives in the yard. Kitchens and sometimes a reception room are three-walled.

When cross-cousin marriage is practised—that is, when a man gives his daughter in marriage to his sister's son—this means the marriage of a couple who are already under the same roof.

Neither do the patrilineal Ga and Adangme live with their wives. There are the men's houses containing sons of the same father, *their* sons and their grandsons. The sisters and daughters of these men, together with their young children, live in a women's house, cooking for husbands in various parts of the town and going to them at night.

Both these systems allow a man to have several wives who may seldom come into contact with one another. The wives take turns to sleep with the husband and to cook for him.

A section of the Akwapim State consists of patrilineal people following a third arrangement whereby the head of a household has all his wives and male descendants with *their* wives in one house with him. When the sons marry they bring home their brides: when the daughters marry they leave. Widowed or divorced daughters or sons' daughters have a right to come back.

All three systems result in large ancestral households, not individually owned, in the home-town. But when a man first goes far afield to farm and founds a "village", he takes his wife and her children, and only in such villages are we likely to find the "elementary family". Later, the Akan man will probably bring one or more of his sister's sons and gradually a larger kinship group will grow up. The elementary family always seems to go against the grain of these gregarious sociable people.

§ 3. CLASS, SUCCESSION AND INHERITANCE

There has never been in Ghana a ruling class descended from foreign invaders and regarded as having blood different from and bluer than that of the populace. In Nigeria there has, and it was this which made "Indirect Rule" possible. Its absence in Ghana made the attempt to imitate Nigerian Indirect Rule a rollicking brawl of de-stoolments, the chiefs finding it impossible to serve two masters—their own electorate and the European concept of chieftainship. In Akan Ghana, from the Volta to the French Ivory Coast, there existed (and still exist) about a dozen exogamous clans, none more royal than another. Each town had a number of elders' stools, each elder was the elected head of a group of clansmen. One such stool, more highly sanctified by past warfare and human blood than the rest, was the chief's, and he was the chairman of the council of elders who ruled the town. In one town the chief's stool might belong to Clan A, in the next to Clan B, or to any other of the existing dozen. The chief, like the other elders, was elected by his own kinsmen, but if the town disapproved of their choice they had to choose again. If after due trial a Chief or Elder was unsatisfactory he was de-stooled. One of the commonest grounds of de-stoolment was the arrogation to himself by the chief of more personal authority than the electorate conceded.* But a chief of high personal qualities was valued as he deserved and given a burden of irksome responsibility which he did not deserve.

There was once a considerable population of slaves, but there was also a continuous process of absorption of slaves into the clans. The slave population has now disappeared without any trace beyond occasional whisperings about people's "origins". The whisperings are mostly those of envy, the "origin" having proved no bar to the attainment of rank—even, in some cases, chieftainship—and unlimited prestige.

Succession to the headship of smaller kinship groups, like that of succession to stools, is a matter of selection by a council of kinsmen. The custodianship of family property similarly is awarded to him—or even to her—who is deemed most likely to administer it wisely and unselfishly. There are no rigid rules that must be followed. In the disposal of the self-acquired property of an intestate dead man, an industrious wife who has helped him to clear and work a cocoa-farm is just as likely to be awarded a share of it as is a graceless next of kin. The discretion of the council has the utmost latitude.

The point which I have here been trying to emphasise, in this necessarily over-simplified picture, is the absence of hide-bound rigidity. Class hardly exists; rank does exist but its attainment is the reward of individual merit. Institutions were made for man. Nothing is immune from criticism. Justice is more than Law. The spirit of the law is more than the letter. Of course, this adaptability and flexibility cut both ways: the self-seeking opportunist has no hampering scruples. One cannot hope for the same undeviating reliability possessed by the rigid and meticulous.

* The idea that Britain introduced democracy into West Africa is quite erroneous. On the contrary, Britain did much to destroy the indigenous democracy. Neither is the idea of an opposition a new one. Alongside every chief was a *mankrado* or *krontinhene* of whom it was said "every *mankrado* is opposed to the chief".

We shall return to this matter of freedom from rigidity when we come to consider mental illnesses.

§ 4. SONS AND NEPHEWS

Among the rural matrilineal peoples it is not easy to assess the amount of modern antagonism between a man's hereditary obligations towards his sister's children and his frequent tendency to favour his own children, The husband–wife bond is still regarded as an ephemeral thing compared with the congenital brother–sister bond. A woman may not even know who is the father of her child, but she does know that her brother will always be its uncle. A man values his sister's sons as his own successors to hereditary obligations and custodianships—such as the headship of an ancestral household—and he values his sister's daughters as the perpetuators of his blood. But since cocoa and other modern enterprises began to bring big financial rewards to individual effort, self-acquired property, with the individual's right to dispose of it as he likes, has undermined the status of family-owned property and its inherent heavy kinship obligations. The rival claims upon a man of his nephews and his sons are a matter, not for a work of this kind, but for a detailed "social study", but there is one aspect which should be mentioned because it is often in the minds of people who frequent shrines, the people usually beset with a feeling of insecurity and a fear of envious machinations. They say that a son loves his father too much to kill him for the sake of the inheritance, whereas he has no such sentiments regarding his uncle.

In spite of the housing arrangements in home-towns, most fathers adore their infant children, carry them about, play with them, indulge them, give them tit-bits of food and praise them to their faces. One ailing child whose parents were on bad terms and whose father was seldom at home was pronounced by the priest to be "getting no *sunsum* from its father". I was surprised, at my weekly clinic* at Mframaso, to see how often it was the fathers and not mothers who brought children for treatment. The small child regards its father as its natural worshipper—unlike the greedy uncle in its own house who sits alone, unfeeling and godlike, at a little low table in the yard and eats a sumptuous meal—for the quality of food eaten is an index to the eater's status. The child returns its father's affection, and some remnant of this bond persists through life. The child does, of course, perceive that the mother sends

* This began as a yaws clinic at the request of the people themselves.

better meals to the father than she gives to the children,* but it is from the tantalising daily proximity of the full-fed uncle that the child gets its reiterated trauma.

§ 5. STATUS OF CHILDREN

In general the infant and the toddler are, by everybody, petted, indulged, admired and applauded on occasions from which they would, in Europe, be excluded. Dignified elders sometimes sit at councils dandling infants. I have seen a shrine *abisa* held up while an infant, not old enough to walk, "danced" to the exciting sound of the drums by travelling rapidly round the yard on its bottom, pumping its arms up and down in faultless rhythm, while the priest and the elders convulsed themselves with pleasure. More than once I saw a toddler with a well-developed sense of rhythm, but hardly enough muscular control to hold the drumsticks, struggling to beat one of the deity's drums and being accorded delighted admiration and patient tuition by a shrine Elder.

But one of the most striking features in the African attitude to the child is the contrast between the lavish affection meted out to infants and toddlers and the harsh disregard which is the lot of most older children†. The adored small child has to suffer the trauma of growing into an object of contempt—even in the eyes of its father. "Small boy" is an opprobrious epithet. A child of either sex is still sometimes sent to live with relatives or others to whom the parent is under special obligation and is there made to work virtually as a little slave. A proverb runs, "It is unpleasant to be a child." Particularly is it unpleasant in the matter of food. Any food which fills the belly is considered good enough for children.

To what extent, if any, the traumatic transition from indulgence to contempt, capricious severity and deprivation lays the foundation of the prevalent sense of persecution I do not know. The age of rejection by the father and the elder sister does not coincide with the birth of a younger sibling, but is later. The father continues to indulge the toddler, and the elder sister to carry it round affectionately on her back, while

---

* In African societies, if a child resents the mother's relations with the father it is less likely to be because she sleeps with him than because she pampers him with food.

† The *possession* of children remains a gratification. Parenthood is more highly valued than marriage, even by educated girls.

the mother suckles the younger child. A man's attachment to and respect for his elder sister often survives throughout their lives.

§ 6. COCOA

It is no part of my business to describe the cocoa industry, but it is necessary to mention that from its start at the turn of the century cocoa-growing has been in the hands of countless independent African farmers who themselves cleared patches of forest of all sizes to plant the trees. After about eight years, with luck and little further attention, the trees yielded an annual gift of money, at first regarded as hardly belonging to this world and quite literally only "to play with". The people who cleared cocoa-farms were enterprising individuals and the cocoa-money had no traditional obligations attached to it. For a whole population of illiterate tribesmen the cocoa industry meant a venture into rewarding individual effort and a breakaway from the old tribal security based on traditional rôles, kinship solidarity and mutual obligation. The old tribal safeguards designed for other days and other ways soon came to be thought inadequate, and between 1910 and 1925, during which years the country's annual cocoa output rose from about 21,000 tons to 206,000 tons, the earliest of the modern protection-shrines was established. These shrines have grown in number parallel to the growing cocoa output. As my case-histories will later show, most rural envy and strife concerns cocoa-profits and the inheritance of cocoa-farms and cocoa-wealth. There is a new proverb, "Cocoa has not shown us the good man."

There are, of course, other and heavier new stresses than cocoa, especially for literates (whose number is now generally estimated at ten per cent of the population), but cocoa remains the widest spread and concerns the mass of illiterate rural people.

There can be no doubt that in spite of seasonal bursts of spending on luxuries cocoa has lowered the basic standards of living and nutrition. It has diverted attention from subsistence farming: the habit of steady diligence has declined. This is not true of the relatively landless Akwapims and Adangmes, whom cocoa has stimulated to heroic efforts of earning and land-buying. Some of the once richly landed Akims from whom the incomers have steadily bought land have reached a pitch of indolence and consequent physical wretchedness which is—or was when I knew them—shocking.

§ 7. ECONOMIC STATUS OF WOMEN

Women are expected to help their husbands on their food farms and to market surplus food-stuffs on the husband's behalf. ("Since God created the world," I heard a possessed priest say to a peevish woman supplicant, "have you ever heard of a wife who didn't help her husband?") But the women also have their own market-gardens and send or take loads of produce to urban centres. They often also have cocoa-farms where they employ labourers—migrants from the Northern Territories. In the home-towns they have their pitches in the market-place, trading in fruit and vegetables, home-made confectionery, haberdashery and imported household commodities. They are—unless quite devoid of "drive"—economically independent. Few wives cannot say to defaulting husbands, "If you want me to leave you, dismiss me at once: I knew how to buy my own headkerchiefs before I met you." Further, there are countless occasions on which women may demand money and ceremonial gifts from their men-folk, but custom enjoins only negligible disimbursements upon women.

By and large, men are improvident and open-handed, women both more reliable and close-fisted, for women have a very early training in the scrupulous handling of small sums. Little girls of four may be seen in the markets selling such wares as kenkey-dumplings, for each one of which they have to account to their mothers.

§ 8. ECONOMIC PASSENGERS

In the forest-country, life at a bare subsistence level is not difficult to maintain. There is no struggle for sheer existence as the northern hinterland of Ghana knows it, and as farm-labourers in England knew it when they brought up families on fifteen shillings a week before the First World War. The population is sparse, the land rich and well watered. Land for cultivation or house-building is free: houses can be built of materials which cost nothing: no warm clothing is necessary. The staple starchy food-crops, once planted, require little attention till they are ready to harvest, and most of them when harvested can be stored. Very few farmers except migrants do anything approaching the amount of work of which they are capable. Those who do choose to work harder than the rest become richer than the rest and inevitably acquire a retinue of partially or totally inadequate hangers-on.

The body of economic passengers which the community carries is considerable. This body contains very few women, for most women produce more than they consume. Old people, too, if they have been industrious, usually have an income from the land they cleared and planted when they were active, which income they share with those who now do the work. Perhaps the most heavily consuming sub-group within the dependent group are the young unemployed literates, disappointed that their literacy had not made them rich and great in some branch of pensionable government service. Each of these literates is fed, clothed, housed and sometimes married at the expense of the illiterate person who paid for his schooling. This supporter may be a father, uncle, grandfather, elder brother or mother, who, having made an unprofitable investment, is now philosophically resigned to throwing good money after bad.

While I was in Mframaso a literate from the next village came to see me and asked for work. He came on a very good bicycle: he said he was twenty-eight and had done no work since leaving school, except a spell of pupil-teaching, from which he was dismissed for seducing a girl. His illiterate elder brother, who had paid for his schooling, thereafter supported him, his wife and his three children. I gave him work of sorts by sending him on his bicycle to surrounding country-towns and villages* where he collected for me the names and particulars of fellow unemployed literates.

He went initially to the chief or headman of each place. Some cooperated, some were suspicious and did not. The list is therefore by no means complete, but I have the names of 182 unemployed literates all within twenty miles of my base.

I did not seek out and interview the persons on this list, but a few of them happened to be known to me. These included two undoubted schizophrenics, both young teachers who had lost their jobs through unsatisfactory work. Only one of these two had behaved queerly enough for his relatives to regard him as mad, though he was well-enough preserved to talk about wanting work. The other (who does not appear in my survey of chronic schizophrenics) had simply become more and more dreamy, forgetful and withdrawn. It is most unlikely that these two were the only sub-clinical schizophrenics who had been tried and proved unemployable.

Of the total 182 whose names my friend collected, 92 were under twenty and had a good chance of obtaining and keeping work if they sought it and applied themselves to it. But the remaining 90 were of all

* No attempt was made upon the three large towns Wenchi, Techiman and Badu.

ages between twenty and thirty, 29 were married and 54 had had jobs which they lost. The reasons they gave for stopping work were:

Sickness	3
Dislike of the work	12
"Redundant" or "terminated"	20
Insufficient pay	2
"No reason"	17

Probably the greatest shock to the newly educated African in paid employment is the discovery that he has to work all day and every day.

Although 29 claimed to be doing *some* farm work, only 8 claimed to be self-supporting. Invariably the supporting relative was the one who had financed the schooling. All such relatives save one, a clerk, were illiterate and 172 were farmers. The rest were 2 chiefs, 2 priests, 1 blacksmith, 1 trader, 1 motor mechanic, 1 driver and 1 goldsmith.

§ 9. STANDARD OF LIVING

It is ingrained in the rural population that basic subsistence is sustained by food from the farm. In "villages" people can and often do exist for long spells without spending money, and at the back of even the urban mind is the feeling that money, with all its exciting possibilities, was not made to be squandered on basic necessities. Money is a luxury and meant to be spent on life's greater gratifications, particularly the enhancement of prestige.

An industrious and fortunate cocoa-farmer may make up to thousands of pounds in a year, but seldom is any of this spent on raising the basic standards of living. He may have a sumptuous car and a driver, a wireless-set, a carpeted sitting-room (seldom entered), a steel safe, a three-storey block of shops and offices in Accra or Kumasi, sons and nephews reading Law or Medicine in England or America, but he lives and eats as his fathers did—in a squalid yard where women cook on the ground and naked children swarm, crawl, and eat dirt. The children may have expensive little imported tricycles, but they have yaws, worms, ringworm and deficiency diseases as freely as other children. The man may have several more wives than his less affluent neighbours, but the wives' way of life is the old one.

The house may be of concrete and sheet-iron instead of mud and thatch, but its design and the pattern of life in it remains unchanged. I have more than once been struck by the apparent want and pathetic poverty of some old woman inhabiting a tumbledown grass-roofed hovel in a forest "village" but have later learnt that she was wealthy. One such woman drew £70 a month rent for business premises which she owned in Accra.

Where does most of the cocoa-money go? Enormous sums are spent on funerals. Cars and lorries account for much: the latter are often run at a loss by young kinsmen. Rich men also subsidise young relatives who are setting up in business or training for—it is hoped, lucrative—careers. They engage in litigation. And they spend incredible sums in travelling about the country to medicine-men and shrines for the treatment of the mental and physical ills of themselves and their dependants. And always there is a remorseless, and usually irresistible, pressure upon them to lend money to people who seldom have much hope, and never any desire, of repaying. "To raise a loan" is such a frequent and absorbing concern that there is even a special personal name reserved for a child who is born on the happy day when this is achieved.

The enthusiastic Akwapim and Adangme migrant farmers, who have practised land-buying and large-scale cocoa-growing in Akim for fifty years, frequently have no idea of using their wealth for any purpose other than further land-buying. As they are prolific people, they usually have sons and grandsons ready to take up work on this new land. The price of land bought by migrants is still rocketing and new purchases absorb extensive wealth. People farming on the "stool land" of their own country-towns pay nothing for the land they farm.

§ 10. QUALITY OF FOOD

The staple food throughout the country is starch, usually starchy roots —yam, cassava, etc., but sometimes green plantain, and a relatively small amount of maize.* The latter has a fair mineral content, the former virtually nil. There is evidence that in bygone times the staple food was

* In about 1937 the late Douglas Benzies of the (now defunct) Prince of Wales College, Achimota, organised a social survey of the purely urban slum quarter of Accra. A large team of his workers questioned some hundreds of people concerning their daily expenditure and their daily food. The results were given to me for analysis. It was found that the poorest people of all lived entirely on starchy food (cassava, yam or maize balls). The slightly better-off added some other vegetable made into a thin gruel or soup, the best-off of all added a third component—protein in the form of meat, fish, eggs. As I was at that time teaching Chemistry to Engineering Degree students and First M.B. (both courses now defunct and not yet resurrected by the new University College) I had access to a well-equipped laboratory and was able to supplement the survey with an investigation into the purchasing power of money at the local markets in terms of food values. The resultant paper, of which no copy had been made, was lent to the Director of Medical and Sanitary Services, Gold Coast, who lost it.

millet, but as millet is more trouble to grow and protect from birds it has been entirely ousted by starchy roots, except in the Northern Territories, in some regions of which the staple food—millet-porridge—especially when supplemented with milk (another food unknown except among the Northern Territories tribes), perhaps partly accounts for the well-developed bony skeletons of these people, though the genetic factor is probably the cardinal one.* The Trans-Volta people grow and eat beans of various kinds and seem the better for it. Coastal people eat plenty of fish and are noticeably healthier than inland people, though here again there are factors other than diet. The dried salt fish which the fishwives send inland is there used chiefly in very small amounts as a flavouring for stews rather than in nutritive quantities.

By and large it may be said that the coastal people and the migrant farmers—the Akwapim and Adangme—are well fed and vigorous, the Ashanti and Akim very poorly fed. The two latter groups were for generations almost entirely preoccupied with warfare and left subsistence farming entirely to the women. There is still some inclination to do the latter.

§ 11. MEALS

In most districts people eat three times a day and usually reckon to do several hours' work in the day before eating anything. In Mframaso I found that many of my neighbours ate only twice daily, the first meal at eleven or twelve o'clock, the last at sundown.

In general the concept of good nourishment is virtually absent: it is known, of course, that life cannot be preserved without food, but the dependence of health on the quality of food is not appreciated. That food is transformed by physiological processes into body substance is too materialistic an idea to be entertained. A woman came from a village to my clinic bringing four children and asking for medicine because "their bodies were weak". And indeed they were: their limbs were but little sticks and they could hardly walk for fatigue. I asked what food she gave them: she replied, cocoa-yam. I inquired what else, but there was nothing else. She was wholly unable to accept, or even consider the suggestion, that cocoa-yam was insufficient: she said they were "only children". I always found it necessary when prescribing good food for convalescent children to diagnose a sulky *kra* which needed propitiation with pleasing food.

* The Northern Territories people, unlike the forest Ghanians, know famine, shortage and hunger, but their staple food, when obtainable at all, is of good food value.

II

THE IDEOLOGICAL BACKGROUND*

§ 1. WITCHCRAFT

The Akan word usually translated as "witch" is *obayifo*, meaning a person who is the abode of an evil entity, the *obayi*.

These witches, in contemporary West African belief, are associated with a secret religious cult of their own. No such cult in fact exists, but the belief in its existence is probably based on remote fact and represents a garbled fragmentary tradition of a widespread pre-agricultural religion,† long superseded. It is believed that covens of witches—numbering usually between ten and twenty—under a group leader, hold secret nocturnal meetings in inaccessible places and travel to these gatherings by flying through the air or by riding on antelopes, leopards and owls. The meetings are cannibalistic feasts: the bodies of the witches' victims are cut up, cooked in a pot (the *bayiseaa*) and eaten. The rank of a witch in the company or coven (*fekuw*) determines whether he or she shall receive the head, the trunk, the hands and so on. Some believers in the cult maintain that the reason for the co-operative group is to enable witches to share in eating victims of other kinship groups, since any one witch can kill only from among her own flesh and blood. It is not, however, universally held that a witch can kill only her own kin.

The fact that a witch has been demonstrably asleep on her mat throughout the night she is supposed to have spent in feasting, and the fact that the corpse of her victim, slain supposedly by witchcraft, has clearly suffered no cannibalistic ravages, are covered by African dogma. It is the spirit of the witch that leaves her sleeping body and flies to the meeting place. It is not the victim's material body but his vital *kra* which is eaten by the witches.

* The purpose of this chapter is not to assess the relative influence of this or that institution but simply to make later chapters intelligible.

† The late Palaeolithic period of Europe has been linked with the Capsian, which is of African origin.

The entity called the *kra* (often translated "soul") is thought of in various ways, but when associated with witchcraft theory is usually pictured as an invisible double and as the essence of physical life. Though a person's *sunsum* (mind, spirit) may leave his body in dreams or in mind-wandering without ill-effects, the *kra* cannot leave without causing sickness and death. If the witches steal away a man's *kra* and cut it up, he becomes mortally sick. If they then relent, reassemble the parts and restore them to him, he recovers. If, however, they have already eaten, say a leg, and hence cannot restore it, he recovers except for a permanently useless leg. If the witches steal only that part of the *kra* corresponding to the womb or the penis, the victim becomes either barren or impotent.

Besides causing illness, death and sterility, witches are also believed to blight crops and to cause accidents, financial losses, ill-luck and disasters of all kinds. Often they are held to bring their male relatives to ruin by making them into drunkards.

Witchcraft must not be confused with other supernatural and evil ways of causing trouble and death. Curses, charms, prayers and bad magics all have their place, but they involve ritual acts and sometimes concrete apparatus. The distinguishing feature of killing or harming by witchcraft is that it is wrought solely by the silent, invisible projection of influence from the witch. Furthermore, she has usually no conceivable motive and bears no ill-will towards her victim. She kills and injures not those to whom it would be natural to wish harm or death but those in whose well-being she may have the deepest interest. This is incomprehensible and therefore the more sinister. No one is surprised to find wickedness among wicked people, but to find it professed by hitherto good and kindly people is mystifying and appalling.

According to witchcraft dogma, a person can possess an *obayi* without awareness of it, and can furthermore use it harmfully without knowing of it. This idea stems, as we shall see later, from the fact that patients suffering from severe depression are, the world over, unshakeably convinced of their own worthlessness and wickedness and irrationally accuse themselves of having committed every unforgivable sin. In Africa the worst sin they can imagine is witchcraft, and they insist that they have abundantly committed it. A witch spontaneously declares that it is she who killed every kinsman whose death she can recall, who ate all the dead infants, who blighted the dead cocoa-trees and engineered all the lorry-accidents. The European counterpart of the self-accused witch often gives herself up to the police. The last of such seen personally by me told the police that she had caused, by her sin, the death of her vicar and had brought disasters to her brother. She also said she was responsible for the illnesses of all the other patients in the hospital.

Although witches are believed able to exert their destructive influence upon their victims from any distance, however great, it is held that the indwelling *obayi* which does the evil work can be initially implanted in the witch only by personal contact with some other witch or by contact with some material object transferred from the other. A favourite vehicle is food, particularly red palm-oil soup. A string of beads or other trinket is another. A self-accused witch will say, "The *obayi* was given me by my aunt. When she came to stay with me she cooked some soup one day and gave some to me. Some weeks—or months—after she had gone home I began to feel ill and miserable and then I knew that she must have given me an *obayi* in the soup." Or the "confession" may run, "My grandmother was a witch and when she died she left me some ear-rings. Later on, when I became a witch, I realised that the *obayi* must have come to me from my grandmother in the ear-rings." Another may say, "My mother had been a witch, and when she was dying and I bent over her she breathed her *obayi* from her mouth into mine with her last breath. I became very sad and ill after her death, and soon I knew that I was a witch and the *obayi* had come from my dying mother." It must be noted that it is only in retrospect that the witch decides whence her *obayi* came.

Every *obayi* is held to have a name. A witch cannot be freed from her *obayi* until she has disclosed its name. There are a number of traditional names for *obayi* (just as Towser, Fido and Spot are traditional English names for dogs), and when asked her *obayi's* name the self-accused witch simply produces one of these. Almost the only things which shrine secretaries think it important to record concerning witchcraft cases are the names of the *obayi*. Sometimes a witch feels that she has several *obayi*.

A few people, it is held, are born witches. The *obayi* comes from the mother into the pregnant womb. Such congenital witches are the worst kind and little can be done to cure them. "Curing them is like plucking a live fowl: after a time the feathers grow again."

Although the belief in societies of witches flying and travelling on animals to nocturnal gatherings almost certainly stems from a forgotten cult, practised not only in Africa but in Europe, it seems quite certain that the idea of eating children, with its attendant abhorrence, has been reinforced from time to time by historic fact. Not only in Africa but in other countries in and around the Arabian Peninsula such cannibalism has been practised in times of famine or siege, evoking a horror which appears to have left an impression on ideology persisting to this day. "And the king said unto her, What aileth thee? And she answered, This woman said unto me, Give thy son that we may eat him to-day, and we will eat my son to-morrow. So we boiled my son, and did eat him: ... And it came to pass, when the king heard the words of the woman, that he rent his clothes."* Here we have an undoubted pact between women to share the flesh of their children.

All this, however, pertains to the African theory of witchcraft. The point here to be emphasised is that no body of dogma alone would suffice to sustain, down the centuries, an *active* belief in witchcraft, with the associated elaborate and costly prophylactic and therapeutic organisations. This is kept alive by that mental illness which Psychiatry calls Depression and the fantastic delusions of sin and guilt which beset the patients. Witchcraft meets, above all else, the depressive's need to steep herself in irrational self-reproach and to denounce herself as unspeakably wicked. If Depression were stamped out, I doubt if even the drunkards and other paranoid failures, with their urge to project blame on others, could keep witchcraft alive. They would probably prefer to blame the more comprehensible machinations of their envious rivals. For people do *in fact* hate their rivals, and do *in fact* often go to Kramu medicine-men and buy bad magics to use against them. Witchcraft exists only in fantasy, in the minds of certain mentally sick people, and is a bewilderment to others. It is therefore likely that, if Depression were to die out, belief in witchcraft would die out also, and the "social function" of witchcraft (of "providing something to blame when things go wrong")† would be taken over by the less perplexing institution of bad magic.

The psychiatric aspect of African witchcraft throws light into some of the dark places in the history of British witchcraft.‡

It has been well established, mainly by the scholarly work of Murray, that the concept and ideology of witchcraft in Britain had its original basis in the survival of a pre-Christian religious cult of great—probably pre-agricultural—antiquity, practised as a persecuted, "underground" movement concurrently with Christianity. But long after this movement had died out and secret meetings and rites had ceased, vague and fabulous ideas about the evil supernatural powers of witches continued

* II Kings vi, 28. See also Deuteronomy xxviii, 53–57, and Jeremiah xix, 9.
† M. Fortes, *Man*, vol. LI, 1956, 172.
‡ M. A. Murray, *The Witch-cult in Western Europe*. Oxford, 1921.

to prevail. It became the custom, when cows aborted, swine took fever, crops failed, floods rose and people perished, to look around for a witch. It has been a matter for much modern bewilderment that the guilt was almost always laid at the door of some lonely, poor and wretched old woman, hitherto submerged in humdrum insignificance. The explanation suggested by the witchcraft of West Africa is that the old woman voluntarily asserted and insisted upon her guilt.*

This is further supported by facts which confront us in the mental hospitals of Britain to-day. There is no more familiar figure in the admission wards than the agitated depressive, weighed down with extravagant and unshakeable self-reproach. Two actual cases must here suffice to show that we have in our midst to-day in Britain people who proclaim, as a spontaneous unlearned response unconditioned by—indeed flying in the face of—their encompassing culture, that they are the very stuff of witchcraft.

Case 1. Mrs. H., a married woman of sixty-nine, was admitted to hospital with a six-month history of increasing depression, sleeplessness and loss of weight. She was in great distress but was rational and gave a moderately good account of herself. She said she could hear accusing voices telling her that she was not fit to live. She said of her mother, who had died forty-five years earlier, "I think I broke her heart", and of her husband's poor health, "It is my fault. He has been a lovely husband and I have been a rotten wife." She said that for her misdeeds she would be hanged. She also declared that she had brought harm to the whole hospital. In terrified apprehension she cowered in corners and tried to hide, thinking she heard the approach of those who were coming to hang her. This picture of guilt and fear is the one often exhibited by African "witches".

She was treated with a short course of E.C.T. and made a dramatic and complete recovery.

Case 2. Mrs. B., a widow of fifty-five, was admitted in an agitated depression. She was retarded, speaking slowly in a whisper. She covered her face, wrung her hands and moaned. The content of her speech was exclusively self-abasing. "I have brought destruction. . . . I'm ashamed. . . . I did it without thinking. . . . I've defied the Lord. . . . No one else

* It is strange that of all the writers on British witchcraft only one (so far as I know), Nigel Balchin, has approached an explanation in terms of mental illness. He writes: "The accused were usually poor and ignorant people who shared the general belief in the reality of witchcraft. Often the evidence suggests that they were feeble-minded or otherwise mentally abnormal." Nigel Balchin, *The Anatomy of Villainy*. Collins, 1950.

has been so wicked as I have. . . . Why should all these people have to suffer for me? I don't know how to put my head in the air at all. . . . I'm not fit to speak to you. . . . All the floods and all the war: it must be me to blame."

She was treated with a course of six E.C.T. shocks. After three she was able to smile, speak freely and help with the ward work, but when told that she would soon be well still replied, "I don't think so: I've done harm to so many people." After three more shocks, she had completely recovered and was discharged.

It needs but little imagination to picture the reception of such self-accusations three centuries ago.

§ 2. "MAGIC"

Classical Anthropology distinguishes between religion and magic by saying that religion involves a deity whom man implores, magic involves forces which man commands. This fundamental distinction still stands. It may be added, first that religion usually postulates a deity who is good and who demands goodness, whereas magic is of two kinds, good and bad. Furthermore, a deity generally has at his disposal a diversity of blessings and punishments, whereas each special magic is directed to one narrowly circumscribed end, such as killing an enemy or making a house immune to lightning.

As might be expected, there is some antagonism between magic and religion, for magics, unlike deities, make no moral demands and, above all, will operate automatically and inexorably for any operator provided only that he operates correctly. Therein magic exhibits an affinity with science. But the similarity goes no further, for scientific procedure is built up on strict observation of facts, whereas magical procedure has no such basis.

Magic, or, as it is more often called in West Africa, "medicine", always involves concrete apparatus (usually called *suman*) and a ritual in which this apparatus is handled. There is no activity in life which cannot be assisted by medicine. A hunter can medicine his gun and his bullets to make them unerring, his dog to make it fleet, himself to make him invisible. A blacksmith can medicine his tools, a fisherman his canoe and nets, a lorry-driver his lorry. A suitor can medicine himself to make his charms irresistible.

Good medicine, which includes in its many branches the therapy of illness, divining and the manufacture of good *suman*, is practised by respected men termed *adunsini*. There were two in Mframaso and they often worked in collaboration with the *obosom*. For instance, if a mental patient was unable to make a confession at the shrine by reason of muteness, medicine would be made to help him to speak. One of these two *adunsini* made large sums of money before the General Election (when strife and bloodshed were anticipated) by medicining people—at £10 a head—to make them immune from bullet and cutlass wounds.

Bad magics for killing or harming others can be obtained only from bad medicine-men. They involve such objects as string, padlocks and needles, the essence of which is sent to "tie", "lock up" or "pierce" the victim. Usually when a culprit is caught with a bad medicine he says he has bought it from a Kramu (Moslem) medicine-man.

A potential bad magic is possessed by all ceremonially unclean (menstruating) women. Such women are not allowed near shrines, near good *suman* or near any medicinal object. Water or cloth which has been in contact with the pudenda can be used not only to destroy good supernatural influences but also maliciously to procure positive evil.

The traditional kinds of *suman* and medicines have been fully described by various ethnographers, so I will describe here only a new importation (I suspect from India) which must be classified as a magic or medicine and which first came to my notice in taking case-histories. This is a book called *The Sixth and Seventh Book of Moses*★ which must be classed as an ambivalent magic designed to commend itself to literates. It claims to be a collection of translations of ancient and mediaeval treatises, originally in Hebrew, concerning "Moses' Magical Spirit Art". It is profusely illustrated with black-and-white representations of "Seals", "Tables", "Magic Circles", "Schemhamforas", "Semiphoras" and so on. Every seal or table is accompanied by a "conjuration" or recitation, for instance:

> I, N.N., a servant of God, call upon Thee, desire and conjure Thee, O Spirit Anoch, by the wisdom of Solomon, by the obedience of Isaac . . . and by the most terrible words Dallia, Dollia, Dollion, Corfuselas, Jazy . . . to appear before me in a beautiful human form and give me what I desire. (This the conjuror must name.)

★ The publisher is anonymous. The book is now, I am told, banned by the Government, presumably because its frequent use by incipient schizophrenics in cemeteries at night led the Government to believe that its use caused madness. Popularly it is believed that the user, by its aid, raises spirits of the dead which he is unable to dismiss.

To the description of each seal is appended some such statement as: "Carrying this seal will cause you to be very agreeable and much beloved and will also defeat all your enemies." However, some of the procedures are beset with practical difficulties:

> The Seals or general characters of The Seven Great Princes of Spirits must be written upon virgin parchment with the blood of butterflies at the time of the full moon. . . .

Although a "beautiful human form" is the guise in which most spirits are expected, this monotony is not unmitigated.

> Aziel is a very prompt treasure-spirit of the earth and of the sea. He appears in the form of a wild ox.
>
> Ariel is a very serviceable spirit and appears in the form of a ferocious dog. . . .
>
> Marbuel appears in the form of an old lion. . . .
>
> Barbuel is a master of all arts and all secret knowledge, a great master of all treasure. . . . He . . . appears in the form of a wild hog.
>
> Anituel appears in the form of a serpent of Paradise. He confers great wealth and honours according to wish.

The book contains masses of closely printed editorial commentary of platitudinous and unexceptionable piety; nevertheless one section is headed:

Tabellae Rabellinae
Spiriti—Commando
id est
Magiae albae et nigrae citatio generalis
Upon all Spirits, Good and Evil.

This chapter opens with a list of about fifty names of spirits, adding: "Pronounce the name of the good or evil spirit distinctly and he will appear very suddenly: you may then address him." Later two other lists are given, one of Good Spirits and another of Acharontica Spiritus. Of the latter it is stated, "Even though evil they are still Familiar or Ministering Spirits and Ready to Serve."

In the dog-eared copy of the book that I have managed to procure—it has evidently had many owners—I find that the section containing "conjurations" is not much thumbed. This is partly because the accompanying injunctions are often neither practicable nor clear, partly because they contain strings of unpronounceable names, but also probably because the idea of a spell—defined as a recitation which must be meticulously word-perfect in order to work—is absent from West Africa and foreign to the African temperament but belongs rather to peoples of a rigid and obsessive mentality.

But the last chapter of the book is very heavily thumbed. This consists of a selection of biblical psalms, to each of which is attributed the power of bringing about a specified end when used in the manner prescribed. In my copy of the book the psalms which former owners have most heavily underscored are those to be used in self-aggrandisement and the discomfiture of enemies. Against some of these is scribbled "Do". Here are some favourites.

> Psalm 7. When evil persons conspire to render you unfortunate, if your enemies watch for an opportunity to overthrow you . . . pray this Psalm. . . .

> Psalm 9. If you wish to secure the love and good will of all men in your business transactions you should pray this Psalm three days in succession after sundown. . . .

> Psalm 38. If you have been so much slandered that the King and the officers of the law have turned against you . . . pray this Psalm . . . and fast the entire day.

> Psalms 41–43. If your enemies have despoiled you of credit and caused you to be mistrusted and thereby reduced your earnings or perhaps deprived you of your office and installed another in your place, you should pray these three times a day. . . .

> Psalm 48. If you have many enemies without cause, who hate you out of pure envy, pray this Psalm often.

> Psalm 108. Write this Psalm . . . and then your coming and going will be blessed and you will be successful in all your business transactions.

> Psalm 72. Write this Psalm . . . and you will become a universal favorite and find favor and grace from all men; you will then live unconcerned, for you can never come to poverty.

§ 3. RELEVANT MYTHOLOGY

Fairies

No one can live long in rural Ashanti—or for that matter in any other part of rural Ghana—without hearing about the elusive dwarfs, said to live chiefly in the thick forest but also known on the southern grasslands and on the sea-shore.

The first collector of lore concerning these *mmoetia* (sing. *aboetia*) was Rattray.* He suggests that the belief in their existence stems from vague traditions of a vanished race of diminutive people.

Further evidence collected, not in Ashanti but among the Ga and Adangme, supports this. The Ga name for these fairies is *asamanukpa*, meaning the Senior Ghosts. Furthermore, they are definitely associated in Ga tradition with polished stone weapons and with stone missiles.† The holed stone discs (often found in hoards and believed by archaeologists to be ancient currency) are used, according to Ga lore, as missiles by the *asamanukpa*, who are also said to dance on flat-topped stone outcrops.

The people of Osudoku, on the Shai Plain, descended partly from immigrants and partly from the people whom the immigrants found there, have two organised cults connected with the veneration of these beings which are known to them as *akotia*, *adope*, *abodo* and *ahulu*. They are said to be of two kinds, black and "red" (mulatto-coloured): the former are friendly and kind and they are worshipped as deities, having a priest, women mediums to practise spirit-possession, a little temple, and annual sacrifices, songs and dances exactly as have the other deities of the district. The "red" dwarfs, believed malicious, are propitiated annually with food and other rites *outside* the town, a barrier being placed across the path to prevent their entering.

Among the texts of songs that I recorded from the singers at an annual celebration was one to the effect that the dwarfs were so acrobatic that they made the dancing of mortals appear clumsier than the first unsteady toddling of a baby. This suggests Negrito people. All the songs were lively and merry, the worshippers declaring that the dwarfs were happy, laughing people. One song declared that "their world was sweet as honey".

It would therefore seem that the early situation almost exactly paralleled—by pure coincidence—that which existed in Britain when the diminutive Bronze-age "moormen" lived contemporaneously with the tall iron-armed immigrants, the two races in much ignorance and shyness of one another, but with tolerance and some courteous exchanges.

Dr. Murray believes that after the moormen had died out the tradition of them as small but mortal men was quite matter-of-fact until Shakespeare transformed them, for purely poetic ends, into tiny, dainty,

* R. S. Rattray, *Religion and Art in Ashanti*. Oxford, 1927.
† The Akan word *aboetia* may have been derived from *abo*, a stone.

coloured, gossamer fairies.* My own postulate is that this transformation was wrought, not by Shakespeare, but by the frequently pleasant and amusing Lilliputian hallucinations of certain mentally sick people. It was probably the bystanders who equated the patients' reported visions with the "little people" of established, matter-of-fact tradition.

Lilliputian hallucinations are well known in Psychiatry.† They usually occur in a setting of clear consciousness and often during temporary infections. They are commonly pleasant and amusing when the patient is comfortable and serene, but pestering and distressing when he is in pain and discomfort. Sauvet in 1847 induced Lilliputian hallucinations in himself with ether.

This is probably but one field of many in which the influence of sub-clinical mental illness on ideology has yet to be appreciated.

In Ghana, I personally have known—over the years—a good many people claiming to have seen and associated with *mmoetia* or *asamanukpa*. Some of these people were psychotics. The others, when pressed for the circumstances in which they saw the fairies, revealed that they were either (*a*) drunk, (*b*) febrile, or (*c*) exhausted and hypoglycaemic. The mood and disposition of the seer determines the disposition of the fairies which he sees.

One habitual drunkard who had been drinking all night went in the morning to visit his traps in the forest and was set upon by a horde of savage *mmoetia* who beat him with sticks and drove him home. This was evidently a variant of delirium tremens.

One childless, lonely and gentle old woman went to bed after unwonted drinking and as she lay she heard little footsteps and little voices and felt her face being stroked and patted.

Another woman, a childless psychotic (described later in this book), derived pleasure from hallucinations of *mmoetia*.

One man told me that he was formerly a hunter living entirely alone in a forest hut. He had become very lean because he had had a good deal of fever. One day he saw an *aboetia* woman. She was about three feet high and had a shaven head. There were feathers on the backs of her forearms, only visible when she bent her elbows. She was friendly, but was followed by a crowd of companions who were not. Her husband was among them and he beat her because she made friendly advances

* M. A. Murray, *The God of the Witches*. Faber, 1931.
† N. Savitsky and S. Tarachow, "Lilliputian hallucinations during convalescence of scarlet fever", *Jour. of Nerv. and Ment. Disease,* Vol. 93, No. 3, March, 1941. Thirty-three references are given at the end of this paper.

towards the hunter. After this incident the hunter was frightened and came back to his people to live. The dwarfs did not follow him home, but he says he still catches glimpses of them sometimes on his farm and they take the palm-wine and food that he places there for them. He is a somewhat withdrawn personality and has a psychotic family-history.

In talking to ordinary people about *mmoetia* one commonly hears that so-and-so saw some when he was out in the bush; he came home and lay down sick and then he saw more, and in a few days he died.

But the people whom popular belief invariably associates with *mmoetia* dwarfs are those lost in the bush, either because they were "driven" there by a possessing *obosom* or because they simply missed their way. If they reach home alive they say that the dwarfs either thrashed them or fed them with bananas. If a "driven" person never comes home, he is believed—at least until many years have passed—to be still alive and fed by *mmoetia*. It may well be that this belief represents a lingering tradition of shy, diminutive forest people who did, in fact, sometimes succour lost people and help them to reach home.

Sasabonsam

The *sasabonsam* is a mythical forest monster which must be mentioned in passing because several depressed and frightened women in my case-histories have dreamt that they were raped by it.

Rattray thinks the *sasabonsam* has evolved out of the gorilla. But I have several times seen wood-carvings of it (one recently at the shrine at Nkyiraa) which give it physical features identical with those of a creature which I recollect among the illustrations in a book on Etruscan Art. The creature has a human form except for huge bat-wings and instead of legs two twining snake-tails. A common source must be sought for the Ashanti and the Etruscan tradition.

§ 4. THEOLOGICAL DOGMA

It is not necessary for the purposes of this study to describe any more of the content of West African religious doctrine than is required for an understanding of the outlook of the common people, most of whom are unacquainted with the niceties of the religious doctrine set forth by earlier ethnographers.*

* R. S. Rattray. *Religion and Art in Ashanti.* Oxford, 1927. M. J. Field, *Religion and Medicine of the Ga People.* Oxford, 1937. E. L. R. Meyerowitz, *The Sacred State of the Akan.* Faber, 1951.

West Africa has been the scene of so many immigrations and fusions of widely divergent cults that our own libraries of comparative religion would be hard pressed to produce any rite or doctrine which is not discoverable, in fragmentary form, somewhere in West Africa. These religious fragments should be likened to rolled pebbles of rare rock in a heterogeneous conglomerate transported and deposited by cataclysmic torrents; there is no question of conformable sequence in a steadily evolving ideology. In odd places we may encounter Children of the Sun, divine twins and priest-blacksmiths: we may witness the renewal of the sacred fire, the death and resurrection of the god, a ritual athletic contest, a communion with the sky-family, the driving forth of a sin-bearing scapegoat, a feast of unleavened bread, the rogation of the crops, the reservation of stone seats for priest-rulers, and a hundred other unconformabilities, all bearing witness to the fusion of peoples.

Yet everywhere we find that, however diverse the original concourse of deities, a process of levelling—hardly to be called theocrasia—has gone on, and indeed is going on, whereby the final hierarchy consists of one supreme sky-god, or rain-god, who is the ultimate giver and destroyer of all power and life, and a great number of his deputies or "sons" (in Ashanti called the *abosom*). These latter are sometimes thought of as *pieces* of the Supreme God. The Supreme God (called *Onyame* in Ashanti) is aloof, and I have heard it said of him, "Onyame has no priests." The *abosom* are the active approachable executives of the Supreme God. The *abosom* are popularly referred to as "the little gods", but each one is treated, in daily practice, as though he were omnipotent, omniscient and omnipresent.

It matters little how humbly or how loftily a lesser deity originated, it is ultimately adapted to this bold, simple pattern. It has been possible to observe the transformation of even a mere *suman* of circumscribed ability into a versatile discriminating *obosom*, and the accretion by specialised war-medicines and fishing-medicines, of the attributes of universal godhead.* Conversely, the degradation of the supreme sky-god of earlier people to the status of a minor god is also seen. An *obosom* called Bruku and another Dimankoma, both practising to-day at ordinary *obosom brafo* shrines, were undoubtedly supreme gods of long-disintegrated tribes. It may even be that the lesser deity Tsaweh (often

---

* I have heard that a statue of St. Anthony brought by the Portuguese into a Fante town is now a commonplace *obosom*. I have not checked this information, but it is quite consistent with the familiar process.

called Nyongmo Tsaweh or Sky-god Tsaweh), of the Accra Plain, was once Jahweh.

It can never be quite confidently forecast when the common man will cry to the Supreme God and when to a minor deity, as the following few instances will illustrate. One night when staying in a remote, wholly pagan village, I woke during the night to the sound of turmoil in a nearby house where, as I soon learnt, an infant boy had suddenly died. After a few minutes I heard the sound of muffled weeping in a quiet spot at the back of my own house. It was the child's father, escaped into solitude and moaning, "Oh, Father Sky-god, why have you done this?" In the same village, during a drought, people often looked wearily up into the sky and sighed, "Oh, Father God, when are you going to send rain?" In Mframaso, however, during a drought, I heard an *okyeame* say, "If this goes on I suppose we shall have to kill a sheep for Mframa." Again there was an occasion in an urban coastal town, when a literate of the third generation of Christians applied to me very late one night for a lift to a destination a mile away as he thought he had enemies who might molest him in the darkness. As my car was in dock I could not help him, whereupon he asked for a little gin in a glass. This was produced and he poured it on the ground praying for the protection of his ancestral deity, Okumaga.

As will be seen later, when we come to examine in detail that flourishing religious institution, the new shrines, the divine attribute most valued at the present day is the power to punish sin. The main defect, in pagan eyes, of Christianity is the absence of this sanction.

A further point which the stranger must understand is that all the lesser gods are believed capable, if they so desire, of possessing or entering into human beings and using them as passive mouthpieces. Not all the lesser gods habitually exercise this power, but they are all believed to have it. Some of them exercise it regularly and often. This subject of spirit possession is so important that I have devoted a whole chapter to it.

§ 5. THE CULT OF THE DEAD

The dead are regarded virtually as small gods, able to send either bane or blessing to their survivors or descendants. But few of them at the present day are given much more than an annual ritual meal, except at their funerals. A funeral must always be grand and expensive for the honour done to the deceased on his departure determines the honour with which he will be received in the next world. If he is dissatisfied with this he may visit his displeasure on his heirs by sending them trouble and misfortune. It is considered recklessly bad policy to stint funeral expenses.

§ 6. THE POPULAR ASSESSMENT OF CHRISTIANITY

More than thirty years ago it was fashionable for anthropologists the world over to deplore Christian missions on the ground that the indigenous religion was a component of that intricate scaffolding of interlocked tribal institutions which sustained tribal unity.

So far as West Africa was concerned such critics were flogging a long-dead horse. Christianity has been in West Africa for five centuries together with, successively, the Portuguese, the French, the Dutch, the Danes, the Germans and the British. Its missionaries' secular fellow-colonists have always been singularly aloof from it, concerning themselves mainly with trade and war, both of which were known, and known on an extensive scale, long before the white man appeared.*

Anyone who has attempted to compile a history of even one small town anywhere in Ghana knows that few towns and states did not begin as heterogeneous settlements of refugees, displaced persons, prisoners of war, slaves, traders, remnants of defeated armies and so on, some of the immigrants driven by the destruction of war and famine from great distances, and all of them bringing fragments of widely divergent religions. West Africa has always been in a state of flux; none of its communities has ever been so stably settled that it could not accept and assess with equanimity another new fragment of religion.

The European, as a bringer of stimulus, excitement and disruption, owed nothing to Missions until he began to require literate African clerks: then he drew upon the products of Mission schools which initially had the main object of enabling Africans to read the Bible, as indeed countless Moslems read the Koran without unfitting themselves for association with those who do not. Had these schools not been already in existence Governments would no doubt have founded them. As it was, they subsidised, and thereby greatly enlarged, small existing Mission schools—on condition that the teaching met their secular requirements.

* Slavery, indigenous to West Africa, was closely bound up with warfare, for war-captives became slaves. The disreputable partnership between Europeans and Africans, whereby the latter bartered slaves in exchange for European wares, was dependent mainly on inter-tribal warfare. Guns and gunpowder were the most sought-after articles of barter and were used to promote further war.

Those anthropologists who thirty years ago were indignant at the ignorant misrepresentation of native religions by missionaries in different parts of the world may now, if they look around Ghana, witness the turning of the tables. Illiterate Africans have always been more shrewdly and critically reserved than either missionaries or anthropologists have suspected. The naïveté has been on the part of the foreigner. Christianity has always been the object of invidious observation by African pagans though courtesy and concrete self-interest have often forbidden criticism to be outspoken.

The main aspersion cast to-day upon Christians by *obosom*-worshippers is that the former trade upon the fact that they are not threatened, in this life, by any retribution for sin. The *obosom* makes stern ethical demands: Christian Church membership demands only that delinquency be not found out.

I recollect an occasion when a supplicant at *abisa*, after confessing under routine questioning to various peccadilloes, mentioned that she was a Christian. The priest thereupon burst into an indignant tirade, said that he himself was a baptised Christian but had given up church-going because Christians were so wicked. Thereafter I sought, wherever I could, for other people's candid views on Christians and was surprised by many another vehement outburst. One such tirade came from my own field-assistant, who also added, "African Reverend Managers are especially wicked. I knew one in Akim who was getting a lot to eat [i.e., making personal profit] out of Church money. Then his seniors told him they were transferring him to another district. He was very annoyed and made up his mind to kill the new Reverend Manager appointed in his place. So he hid a bad *suman* under the pulpit, and the first time the new Reverend Manager mounted the pulpit to preach he fell down with pains in his heart. He went to hospital and died. The congregation felt quite sure that this was due to bad medicine, so they searched and found the bad *suman*."

The point of this anecdote is not whether the departing minister did or did not attempt to kill his successor with a bad *suman*, but that all his flock felt that this was the obvious explanation of the incident. The narrator was a good-natured, well-adjusted, happy and tolerant person with no personal grudge against Christians. Since he knew that he would not be sacked or in any way penalised if he divulged his honest opinions, I pursued his sentiments further by asking him to write me an essay on "Why people become Christians". He himself had been educated—to Primary School Leaving Certificate—in a Mission school, brought up to church-going, baptised and confirmed, but had long been only a casual and occasional worshipper. His views on all current topics were commonplace, matter-of-fact and representative of his class. This is the essay he wrote.

"HOW PEOPLE LIKE TO BECOME CHRISTIANS

"There are two religions in this world, some of people serve God, and some people also serve gods. The reasons why some people like to become Christians is when they are financially poor, and they find that when they die they cannot get money for their funeral customs or have not got relatives to make funeral, then they join Church because if you are a member of a Church and you die, the Church has to provide everything about the funeral expenses, if you have not got any relatives and you have no means.

"Some people become Christians because they have followed *obosom* for many years and the *obosom* has failed them and had ran into many expenses. Someone may become a barren woman or a barren man, so she or he will follow some *obosom* but he or she will not have a child, in this case they run from the *obosom* and become Christians. Some people have temptations [tribulations] from changing world, (the kind of temptations lose of children by death or wife or mother or father or uncle or brother unexpectedly) so they say they will follow *obosom*, but afterwards they find that the *obosom* cannot help so they join Christians. Some people are witchcrafts and they found that their bottom is going to leak,* then they run away and join Christians. Some people also become Christians when they have practised bad *suman*, and they found out that their sins are coming out, they run and make Christians. Some people be highway-men, then later they repent and become Christians. Some one may be a murderer and then he become a Christian he has repent from his sins. Some one may be a theif he repent from stealing and become a Christian. Some one may have lorry accident, he may call his *obosom* or *suman*, he will not have any believe in the *obosom* or *suman* and then runs to a Church and join Christians. Some one may want child birth, the various *obosoms* will try but will fail. Some Christians will have prayers, and the child will come, in this case she will not have any believe in such *obosom*, she will follow Christians. Some one may have a case in court, he will go to *obosoms*, *suman* and *kramos* but he will not have any help, he will make some few prayers to God and he will win his case, in this case he will follow not the *obosoms* and *kramos* again, he will follow Christians.

---

* Literal translation of *ne to ada adi* = Rabelaisian metaphor meaning to be found out.

"Some people may go from one *obosom* to other *obosom* to help him in his trade, but will fail so they will run away and become Christians, I know a friend of mine who was a Christian, he stopped going to Church and follow *obosoms*, he went to Abijan, Dahomey, Dakar, Atakpame for *obosoms* help, but they couldn't help him so he had return to Christians again, and now he has nothing to do with *obosoms* he stays in his village and doing his farming work and he is prospering more now than when he was following *obosoms*. He is a friend of mind call Mr. A. S. staying at a place in Twifu State.

"Some women are also prostitutes in order to be free and will not go to *obosom*, they run and join Christians because if they are Christians they will not be compelled to go to *obosom* [for censure or punishment].

"Some one may have more children and they will all die, so he finds that when he dies he will not get anyone to make his funeral so he runs and joins Christians.

"Some people may join Christians through their children they sent them to school.

"Some one may be an *okomfo*, but later he or she found that the *akom* can not help, therefore he or she runs to a Church and join Christians.

"Some one may enjoy himself with a ball-dance, follow women, and when he falls into sickness and he found out he was going to die, then calls a minister and put before him, that I have offended God by giving my life to the world by ball-dancing and following women, now I have seen the light of God therefore minister I want you to baptise me to become a Christian, God only is my light.

"Some one may be a drunkard, waste all his money in drinking, now he goes straight to a Rev. manager and put before him I sin before God by drinking, and now I have come to the light of God, therefore Rev. manager I want you to baptize me and become a Christian. The Rev. manager will agree and baptise him and then he become a Christian.

"Some one may be a chief, he will order his subjects to kill people in an occasion, now he will sleep and think over that killing people is a sin before God, he orders his subjects stop, then he runs and joins Christians.

"Some one may be a *kramo* he will kill more people by tie them, and kill them with bad *suman*, then later he repents and become Christian.

"People join Christians because they know that when they are Christians and do wrong God will not kill them."

§ 7. "CONFLICT"

Literate Africans, perhaps educated in Mission schools, accustomed to attend church on Sundays, employed as clerks, teachers, store-keepers, and in a hundred other "detribalised" jobs, are frequently pictured by the European as being in a state of moral and religious "conflict". They are popularly accredited with "split minds"—minds supposedly rent in twain by the opposing pulls of tribal gods and the dictates of Christianity. It is further believed that they escape from this melancholy situation only by erecting "watertight compartments", which latter have the evil effect of producing "all sorts of mental trouble and neurosis".

Let me say at once that I do not now believe that any such "conflict" exists. It is true that literates have more serious mental trouble than do illiterates, for they have heavier demands made upon their diligence, adaptability, endurance, judgment and integrity. But their difficulties are on a perfectly manifest plane. They are often disappointed that the rewards of literacy are so meagre compared with the worries, and that its prestige is diminishing as its rarity diminishes. Their envy of their relatively carefree, illiterate brethren may sometimes be unrecognised by themselves and may thus bring unconscious conflict, but more often they say, quite candidly, "The illiterate is better off than the literate." Certainly there is no conflict between incompatible creeds.

So far as Africans think at all about creed, they see—and it seems to me quite logically—no incompatibility between Christianity and paganism. Christians teach that God begat one son who still—on rather poor evidence in pagan eyes—works in and for his adherents. Pagans believe that God has many sons—all the *abosom*—who work for him most dramatically and convincingly. I have more than once heard the *obosom*, speaking through the mouth of the possessed *obosomfo*, declare with some complacency, "I am the last-born son of God." Many of the *obosomfo* whose shrines I frequented are baptised Christians. One of them always wears a crucifix and has another surmounting the roof of his sanctuary. The first *obosomfo* at Mframaso not only founded a Christian school in his village but intended to build a church and in it to worship God every Sunday morning between his two sessions at the *obosom's* shrine. One of the present elders of the Mframaso shrine is also a pillar of a Christian church a few miles off, and does most of the organising when the Bishop visits it. He is valued by both pagan and Christian communities for his good sense, fibre, fidelity and generosity. I asked him once why he, as a baptised Christian, became an elder of the *obosom's* shrine. He replied, with serene innocence, "Anyone can see that the *obosom* has power."

Converts to Christianity have a variety of reasons for joining Christian churches. But even the small proportion who join from a positive conviction of the superiority of the Christian faith and its consolations do not thereby embrace any belief in the *non-existence* of the gods they are ceasing to serve.* New converts usually go with gifts and take a courteous farewell of them, explaining that they intend no offence and hope that none will be taken. They ask their old gods not to "follow" them, "trouble" them or bring them misfortune. They explain that they are making arrangements for their obligations to these gods to be taken over by some responsible kinsman.

The convert may perchance be a person who has "taken a scunner" at the whole pagan system because it is personified, in his eyes, by some senior kinsman devoid of all human graces. This convert does not cease to believe in the existence of pagan supernatural forces: he simply believes that they are either evil or not on his side.

It is not possible to know what proportion of the ordinary supplicants at shrines are Christians, for they seldom mention this unless the priest inquires, but it is certainly as high as the proportion to be found among the patients in my detailed case-histories. And not only do unsophisticated illiterate or semi-literate Christians come to the shrines: I have met there training-college teachers, lawyers, members of the Legislative Assembly and some of the most highly educated men in the country. One man was of the third generation of Christians, the grandson of an ordained pastor. He himself was an excellent personality, urging his own sons and daughters into higher education, but he told me that the country had become very unsettled and unsafe, witchcraft was spreading to seaside areas where it was formerly unknown and that precautions must be taken against it.

It is quite true that Christian Church officers and employees—such as presbyters and school-teachers—when they consult shrines, go to distant ones and conceal their visits from their senior Christians, but this implies no conflict in their own minds, only a criticism of the missionary's abysmal ignorance of supernatural things. Not only does he lack understanding, he lacks the desire and the capacity for it: therefore he must be humoured and deceived. But the African does not deceive himself, though he does, for purely prudential reasons, deceive those who can sack him or withdraw his scholarship. His own conscience needs no squaring and his own actions no rationalising.

---

* The first of the Ten Commandments runs: "Thou shalt have no other gods *before* me." It does not say: "Thou shalt deny the existence and activity of all gods but me."

III

SPIRIT POSSESSION

Introduction

Of the new shrines which we shall examine later, those belonging to the Ashanti type appear to be increasing in number and popularity at the expense of the "drinking-medicine" type. This is undoubtedly due to the arresting phenomenon of "spirit possession" and the unmatchable authority with which this endows the priest. The deities who dispense "drinking-medicines" are admitted by all supplicants to be just as effective in "catching" evil-doers, but the initial ritual which the priest almost mechanically performs for the supplicant contrasts sharply with the unique attention the latter feels himself to be getting when a "possessed" priest, undeniably divested of his own everyday personality and invested with another, speaks with a voice believed to be divine, on the topic of the supplicant's individual troubles.

So ancient, so widespread and so perennially persistent is this spectacle of spirit possession that it calls for examination in some detail, first as an isolated natural phenomenon, next in its contemporary rôle, and lastly in its contribution to an understanding of the wider history of religious ideology.

The Nature of Spirit Possession

A person in the "possessed" state is in the condition known in psychiatry as "dissociated personality". By psychiatrists it is usually called "hysterical dissociation", for the classical clinical studies of dissociation made in Europe and America were of hysterical and maladjusted patients exploiting their aptitude for dissociation to escape from responsibilities or disagreeable situations. In other times and places it has happened that outstanding and even gigantic personalities (such as Moses) carrying without a falter immense burdens of responsibility and leadership have also been dissociation adepts and seem to have used this power of shuttering off the distracting irrelevancies of normal consciousness to concentrate more intensely on a narrowed field. There seems no more reason to suppose that dissociation is *necessarily* hysterical than to suppose this of the equally weird, more undignified, though almost universal phenomenon of laughter.

The possession fit* has some well-marked features. It is essentially an excitement, usually of short duration, not often more than two or three hours, though a whole day's possession has been sometimes reported. The excitement is preceded by a few minutes of dazed and dreamy inaccessibility. The person is speechless, sometimes fidgetting as in an insulin sopor and usually looks oppressed. He sits head-in-hands, or huddles himself on the ground with his head over his knees, or, if he is standing, he may sway with drooping eyelids as if "asleep on his feet". Sometimes the fit aborts and never gets beyond this stage of confused inhibition. If this happens at a dance and the person is slumped on the ground obstructing others, he is picked up, usually quite limp but perhaps feebly wriggling, and carried behind the scenes or to his house where he sits dazed and mute.

But more often the short confusional phase suddenly gives way to intense motor excitement. The medium leaps to his feet with flailing arms, quivering, dancing, leaping, singing, shouting and perhaps "prophesying" † with words regarded as not his own. Great feats of strength and endurance may be performed under this excitement. Sometimes the medium runs for miles, sometimes he spins like a top for minutes on end with no appearance of vestibular embarrassment. Often he throws off his clothes, but never outrages decency. Once, when military *asafo* companies of excited young men were dancing at a chief's funeral, I saw a youth become possessed, seize a passing hen, tear it limb from limb and eat it—or partially eat it—alive. More often the performance is quieter, but never is the medium quite still. He is always in a quivering vibration. If he stands in one spot he usually jigs from one foot to the other. The unceasing tremor may be either coarse or fine: his head may look as if it must soon be shaken right off, or he may walk so sedately that only close observation reveals that his toes and fingers are finely trembling. The facial expression is usually mask-like. The eyes may be either fixed and staring, almost closed, or they may roll, in all these cases

* The number of these fits that I have witnessed since first frequenting the sidetracks of West Africa in 1930 must now be a matter of thousands.

† προφητης = one who speaks for another: an interpreter of the will of a god (Liddell and Scott). The popular connotation of the word—to foretell the future—has comparatively rarely been employed, in either ancient Hebrew, early Christian or contemporary West African religion. To foretell the future, David employed a "*seer*", not a prophet.

appearing useless but proving adequate. The medium sweats freely, and if rubbed with powdered white clay, as is sometimes the custom, this pours off in runnels.

The end of the excitement is abrupt. The medium flings himself against a wall, on the ground, on a seat or into someone's arms and becomes limp. A genuinely bewildered expression overspreads his face— that of someone waking from sleep in unfamiliar surroundings. In an elderly medium, the face, as it abruptly gains awareness, seems suddenly to age. An expression of appropriate pain and discomfort appears as the medium becomes aware of his aching limbs, his bruises, his thirst and so forth. The exhaustion that follows is appropriate to the amount of physical energy expended and the medium usually falls asleep, sometimes then and there, but more often after staggering home to his house.

The behaviour of the professional medium, whether priest, priestly auxiliary or private soothsayer, becomes modified and controlled according to traditional ritual. We shall return to this important aspect of the topic.

The genuinely dissociated person describes a complete amnesia for the period of dissociation.

Another feature described by some subjects is an aftermath of peaceful euphoria. This, of course, may be masked by extreme exhaustion, bruises and other discomforts of over-exertion.

It is clear that the dissociated state has some ground in common with sleep-walking and hypnosis. This being so, it is not surprising that three outstanding claims to "paranormal" quality have been made for the oracular utterances of dissociated mediums.

The first of these is the superlative wisdom of the advice offered by the oracle. The dissociated mind may indeed be endowed with the ability to concentrate upon a circumscribed set of relevant facts, marshall them and draw conclusions from them more swiftly and ably than the mind beset with the distractions of normal consciousness. Many of us have had the experience of solving a problem during sleep. A swimmer who has failed to master a particular new stroke may dream that he succeeds and find when he next enters the water that the mastery attained in the dream is in fact real and persistent.

The second claim, that oracular utterances at times penetrate the future, is, in the light of the similarity between dissociation and sleep, not extravagant. Although J. W. Dunne's mathematical explanation of the fact that dreams often rehearse future events has come under criticism, his observation of the facts of dream foreknowledge has not been gainsaid.* It is not unreasonable to grant the dissociated mind an extended awareness similar to that of the dreaming mind.

It need not, however, be emphasised that neither dissociation nor sleep can make a silly or commonplace mind into a great mind. The man who solves a mathematical problem in his sleep is a mathematician with a mathematician's grasp of that problem. The man who masters a new swimming stroke in his sleep is a competent swimmer. Africans sum up oracular utterances much as they do those which men make in their cups. "If you are a wise man, drink makes you wiser still: if you are a fool, drink makes you even more foolish." And regarding oracular priests they emphasise that a good priest must be not only a wise and sensible man but also a man of "strong spirit".

Another paranormal faculty occasionally attributed to possessed persons is the "gift of tongues". Although meaningless gibberish invented by the speaker is often thought by the hearer to belong to a foreign language,† there is nevertheless a rational basis for a limited gift of tongues in that the dissociated mind may well have access to recesses of memory containing fragments of language acquired in childhood and since forgotten. At the feast of Pentecost, Parthians and Medes, Cretans and Arabians and the rest, no doubt lodged annually in the houses of Galileans, the same strangers returning perhaps year after year to the same house and exposing the quick-eared Galilean children to the sound of their language. Certainly in Ghana whenever a possessed person speaks fragments of another language, that person's history reveals that he has, at some time or other, been in contact with its native speakers.

However, paranormal cognition is not the blood and bones of oracular utterances. These, as ethnological observers the world over have often emphasised, are seldom either original or surprising, but are commonly an enunciation of hitherto unexpressed but strongly held public opinion. Where the oracular utterance startles, it is by reason of its daring. When the speaker is held to be but the passive instrument of the voice of the god, this not only endows his dicta with authority but exonerates him from responsibility for them. We shall return to this topic from time to time.

* J. W. Dunne, *An Experiment with Time*. Faber, 1942; *The Serial Universe*. Faber, 1934.

† The sterile tedium of such gibberish in the mouths of "prophets" is the subject of a special discourse by the Apostle Paul (I Corinthians xiv).

The Induction of Dissociation

The sound of excited drums, gong-gongs, rattles, or rhythmic clapping and singing is the usual agent for precipitating a dissociation fit, both in the novice and the habituated *okomfo*. I have seen a young *okomfo*, desiring to be possessed, go and stand quietly in front of the clanging iron gong-gong of the orchestra where, after a few minutes, his head sank slowly to his chest, and just as I was expecting him to slide to the ground he suddenly leapt quivering into the air and danced.

Other strong emotions—such as wonder, fear or grief—may precipitate a dissociation perhaps in someone who has never been dissociated before. As we shall see later, the emotional experience of baptism or ritual anointing has been, in other cultures, a potent agent in precipitating a first dissociation. Young Christians in Ghana are often possessed for the first time in church, and if the missionary or catechist-in-charge fails to endorse the view that the Holy Ghost is the possessing spirit, the new medium assumes that an *obosom* has called him to its service. The terrifying experience of seeing a companion killed or damage done by lightning has sent more than one person into his first dissociation fit, wherein no doubt lies the origin of the belief that some new *abosom* first come down from heaven in a flash of light.

Probably the greatest aid to dissociation is hypoglycaemia. On shrine working-days the priest eats nothing. Often when one seeks out the history of someone possessed for the first time one learns that he had gone out early in the morning without eating, to hunt, to farm or to collect firewood, had stayed out, fasting, all day and had come home in the evening possessed.

Another aid is conditioning. The priest at Mframaso before routine *abisa* always retired into the sanctuary to await the descent of the spirit upon him. On one occasion when he had had influenza and had decided to do only a short day's work, he deliberately avoided entering the sanctuary because, he said, the spirit would come at once if he did.

It is well known to psychiatrists that the induction of the hypnotic state is sometimes assisted by chemical means; for instance, the inhalation of sub-toxic amounts of ether.* In West Africa, so far as I know, chemical aids to dissociation are not generally used, though I have seen priests chewing herbal "medicine", the nature of which they never divulged.

* It is necessary to distinguish between a chemical intoxication and a chemically assisted induction of the hypnotic state.

Though alcohol is taboo to priests on working-days, it sometimes precipitates dissociation in laymen. One supplicant at a shrine, a young man well known locally as a poorly endowed personality, both mentally and physically, came complaining that *akom* came to him if he took the smallest thimbleful of alcohol. Thus possessed, he danced and often ran a dozen miles along the highroad. His relatives corroborated this. At the shrine he begged the deity—amid the derisive laughter of the by-standers—to forbid his drinking. The deity said that an ancient *obosom* who had once had a priest among the young man's forebears and had lapsed into desuetude, was "troubling" him, not because it wanted to "come back" to revive its priesthood, but because it wanted due annual propitiation. The head of the supplicant's family was called and ordered to offer appropriate sacrifices, after which the *obosom* would trouble the youth no more.

Though incense and smoke are used in the rites of some ancient gods in other parts of Ghana, I have never seen fumes inhaled to induce dissociation.

Associated Hysterical Stigmata

I have met only one case in which dissociation seemed to be linked with another hysterical phenomenon. This was a conversion hysteria.

The patient was a supplicant at a shrine, a Trans-Volta woman of about thirty, a Christian married to an Akim collector of lorry-park tolls. She had six children and had lived serenely till several months before I met her, when her husband took a concubine whom he intended to marry. One day the patient found under her pillow a strange hand-kerchief which she assumed to be part of a bad magic made against her by the interloper. From then on she became possessed every week or so. The episodes of possession lasted one or two hours. She had no recollection of them herself, but spectators told her that every attack began by "shaking her", after which she danced and then always developed a paralysed right hand and right foot, which recovered as soon as the spirit left her. She consulted a medicine-man who told her that the paralysis was caused by the bad magic made against her and that the *obosom* which possessed her had come to save her from it and from her other troubles. At the shrine she spoke only of the bad medicine against her and asked for protection from it. In a private interview she told me that she had the idea of becoming a pro-fessional *okomfo*. I do not know the outcome, as she went home the same day.

The Making of an Obosomfo

A great many ordinary people become mildly possessed in a casual way at religious dances. They usually remain inconspicuous and go quietly home after the dance, doing their daily jobs till the next festival. But occasionally a person, possessed for the first time, is so "strongly" seized that he is at once believed to be marked out for a dedicated career. "A big *obosom* wants to come to him and work."

The cardinal sign of this "strong" calling is that the spirit "takes" him or "drives" him forth into the wilderness. He dashes so furiously, so fleetly and so far away into the bush that there is extreme danger that he will never find his way back and will perish. So he is always restrained, if possible, by his friends, from rushing away or, if he eludes them, he is diligently sought.

If the search-parties fail, his friends' first hope is that he will spontaneously come back after forty days—the traditional period not only for such sojourns in the bush* but of other ritual periods of time in Akan worship.

If he returns, he usually reports, as might be expected after the loneliness, panic, exhaustion and hypoglycaemia, visions and voices. The usual hallucinations are of *mmoetia* (mythical forest dwarfs), who may beat him and terrify him but who may also minister to him. When friendly, they feed him, traditionally with bananas. And indeed a banana-farm near a stream would be the most likely life-saving circumstance for him to stumble upon.

Some years before I stayed in Mframaso, the twin brother of the "owner" of the shrine was taken by the spirit to bush and never came back. Probably the dementing diseases pellagra and beriberi claimed him, for he remained alive for several years and was occasionally seen in glimpses, naked and with hair grown long. One witness tried to lead him home, but after a tussle he escaped and ran away. During my stay the problem of the disposal of his wife became acute. Should she be treated as a widow and sent home to her kinsfolk or would her husband come back? The priest and the elders of his family went to the shrine of another deity and made *abisa* concerning him. There they were told that he would not return, but the deity did not commit himself as to whether he was still alive.

Though it is usually at a festival amid excitement and drumming that

---

* Festivals with drumming are held at forty-day intervals. A person who goes to bush during one festival and survives, may well be guided home by the sound of the drums of the next.

the spirit makes its first perilous onslaught on the new *okomfo*, it may happen as he goes about his farming or other work. Then, if no one sees him taken to bush, his danger is the greater.

The man marked out for priesthood by rushing, or attempting to rush, away to bush is sent for training to some experienced old priest. Under this training the novice's behaviour while possessed to the sound of drums becomes controlled and conditioned according to traditional ritual and he becomes no longer prone to rush to bush. A further result of training is that he becomes able to speak while possessed, the novice being, as a rule, mute. When he begins to speak and reply to questions he has become the mouthpiece of an *obosom*.

There was one occasion during my stay in Mframaso when consternation reigned because it was thought that the priest was gone, for good, to bush.

The occasion was out of the routine. The *obrafoso* grove, which had not been in use since the death of the old priest, was reopened during the *Fofie* festival in May. There was a procession to the grove with much gun-firing, drumming, sacrifice of sheep and fowls and excited dancing and singing by the populace and the women's *Apo* choir. Several ordinary people were possessed as well as the priest and the young *okomfo-in-training*. Both these latter, during their possession, made mad rushes to bush and were pursued, caught and dragged back by gangs of strong men after violent struggles. The day's dancing and singing went on without a break from dawn till evening. The following day, the priest, instead of resting, went with a party to a kinsman's funeral in a neighbouring town and there had a second day of fasting together with some drinking. In the evening, after dark, the party returned, all rather excited, and when about to enter his house the priest was suddenly possessed and driven away to bush, in exactly what direction it was too dark for anyone to see. The town-crier beat his gong-gong calling out all the men to form search-parties and all the drummers and the *Apo* women to beat their instruments and sing. The musicians worked furiously, and their loud and clamorous music, penetrating through the night far out into the bush, reached the wandering priest and he returned, still dancing wildly, into the *obosom's* yard. There he continued to dance, surrounded by frantic music and singing. At last, still possessed, he put up his hand to silence the music and then spoke. The deity, he said, had been so much grieved of late by the laxity and folly of many villagers and shrine servants that he had decided to desert his shrine for ever, first driving his priest away to bush for good. However, he had heard the singing of the women and out of pity for them and their children he had relented and returned to watch over and care for them. He then enumerated some of the misdeeds that had pained him—these included peculations—and said they must cease lest he should leave them "to sit in desolation under their grass roofs".*

If the hysterical basis of dissociation be accepted it might be supposed that the dissociated subject would see to it that he did himself no physical hurt. There seems no doubt, however, that untrained novices do sometimes lose their lives. They may, of course, die of thirst, starvation, fear and associated dementia when they run away to bush: getting lost may be regarded as an accident akin to the actual suicide of a person who intends only a suicidal gesture. But they may also, if witnesses are to be believed, die of exhaustion, without going to bush at all, under the eyes of their friends. I was told by an excellent witness concerning the "very strong *obosom*" that intermittently possessed the youth in training at Mframaso that it had killed twelve other novices by "repeatedly keeping them possessed all day long". The witness said, "Three of them died here, and we all saw them die. We knew it was one and the same *obosom*, because every time it said, 'When I go away to sleep [i.e., when the dissociation fit ends] you will die.' This *obosom* is a very strong one and often stays with its *okomfo* for a whole day and tires him till he is too weak to live."†

When an *okomfo* spends a matter of years in the bush with enough self-possession to keep himself alive, but insufficient to bring him home, it is difficult to escape the conclusion that he is a schizophrene—with his madness no doubt reinforced by dementing deficiency diseases. We know (*vide* case-histories) that fear often induces its own psychosis and in a potential schizophrenic can precipitate a florid attack. Anyone who has run to bush impelled by a temporary dissociation and comes to himself lost and famished must be beset with fear. I do not think there is any direct connection between schizophrenia and dissociation, but neither are they mutually exclusive and an *okomfo* has probably the same chance of becoming schizophrenic as anyone else.

Of the practising *obosom brafo* priests who came within my ambit in Ashanti several told me how they started their careers.

One said his *obosom* drove him into the wilderness many times

* The modern symbol of prosperity is the sheet-iron roof.
† There seems no reason to attribute such a death to an uprush of death-wish. It is sufficient to invoke only the apathy reactive to exhaustion. It will be recalled that Elijah after one of his prodigal outpourings of energy lay under a tree and "requested for himself that he might die".

during seven months, and each time he had to be sought and brought back.

Another said he was five days in the bush before the search-party found him. For yet another fortnight he ate nothing. At the end of that time it was resolved to send him to an old priest for training, whereupon he resumed eating.

Another *obosomfo*—a woman with a son of about eighteen—said she was first possessed at the age of twelve, and thereafter, for a good many years, only at festivals. About a year before I met her the spirit drove her to bush, but only long enough to show her pursuers a boss of rock, the spirit of which had spoken to her and told her that its name was Obo Kofi.* Her two uncles, both senior chiefs, established her at a shrine in the "village" in which she had been living when the *obosom* first came to her.

Another *obosomfo* who claimed to have been fifteen years in practice said that his career began by his *obosom* driving him to bush "for more than forty days". On his return, he said, he had no recollection of the episode and knew not how he was fed. His insignia were not ceremonially brought down from heaven, but he himself, becoming possessed, led his friends into the bush, showed them an object lying under a tree, said an *obosom* had entered it, and that it was to be brought home in a brass pan and enshrined.

Yet another, who had been six years at work, said, "The *obosom* took me to bush for twenty-nine days. My friends said that I was like a madman, but I don't remember that. I knew that if it had not been for the *mmoetia* forest dwarfs I should have died, though some of the *mmoetia* beat me, pulled my hair and flung me to the ground. I still see *mmoetia* sometimes when I go to hunt. Sometimes they pull my hair but they tell me not to run to bush again. Sometimes they come home with me and dance and sing. They are men, women and children and have *mpese-mpese* hair like mine. Some are naked and some have loin-cloths. Whenever they come home with me the *obosom* comes upon me as soon as I reach home. I always put food in the grove for them and always I find that they have come and taken it. After the *obosom* first came to me and took me to bush for twenty-nine days a stranger from Sampa came and caught three *abosom* for me: they were drummed down out of the sky and came like a fire."

Another prosperous priest of some years' standing told me that he did

---

* Obo is a widespread ancient deity. The name means a rock or stone. I do not know whether the cult originally had megalithic associations or whether it was a part of the Nature-worship cult and was associated with a mountain.

not open his career by going to bush but became "just mad". *Obosom* possession was diagnosed and he was sent to an old priest for training. No ceremony of *obosom* capture was performed. "We just waited—for three years—till it made me able to talk."

The story of another very successful elderly priest was told to me, not by himself, but by some of the other inhabitants of his native town. He had been out in the bush all day, hunting, and in the evening heard a sound of whistling and someone repeatedly calling his name. He came home frightened and trembling, and when he reached home was "shaken" still more. He sought advice at an old shrine and was told that an *obosom* wanted to come. He set up a shrine on the site of his old hunting camp and became highly prosperous and respected.

A middle-aged *okomfo* woman in private practice, not in Ashanti but in Akim, told me that she first became possessed at the age of about twelve. The spirit drove her away to bush, search-parties failed to find her and she was assumed to be dead. Then she was seen one day in the cemetery, drinking rain-water from the vessels left on the graves. Friends tried to bring her home, but she ran away. For seven more *months* she was in the bush, but was occasionally seen drinking water in the cemetery. (Probably people left food there for her, but she does not recall this.) After seven months she came home voluntarily and shortly afterwards was one day suddenly possessed, danced and said that her *obosom's* name was Gyenang Kweku. A medicine-man said that he knew where this deity came from—Yiripina in the Northern Territories— and that he could carry out the rites to establish the girl as this deity's *okomfo*. This he did, and she became a private soothsayer and giver of advice both medical and worldly. When I met her she had been many years in practice and had been twice widowed. Her second husband was a Christian catechist who on his death-bed confessed that he had often stolen money from her and had attempted to poison her out of envy of her wealth and status.

Some Candidates for Priesthood

I. During my stay in Mframaso a young *okomfo* completed his training there and I was able to witness all the major stages except the earliest. Psychiatrist readers will discern a curious blend of gainfully directed hysteria and patient self-discipline.

When I first knew this youth, Kwesi Y., he had been in Mframaso about five years. He himself told me his previous history, which various good witnesses corroborated.

He belonged to an Ashanti country-town which I shall call Nsuso. He was the eldest of his mother's nine surviving children. His father died soon after the birth of his mother's second child and the mother married again, but left her second husband after the birth of her ninth child.

The youth, Kwesi, was the only child who was not sent to school. He told me he had never wished to be sent, but it may well be that his later ambition to become a powerful and wealthy *obosom brafo's* priest was explicable in terms of this situation.

At the time when the *obosom* first came to him he was about fifteen and was living, in the traditional manner, in a large household with his mother, his maternal uncles and aunts and the latter's children. All the young males in the household ranked as "brothers" and some were literate Christians. The youth, Kwesi, was in his own words "the least of all the brothers". He had made himself a farm and was a good hunter, but was also training as a bricklayer and mason.

When he first started behaving strangely no one could decide whether he was mad or whether "an *obosom* wanted to come", though it seems certain that the strange behaviour came in fits and starts. He often flung off his clothes, strode about naked and staring and made attempts to run to bush. Sometimes he seized hold of a passing sheep, cut its throat, carried the carcase to the *abonsam* stone, and came back, remaining quite mute the while. On recovery from the attacks he remembered nothing of his actions and was startled when told of them. In some of his attacks he would career wildly up and down the town, gibbering an unintelligible "language". Sometimes he had ten or a dozen attacks in one day: he told me, "It hardly left me alone long enough to let me eat." He was taken to all the country's most famous oracles and medicine-men for diagnosis and treatment and cost his kinsmen, in all, about £300 before one medicine-man diagnosed "a very strong *obosom*, too big for us to control" and recommended a visit to the shrine at Mframaso. This was made. The old priest of Mframa was then alive and he not only endorsed the diagnosis but undertook to keep the youth under his care, train him and, after training, help him to set up in practice in Nsuso. The old priest accepted nothing for his training, board and lodging, but said he could pay off his debt when he started to work.

As soon as these promises were made the youth settled down in Mframaso. There his tormenting *obosom* left him entirely in peace except on festival days, when it seized him with great fury and danced him into utter exhaustion. During possession he was, however, quite mute and it was accepted by everyone that until his *obosom* should start to use him as a mouthpiece there could be no question of his independence.

This was the stage of training he had reached when I first met him in Mframaso. He was a pleasant, unassuming youth and seemed well endowed both mentally and physically. He was stockily built and heavily muscled, with a broad, square face and a good gleaming skin. He worked quite hard, but in leisure hours was always conspicuously clean in a well-washed white smock, and even his acolyte's uncut hair was neat. His room was meticulously tidy. On the *obosom's* working days he helped the *sinkwafo* with drumming and other shrine duties. He was supposed to remain chaste during his training, but he broke the rule once, reported his offence and was fined one sheep.

When I first went to live in Mframaso he was very friendly and often came to call and sat and chatted. When I asked him his exact standing he said he was an "*okomfo ketewa*"—a very small *okomfo* indeed. He often seemed somewhat worried and said his lot was hard, but I think he was feeling uncertain as to how far the new priest of Mframa would repudiate or accept the commitments of his predecessor.

I first saw him violently possessed at the Fofie festival in May when I had been living in the village about three months. The *obrafoso* grove was in use at that festival for the first time since the death of the old priest and there was much tumult of drumming, singing, gun-firing and dancing. The possessed youth appeared to be making some effort to carry out *obosom* ritual. He several times stood in one spot, shaking violently and seemed trying to speak, though no sounds came out of his moving lips. Then he held out his hand for an egg, took it, made as if to throw it in the ritual manner but seemed unable. He dropped several eggs irresolutely on the ground, but they did not smash. At last he seemed determined to smash one and stood facing a big silk-cotton tree, the egg poised in his hand, while the populace scuttled out of the line of fire. Eventually he flung it, but feebly and inaccurately. It missed the tree and fell into the undergrowth, whereupon the spirit seized the thrower and sent him charging off, blindly stumbling through the vegetation, whither his friends pursued him and brought him, struggling, back.

Some weeks after this he appeared as an ordinary quiet supplicant at *abisa*. He said a message had come that his mother was sick in hospital and he asked the *obosom* to restore her to health. His attitude was blatantly selfish. He said, "My mother is my right hand. If she dies I am done for. My uncles and my father's brothers and my own brothers have always refused to help me. My lot is very sad, so I implore you to make my mother to recover, for I depend on her."

A few weeks later the mother, duly restored to health, came to visit her son and at *abisa* asked about the progress of his training. She was told that until the Wawaase priest's case* was settled nothing could be done for her son, as the deity was weary of setting up perfidious new priests.

After another week, however, while the mother was still in Mframaso, the spirit came upon the youth before the routine morning *abisa*. He danced in the yard and as soon as the possessed priest emerged from the sanctuary he leapt the parapet and flung himself at the priest's feet, embracing his ankles in an attitude of supplication. He did not rise till the priest has kicked himself free and gone forward on to the dais. Later the priest, still possessed, announced that the new *okomfo's obosom* was "ready to come and work" but repeated that nothing could be done till the Wawaase case was settled.

A few weeks later the youth and his mother appeared again at *abisa*, the mother saying that she was going home and asking for blessing in her enterprise of raising enough money to establish her son as an *obosomfo*.

About four months later she came again to visit her boy. One morning she came to routine *abisa* complaining of lumbago. The deity replied that this was the result of her having had lately extra-marital intercourse with a number of men. She admitted this matter-of-factly, explaining quietly that this was the only means by which she could hope to raise money for the approaching expenses of her son. This was accepted as reasonable, as she had no husband to reproach her with infidelity. She was a dignified woman with a quiet, gracious air of authority, and rumour had it that she was the courtesan of chiefs and other "big men" who rewarded her as befitted their own exalted rank.

The mother went home, and six months later came again bringing a deposit of £60, and asking for meetings with the priest and his elders to arrange about her son's installation. At a Kwesidae festival when the priest was possessed the spirit came upon the young novice and for the first time he smashed eggs competently and also shouted and whooped, having theretofore been mute while possessed. He then flung himself repeatedly at the feet of the possessed priest ("one *obosom* was imploring the other *obosom*") till the priest, after shaking him off several times, at last took him petulantly by the back of the neck and thrust him into the sanctuary. After a few minutes he emerged dancing furiously and

* Page 72.

holding in his hand the neck of a smashed rum-bottle. He brandished this in threatening fashion. The elders restrained him by clutching his wrist and at length succeeded in confiscating the weapon. He then filled his mouth with bits of broken glass and chewed them. After a few minutes he mounted to the doorstep of the sanctuary where he collapsed on the ground as the spirit suddenly left him. He then dazedly grimaced, spat out the broken glass and sank with a few shuddering quivers into his usual exhausted sleep. He came to me the next day with a badly cut, swollen and infected mouth.

It was thereafter accepted that his *obosom* was resolute, could be fierce and destructive and was imperiously demanding attention. His mother had meetings with the priest and elders and it was decided that a party of officials, drummers and singers of Mframa's shrine should go to Nsuso with the *obofohene* who would organise the ritual of calling the obosom's insignia down from the sky and housing it in the usual kind of receptacle. Mframa's clerk drew up a document to the effect that the total sum to be paid for all these rites and travelling expenses was £400, of which the youth's mother had already paid £60 and would pay another £40 before the rites started. The remaining £300 was to be paid when the new deity was ready to start work.

After a further four months the mother came again bringing the £40. When she made her report at the shrine the youth was wildly possessed and at the next Kwesidae festival he shouted, seized a sheep and scrambled, dragging it, up to the top of the portico of the sanctuary. There he bit it till it bellowed and then jumped down eight feet with it, falling heavily. A few weeks later the *obofohene*, *obrafohene* and a lorry-load of drummers and singers went home with the mother to entice down out of the sky, capture, imprison and bring back to Mframaso, the insignia of the new *obosom*. The youth was left behind in Mframaso, where, the next day, he was possessed and shouted, using his voice freely.

Meanwhile the party at Nsuso drummed and sang in the bush near the town every night for a week, and on the seventh night, it was related, three insignia were enticed down out of the sky, each coming in a display of fire, were "captured" by the *obofohene*, placed in a brass pan, brought home to Mframaso in the lorry with joy and singing, and housed in Mframa's sanctuary. The returning party described the excitement and awe that had prevailed in Nsuso. The young *okomfo's* mother, his sister and a variety of other townspeople had become possessed and a "scholar" had become weak-kneed with fear and had collapsed on the ground.

The three sacred objects reputed to have been enticed out of the sky were exhibited to the shrine elders at *akyima*. (I myself did not see them, having gone to a case in another village.) They were said to be roughly spherical, a little bigger than a fist: two were grey (probably clay) and one was, from the description, covered with gold-leaf.

Two days later Mframaso celebrated its own *obosom's* July corn-festival. There was a whole night's drumming, dancing and singing, and the next day intense excitement when Mframa's insignia were carried in the palanquin to the grove, but throughout this the young *akomfo* of the new *obosom* remained quietly unpossessed. This was because the *obosom* Mframa had announced that he was holding the new *obosom* "in prison", unable to function, until the remaining £300 should have been paid. The youth's sister, however, a young woman of about twenty with an infant, was possessed strongly and often.

Meanwhile the mother in Nsuso had succeeded in enlisting the sympathy of the paramount chief of her district. He sent his emissaries to Mframaso with ceremonial gifts to ask that the new *obosom* might be allowed to go to Nsuso and start work. They were told politely but firmly that it would do no work till the £300 was paid, but they were given a month in which to help the mother to raise the money.

However, in spite of Mframa's interdict against any activity of the new *obosom*, the latter possessed the young *okomfo* and announced that its name was Kofi Gyata Kyereapem (Kofi The Lion who catches Thousands). It seemed, then, clear that the new *obosom* was determined to be active, so Mframa told the Nsuso emissaries, through his possessed priest, to return to their town and build a suitable sanctuary. They were to take the young *okomfo* with them and his *obosom*, possessing him, would reveal a suitable site for the building. The mother and the sister then made *abisa* asking for blessing in the enterprise of raising the £300, and the Nsuso people went home.

Nothing further happened for another three months. Then the young *okomfo* returned bringing his sister and her husband. The sister had been "caught" by the *obosom* and spontaneously declared herself a witch. Although she was under the protection of the *obosom* Mframa and had come to make peace with him, it was assumed to be her brother's new *obosom* who had "caught" her. The young *okomfo* could not conceal his satisfaction at this striking demonstration of its power, though her husband was in tears at his young wife's plight.*

* See case-history, No. 35.

The Nsuso chief sent his head ambassador to reiterate that it was difficult to raise £300, but the deity, though polite, was unrelenting and even warned the messenger that if the new *obosom* was not speedily installed in its own new house it might become "*basaa*" and unmanageably destructive.

A month later the paramount chief himself came from Nsuso on behalf of the young *okomfo* and his mother. He said that the sanctuary was now ready and if work might begin the money could be paid by instalments as the shrine began to earn: he himself would stand as guarantor. Mframa consented, documents were drawn up and shrine officials and drummers were sent to instal the new *obosomfo* and open the shrine.

So far as I know, the new shrine is now in full swing.

II. Another person thought to be called to a priest's career was associated with Mframaso when I was there.

This was a youth of about eighteen, a relative of the old priest who trained the present incumbent of Mframa's shrine. I did not think this candidate a very good personality and doubted whether his aspirations would have been encouraged by the Mframa priest had the latter not been under a personal obligation to the aspirant's senior kinsman.

The youth turned up in Mframaso one day—some twenty-five miles from his home—apparently possessed and dancing from house to house. Some people thought he was mad. It is noteworthy that whatever the state of his volition he came to the right place. He was brought to the priest, who said he would look into the matter. The youth then became rational and was sent home by lorry in the charge of the priest's nephew. On the way he became possessed again, tried to jump out of the lorry and gave his escort much anxiety.

During the next six weeks he came to Mframa's shrine several times, brought by his senior kinsman. On the first of these occasions Mframa was asked to cause him to take food as he had eaten virtually nothing for several weeks. He had several times been driven of the spirit into the bush, where he had once been lost till a search-party found him after several days.

When he had resumed eating, his kinsmen were told by Mframa that a big *obosom brafo* was involved and that they should not lightly set up a shrine. "There is life and death as well as money in this work . . . to take up an *obosom brafo* is not like picking up a snail from the ground. . . . Some of you may die before the *obosom* settles down with you. If it stays you must treat it well and keep its rules: then you will prosper and be happy, but if you treat it carelessly it will bring death and suffering."

The party were told to take the youth home and when his *obosom* had become manageable and his friends had collected the requisite funds the *obofohene* would go and entice the insignia down from heaven.

There the matter was resting when I left the district.

III. Another candidate for the priesthood was brought by his father with the request that the *obosom* might be induced to leave him. The young man had been trained at Mframaso, had reached the stage of talking while possessed, but needed more capital if he was to open a shrine. The father had borrowed and already spent all he was able and wished to abandon the project. He was told to propitiate his son's *obosom* with a cow and to pray to it enunciating his situation. If this was not done the *obosom* would worry the boy to death.

IV. On another occasion a youth attended *abisa* saying that *akom* dancing had come to him and that he would like Mframa to help him to establish himself in practice. He was told roundly that he was a fool, that fools always suffered for their folly and that he must come with his senior kinsmen if he wanted to be taken seriously.

Loss of Ability to Dissociate

When I first went to live in Mframaso one of the familiar figures in the village was a wretchedly unhappy-looking man with *mpese-mpese* hair who spent his time sitting in the street outside his lodgings, dressed in mourning clothes. He walked ataxically, and only with help, seeming to have peripheral neuritis.

His history was that four years previously, during the lifetime of the old priest, he was brought from his home (which I shall call Wawaase) to Mframaso, apparently mad, naked, and for ever rushing away into bush. The old priest's diagnosis was unhesitating: "He is not mad, but a very big *obosom* is wanting to come to him." The priest gave him some consecrated water to bathe in, and before the day was out he was quiet, rational and asking for his clothes.

He was then trained in Mframaso till his deity could possess him in a disciplined ritual manner and could use him as a mouthpiece. A responsible younger kinsman was trained as his *obrafohene*. His deity was a very vigorous one and sometimes possessed him strenuously for the greater part of a day without intermission.

When training was complete the new priest was sent home to Wawaase where a sanctuary was built for his deity. The *obofohene* from Mframaso, with a large party of elders, drummers, singers and mus-keteers followed, and after five weeks' hard work enticed down out of the sky and enshrined the insignia of two *abosom*. The new *obosomfo* was established in practice.

The total expenses of his training and installation amounted to more than £1,200, of which only a part was paid, the remainder standing as debt to Mframa's shrine. An agreement was signed, witnessed by the two paramount chiefs of the Mframaso and Wawaase districts, whereby the new shrine was to pay one-third of its yearly takings to Mframa till such time as its debt should be discharged.

After one year's work the new shrine sent Mframa £200. Then nothing more was heard from Wawaase till shortly before I went to stay there, when the priest from Wawaase appeared as a supplicant before Mframa, sick and abject, complaining that the spirit had departed from him and had not possessed him for nearly a year.

The dictum of the deity at Mframaso supported the supplicant's own conviction. He had offended his deity on three counts. Firstly, he had failed in his promise to pay off portions of the debt. Secondly, he had drunk habitually and excessively of the rum offered by supplicants at the shrine, and when supplies of this diminished he had taken to drink-ing the locally distilled raw spirit—a poisonous fluid very wisely taboo to all reputable *abosom*. Thirdly, he had sought to bolster up his failing powers and reputation by installing, as an auxiliary, a large *suman* which he had bought.

The dejected and disgraced priest stayed in Mframaso for about six months. He was told at the shrine that if he did not eschew drink he would die before the year's end. His financial guarantors were told that they too would die if they did not speedily pay their debt. The chief himself came from Wawaase and, after some months of acrimonious negotiation and sacrifice of cows and sheep, he brought £150. The *obofohene* and some assistants were sent to prepare the Wawaase shrine for reopening.

Meanwhile the delinquent priest had been living in abstemious re-pentance and was much improved in health. He could walk without assistance, though with some slight residual ataxia. However, at one of the forty-day festivals he became mildly possessed, and after a fashion, danced. With hope restored he made further improvement and was sent home, the priest of Mframa accompanying him to perform a ceremonial reopening of the shrine. There the regenerate priest was left, with his re-established shrine and Mframa's injunctions concerning his religious and financial obligations.

At the end of nine months messengers came again to Mframaso saying that the shrine had been working satisfactorily and had made a profit of £204.

The point of this story is that dissociation, whether an hysterical phenomenon or not, can be successfully exploited only in conjunction with self-discipline and by a good personality. I shall be surprised if the Wawaase shrine lasts long.

Another established *obosomfo* for whom things were not running smoothly came one day to *abisa* at Mframaso and asked for help. He had been several years in practice in a village some twenty-five miles away. He said his shrine was not prospering, that he was £160 in debt and that he was afraid the *obosom* would cease from possessing him if people did not respect him more. He said that supplicants often brought the taboo drink *akpateshi* (illicitly distilled raw spirit) and he thought this insult was enough to scare the *obosom* away.

He seemed very anxious and also said that one night when he was out hunting he saw something in the bush "like fire", thought it concerned his *obosom* and was frightened. The consultant priest replied that the fire had been an ordinary fire lit by people, and that if he had fired his gun at it there would have been trouble.

It seemed to me that this man, though quite earnest, simply lacked the capacity to succeed in his work.

The Charlatan Priest

Although it is necessary to impute gross imposture to the medicine-men who exploit the credulity of both priests and populace in the bogus ceremonial of calling a new *obosom* down out of the sky, the *akomfo* priests themselves are, for the most part, honest men. The phenomenon of dissociated personality, on which their claim to veneration is based, is genuine and impressive. The priests themselves reverence it and submit to severe discipline in its service, though not disdaining its material fruits.

I can give, however, one example of a charlatan priest. It is to be noted that his priesthood did not last long.

He was a literate youth who had left school three years previously after obtaining his primary-school leaving certificate. Since then, he had been helping his uncle, a farmer, who had promised to send him to

74

a secondary school with the intent that he should ultimately become an engineer's mechanic. The uncle was dilatory and the career of priest no doubt seemed to the youth a short cut to wealth and prestige.

One night a Ga stranger—a migrant farmer who had come into the district to grow cocoa—took the youth out hunting. The hunter fired at an antelope and a few seconds later the youth shouted that he could see "something like a lump of fire giving out sparks". It had come out of a hole, he said, rushed towards them, halted and gone out, but kept lighting up again in bursts. The hunter could see nothing of the sort, but impressed by the boy's insistence, joined him in bolting home. The Ga, a very good personality, himself narrated this to me and was quite definite that he himself saw nothing.

Some days later the youth's uncle took him and a Fante labourer to hack weeds out of their farm, the youth almost certainly in resentment at this menial task. He began to use his cutlass so wildly that his uncle thought "something had come to him" and brought him home. For three days he was speechless, but made signs indicating his wants and wishes and had intermittent attacks of "shaking". On the third day the uncle, a Christian, took him to the local *obosom*, who said that a new *obosom* had come to him and must not be disregarded.

Shortly after this the boy went to his parents one evening after dark, shaking, dancing and signing to them to follow him to the outskirts of the town. There he pointed out to them a flickering light among the trees.* He signed to his companions to stay at a respectful distance while he himself went forward, dancing and smashing eggs. After a short interval he returned holding an object enveloped, except over its top out of which flames came, in white calico. When the flames had died out the youth carried home the object, which was a little smaller than a coconut, wrapped entirely in brand-new trade calico, of which no one dared to divest it. The boy then poured a libation on the bundle and took it to the local *obosomfo* who agreed to house it in his sanctuary till it should have one of its own.

After this there was a sound of mysterious drumming from the place where the sacred object was found. It lasted for three days, but as no one dared to go and investigate, it was impossible to say what sort of drum produced it. The youth may well have had confederates.

The aspirant then enlisted the co-operation of the town's chief—a

---

* I suspect that calcium carbide, used by all night-hunters in their acetylene forehead lamps, played a part. I witnessed a similar deception years ago in Akim Kotoku and found the spent carbide on the ground the next day.

literate who has since been de-stooled. The chief lent him some drums and some helpers, and a very unpretentious and inexpensive tabernacle was built to serve as a sanctuary till such time as a more imposing one could be built. A profit-sharing agreement was almost certainly made between the youth and the chief.

The first time I saw the new *obosomfo* at work I felt very dubious about his integrity. He was a sulky-looking boy and I thought also shifty. He danced to the drums outside his new sanctuary purporting to be possessed, but I did not think him genuinely dissociated. He grimaced and spun about, but had not the characteristic mask-like face and fine tremor. I do not think I was alone in my misgivings* and probably no one was more surprised than the boy himself when his new *obosom* "caught" someone.

Some months later he fell into the hands of the police for obtaining money under false pretences in a connection quite unrelated to his religious pretensions, and was given a long term of imprisonment which he was still serving when I left the district.

Rôle of Dissociation

In Ashanti, as we have seen, dissociation is a part of the technique of certain priests. The profession of priest, like that of any of the professions in our own country—Medicine, the Stage, the Bar, the Police—contains its quota of poor and base personalities, its leaven of richly endowed excellent personalities and its body of inoffensive pedestrian members. By and large, the people who do well in it exhibit the same personal qualities which would bring them esteem and success in any other calling.

The function of dissociation or "possession" in priestly duties is to endow the priest's utterances with authority and to exonerate him from personal responsibility for them. Public opinion and the moral judgments of society find in him vicarious utterance.

For the individual supplicant his own personal problems are weighed, summed up and clarified for him by the possessed priest with complete detachment, and judgment and advice are given in accordance with orthodox tenets. It is not derogatory to the dignity of a supplicant to accept the advice of an *obosom* when his dignity might compel him to reject the same advice if proffered by his parent or his wife.

Away from Ashanti, there are some districts of Ghana where priests never become possessed but simply officiate at the rites of ancient gods.

* See case-history, No. 38.

At big annual festivals, though these priests do not become possessed, they have a number of women auxiliaries who do and who then express in speech what are accepted as the wishes of the gods.

In these tribes people seeking personal and medical advice go to private practitioners. Soothsayers and medicine-men may either work in partnership with dissociation adepts or may themselves practise dissociation to enhance the authority of their diagnoses and treatments.

In some southern districts I have witnessed the custom of "carrying the coffin" round the town before taking it to the grave. The bearers become dissociated and "the spirit of the dead man drives them"—often with furious speed. It is held that if the deceased died from malicious poisoning, magic or witchcraft the coffin will refuse to pass the house of the evil-doer. Clearly, when public opinion has strong suspicions of any individual, that opinion, shared by the bearers of the coffin, finds expression in their dissociated action.

I have mentioned in passing that a phase of euphoria is often described after dissociation. Among the coastal Ga, dissociation is on this account sometimes used therapeutically. The patient is a person afflicted with a bad *gbeshi*, which may be roughly defined as a spirit of bad luck which brings him unaccountable failure when circumstances appear propitious. To remove this tiresome entity, the patient is taken by the medicine-man and his assistants to the outskirts of the town or on to the sea-shore and there dissociation is induced. The patient is made to hold either a large pan of water or a fowl on his head. A rhythmic din is produced by gong-gongs, clapping and chanting until the *gbeshi* "gets up", that is, till the patient becomes dissociated and dashes off to bush, pursued by insults and threatening cries directed at the departing troublesome *gbeshi*. When a fowl is used it is hoped that the *gbeshi* will enter it,* and it is accordingly abandoned in the bush. After this dissociation, for which the patient describes the usual amnesia, he feels relaxed, peaceful, happy and hopeful. Convinced that his troublesome *gbeshi* has departed, he embarks on a fresh start in life.

One of the most interesting religious spectacles of the last thirty years in West Africa—not only in Ghana—has been the rise of African-organised Christian cults which make regular use of the indigenous type of dissociation, not only to aid the recovery of the sick, if it can be induced in these patients, but to bring a feeling of peace, refreshment

---

* The theory that an evil spirit deserting a person could enter an animal was acceptable to the Hebrews and was invoked to explain the stampede of the Gadarene swine.

and well-being to any of the congregation who achieve it. In their belief, the afflatus which possesses them is the Holy Ghost of the early Christians.

It was in the Axim district of the Western Province, about eighteen years ago, that I first witnessed these Christian meetings, held out of doors and sometimes conducted by a woman minister. Since then such communities have proliferated and reached all parts of Ghana, though they are still most plentiful, I am told, in the Western Province. Their members, in my limited experience, seem happier, more generous and harder-working than most of their compatriots and their zeal is unparalleled by that of any other religious body. There can be no doubt that these worshippers have recaptured something of the atmosphere of the primitive Church and that it suits them better than the now orthodox "atmosphere of Christian worship" against which they have, with characteristically African independence of judgment, revolted.

Ashanti and Hebrew Spirit Possession

That Hebraisms exist in West African religions, particularly in Ashanti, has long been known, Egypt having been postulated as the common origin. But it has not been recorded, so far as I know, how strikingly similar are the technique and tradition of spirit possession in Ashanti to-day to that of which the Hebrew "prophets" were exponents, and how the two cults illuminate one another.

It appears from the Old Testament that there were three kinds of Hebrew prophet. Firstly there were those who simply had dreams.* Secondly there were those who were hallucinated, either visually like Gideon or auditorily like Samuel and many others. Of these latter, it was said, "the *word* of the Lord came". Thirdly there were the far more numerous prophets (even more numerous than in Ashanti to-day, for they went about in "bands") who were intermittently possessed by the "spirit".

The prophets of this last kind were, as in Ashanti, literally and physically *moved* by the possessing spirit without any conscious volition of their own. While thus moved by intense motor excitement they could perform incredible feats of strength and endurance, and they often ran uncontrollably to bush, sometimes, as in Ashanti, never to return.

The biblical descriptions of seizure by the spirit are variously worded, but always the prophet is suddenly and physically "moved" by it as a

---

* "The prophet that hath a dream let him tell a dream; and he that hath my word let him speak my word faithfully", Jeremiah xxiii, 28.

passive agent. We are told of more than one prophet that "the spirit of the Lord came upon him *mightily*". Of many another we read that the spirit "took" him, "drove" him, "rested upon" him, "entered into" him, "fell upon" him, "moved" him, "caught him away", "lifted him up", "set him on his feet" and so on. Sometimes it was said of the possessed prophet that "the *hand* of the Lord was upon him". Of Enoch it was said that he "walked with God", almost certainly meaning that he was physically—and, as it happened, fatally—made to walk away by a volition not apparently his own.

The "spirit" that produced these fits of motor excitement is designated in the Greek New Testament by the word πνευμα (air or breath), not only when the writers are describing contemporary happenings but when they are referring to the Old Testament prophets, thus leaving no doubt that, in their own minds, there was unbroken continuity with the old tradition.

Similarly in Ashanti, all the *abosom* who enter into and possess their priests come under the generic term *honhom*, a word which also means a wind or breeze and is related to the word *home*, to breathe. The idiom used of spirit possession in Ashanti is also identical with the biblical one, "the spirit rested upon them and they prophesied".*

Some of the Old Testament prophets appear to have experienced both hallucination and possession by "the spirit". Ezekiel seems at times to have experienced them in rapid alternation: probably the emotion engendered by visions and voices precipitated dissociation, and the exhaustion and hypoglycaemia after a period of dissociation brought more hallucinations. He says: "The spirit of the Lord entered into me when he spake unto me, and set me on my feet. . . . Moreover the spirit lifted me up and brought me to the East gate. . . . He said unto me, therefore prophesy against them, O son of man. And the spirit of the Lord fell upon me."

Moses similarly refers to a clean-cut break at the point when the "hand" of the Lord is removed and visions begin. God says to him, "I will *put* thee [Moses being, presumably, passively put] in a cleft in the rock . . . and I will *take away mine hand* and thou shalt see my back. . . ."

Besides the three types of accepted prophets there were inevitably the "false prophets", often denounced by the true prophets because they "prophesied out of their own hearts" without either dissociation or hallucination, and might even fake a spirit-driven run to bush. "I sent

* Numbers xi, 25. In Ashanti the equivalent expression is *"obosom no asi no so"*, the phrase *"si . . . so"* meaning to descend upon, or perch upon.

not these prophets, yet they ran, I spake not unto them, yet they prophesied."★

Let us now glance at a few Hebrew prophets, one by one.

The earliest record of the disappearance into bush of a dedicated man is that of Enoch. The clue to this was given me in Ashanti by my cook, a member of a remote Moslem tribe north of Bawku, in the Northern Territories, apropos of the disappearance of an Mframaso *okomfo* into bush. He told me of a countryman of his, who was driven, in similar fashion, of the spirit into the wilderness, and not seen again for five years, after which he returned and settled down. I enquired what *obosom* would drive a Moslem. The reply came simply and without hesitation, "God took him." The phrasing at once recalled Enoch, "And Enoch walked [not metaphorically] with God, and he was not, for God took him."

Moses' shamanistic career started—not surprisingly to any Ashanti—with danger to his life. "The Lord met him and sought to kill him." Later Moses made himself unique among Hebrew prophets by using chemical aids to hallucination when he conducted what Ashantis know as *abisa* at the door of the "tabernacle of testimony" or at the door of the "tent of meeting" where people brought their problems and where "Moses brought their cause before the Lord" always enveloping himself in fumes before giving utterance. "And it came to pass when Moses entered into the tent the pillar of cloud descended and stood at the door of the tent: and the Lord spake with Moses. . . . And the Lord spake unto Moses face to face as a man speaketh unto his friend." This was evidently clear hallucination, but it seems that on one occasion Moses employed fumes to induce dissociation in no fewer than seventy elders whom Moses set round about the tent. "And the Lord came down in the cloud and spake unto him, and took of the spirit that was upon him and put it upon the seventy elders: and it came to pass that when the spirit rested upon them they prophesied, but they did so no more." Two other men who remained in the camp on this emotional occasion were spontaneously possessed "and the spirit rested upon them . . . and they prophesied in the camp"—to the indignation of Joshua, who was astonished that Moses was not jealous.

On at least one occasion, it seems, the fumes were too thick for safety. "And Moses was not able to enter the tent of meeting because the cloud abode thereon."

★ Professor Dorothy Emmet takes a different view of false prophets. "Prophets and their societies", *J. Roy. Anth. Inst.*, Vol. LXXXV, pp. 13–24.

The secret of the fumes,* which no doubt Moses brought from Egypt, did not long survive him.

Although Moses was in the habit of going off into the mountains for forty-day periods, he does not appear to have been "driven" there and his fasting was self-imposed. † His final departure to die alone also seems deliberate. "And the Lord spake unto Moses . . . saying: Get thee up into this mountain . . . and die in the mount whither thou goest up. . . . So Moses died there in the land of Moab according to the word of the Lord and he [the Lord] buried him . . . but no man knoweth of his sepulchre unto this day."

The history of Samuel—a conventional priest of no great character as a prophet—affords an illustration of the principle that a prophet is exonerated from personal responsibility for his utterances. An older "man of God" had reproved the priest Eli for condoning the immorality of his sons, whereupon the child Samuel heard voices bidding him also to denounce the old man, and was not chidden for impertinence.

Saul and David are examples of young men who were first moved to prophesy "mightily" after the strongly emotional experience of ritual anointing into a high calling. Later, Saul became the prey of savage jealousy, which emotion also informed his prophesying with a murderous

* I consulted Mr. Robert Graves concerning what seemed to me a possible identity between the volcanic gases inhaled by the priestesses of the Delphic Oracle in their cleft in the rock and the gases inhaled by Moses in his cleft on Sinai. Mr. Graves tells me that neither the Delphic mountain nor Sinai is volcanic, but there is oil shale on Sinai. He also affirms that the Delphic sibyls inhaled the hallucinogenic fumes of a poisonous mushroom. He thinks that Moses used the same mushroom.

My own guess (as an ex-chemist) concerning the fumes used in the tent of meeting is that they may well have been impure nitrous oxide prepared by dropping crystals of ammonium nitrate (obtainable in an impure form from manure heaps in some climates and, like other nitrates, known to the Egyptians) on to a hot, but not red-hot, metal dish. This would account not only for the explosion which blew up the two meddlesome and inept sons of Aaron who "offered unto the Lord strange fire that he had not commanded" but also for the fact that Moses lived to be exceptionally old with no impairment of eyesight and vigour, whereas the habitual users of the toxic Delphic vapours never lived long.

Concerning the oil shale on Sinai, it might be that it was set smouldering by lightning, so producing the fiery glow and smoke so often seen on the mountain. Also, if oil vapour condensed on Moses' skin as he sat in the cleft, this could explain why "the skin of his face shone".

† Alongside of Moses, we are given a striking picture of men whom no experience of awe and wonder was able to stir out of their normal stolid consciousness. "Then went up Moses and Aaron, Nadab and Abihu and seventy of the elders of Israel: and they saw the God of Israel: and there was under his feet as it were a paved work of sapphire stone and as it were the very heaven for clearness. And upon the nobles of the children of Israel *he laid not his hand* and they beheld God and did eat and drink."

bent. Nevertheless, his chronicler and no doubt his associates exonerated him from personal responsibility for the actions of his dissociated personality: "An evil spirit *from God* came mightily upon Saul and he prophesied in the midst of the house."

Elijah the Tishbite appears to have been always prone, when "the hand of the Lord was upon him", to run capriciously to bush. When he gave his friend Obadiah a message to take to Ahab, Obadiah, admirer though he was, could not trust Elijah not to be "carried" off during the messenger's absence. "And it shall come to pass, as soon as I am gone from thee, that the spirit of the Lord shall carry thee whither I know not: and so when I come and tell Ahab and he cannot find thee, he shall slay me."

Elijah, like the Ashanti *okomfo* to-day, was prone to run himself to exhaustion and sleep. During one of these sleeps under a juniper tree an angel of the Lord came and fed him. In Ashanti the traditional ministering figures are the *mmoetia* forest dwarfs. The Old Testament itself provides the explanation of these ministrations to hungry and hallucinated people. "And it shall be as when an hungry man dreameth, and behold, he eateth . . . or as when a thirsty man dreameth and behold he drinketh.' Hallucinations, no less than dreams, can be wish-fulfilling.

In Elijah, also, we have an outstanding example of the desire for death which may be expressed by the exhausted *okomfo* whose vitality has been drained by over-exertion to the very dregs.

The end of Elijah appears to have been in the tradition of Enoch: he made off into the bush and did not return. Evidently he had prodromal symptoms of this final impulse, for he appointed a successor and gathered a band of sons of the prophets to see him off. A whirlwind,* together with the clatter of a passing bright metal vehicle on the road,† apparently precipitated his dissociation and into the dust of the whirlwind he disappeared. The sons of the prophets, in spite of the discouragement of the vain and ambitious successor Elisha, insisted on organising a search-party as their Ashanti counterparts would certainly do to-day.

The prophet Jephthah seems to give us another example of a spectacular cross-country run at the outset of a dedicated career. The story goes that Jephthah, having consented when asked by the elders of Gilead to lead a fight against the Ammonites, began irresolutely by parleying, unsuccessfully, with the enemy. However, "then the spirit of the Lord

---

* It could not have been a very strong whirlwind or it would have carried the cloak further before dropping it.

† Elijah appears to have found chariots exciting and apt to produce dissociation. We are told how the "hand of the Lord" upon him once caused him to run before Ahab's chariot.

came upon Jephthah and he passed over Gilead and Manasseh and passed over Mispeh of Gilead and from Mizpeh of Gilead he passed over unto the children of Ammon. And Jephthah vowed a vow unto the Lord. . . ." I do not wish to stress my interpretation of this quotation as another run under the influence of "the spirit", for it is not certain that Jephthah ran or that he went alone, but at any rate the spirit was upon him and he paused at the end of the journey to make vows before opening his military campaign.

Another prophet worthy of attention is Samson. Like Samuel, dedicated to the Lord from the womb, he appears to have attained young manhood when "the spirit of the Lord began to move him in Mahaneh-Dan". In his later years, like his contemporary consultant prophetess and "judge" Deborah, endowed only with the authority of spirit possession, he "judged Israel" for twenty years. Like many Ashanti *akomfo* to-day, he was capable, when "the spirit came mightily upon him", of spectacular feats of strength and valour. But when shorn of his *mpese-mpese* hair, the outward and visible sign, as in Ashanti, of his calling, he failed to achieve the orgasm of possession, presumably inhibited by the same kind of anxiety which makes a man impotent with a new wife when he believes the old wife to be making bad magic against him. When his hair grew again his confidence returned, as does that of the re-assured husband after putting himself under the protection of an *obosom*.

In the first century A.D., there appears to have been perfect identity, to the minds of the apostles, between the Holy Spirit that moved Moses and the other prophets and that which descended upon the prophet Jesus at his baptism, and after his death possessed his disciples, first in a scene of intense excitement at Pentecost and later spreading among converts till the apostles perceived an approximation to the state of affairs, "I will pour out my spirit upon all flesh."

No prophet ran truer, at the outset and close of his dedicated career, to Hebrew tradition than did the prophet Jesus. He began on the ritual occasion of his baptism by an older prophet when he was "driven" for the usual forty days into the wilderness, at the end of which time traditional "angels" ministered to him as do the traditional *mmoetia* to the driven Ashanti novice to-day. "And straightway, coming up out of the water, he saw the heavens rent asunder and the Spirit as a dove descending on him, and a voice came out of the heavens. . . . And straightway the Spirit driveth him forth into the wilderness. And he was in the wilderness forty days . . . and the angels ministered unto him."*

* The dove which came blundering into the assembly in the river was probably a real one which afterwards became charged with significance by the onlookers, as

The final disappearance of Jesus was in the tradition of Elijah. Reviving in the rock-hewn tomb (Pilate had "marvelled that he was already dead," for death by crucifixion usually occurred on the fourth day), Jesus spent a further ritual period of forty days, elusively in the wilderness, but sometimes joining his friends at dusk or dawn to take food. He looked—as very sick men often do—so changed that they hardly knew him, but he assured them that he was flesh and blood and not a wraith. "When forty days were fulfilled ", he gathered his disciples on a hillside as the sons of the prophets had been gathered to take farewell of Elijah, and in the act of blessing them he was "taken up" ($\epsilon\pi\eta\rho\theta\eta$ —stirred up, roused, excited, elated) and went up the hillside into a hill-top mist which "received him out of their sight".* It was not new for prophets to go to meet God in a cloud. "And Moses entered into the cloud and went up into the mount." We gather, moreover, from the disciples' later history that they expected Jesus to come back, for he was, unlike Elijah and Moses, but a young man. They forgot, however, that he was a very sick man,† and, like the Ashanti to-day when a man is "taken" to bush, they continued to believe that he might be alive. Much earlier, the same reluctance to believe that the "taken" Enoch could be dead had resulted in the legend that he never died at all but was "translated".

Shortly after the departure of Jesus the Pentecost meeting of the disciples, when they were all simultaneously possessed, inaugurated a period when possession spread like an epidemic among the converts to the new faith. A striking feature of the New Testament narratives is the clear distinction drawn between those who were possessed and those

were several birds which appear in my Ashanti case-histories. (See cases 24, 99.) Doves are sacred and significant birds in West Africa also.

The voice from heaven we may safely take to have been thunder, for there is elsewhere an account of another "voice" which runs, "There came a voice out of the heaven. . . . [The multitude that stood by and heard it said that it had thundered] Others said, An angel hath spoken unto him." Jesus himself denied that this "voice" had any significance *for him*. John xii, 29–30.

* I find that in the edition of the Greek Testament annotated by Dr. Brooke Foss Westcott in 1885, certain passages are marked by him as "suspected readings" and certain others as "rejected readings". The latter he declares to be "interpolations containing important matter apparently derived from extraneous sources". These rejected readings include all the accounts of the "ascension" except that in Acts, indicating that it was a favourite subject for embellishment. Nevertheless, there is still no evidence that the evangelists wished to convey a picture of Jesus soaring into the air. Ezekiel and others had been "lifted up", and Jesus himself had been "taken" up a mountain on his own feet before.

† A soldier's spear had probably pierced between his ribs ($\pi\lambda\epsilon\upsilon\rho\alpha\nu$, John xix, 34)—That the wound bled is evidence that he was alive.

who were not, or, in the chroniclers' idiom, those who received the Holy Ghost and those who did not. "Now when the apostles which were at Jerusalem heard that Samaria had received the word of God, they sent unto them Peter and John: who, when they were come down, prayed for them that they might receive the Holy Ghost: for as yet he was fallen upon none of them: only they had been baptised into the name of the Lord Jesus. Then laid they their hands on them and they received the Holy Ghost." Again, to the astonishment of Peter, a group of Gentiles were affected even before they had been baptised. "While Peter yet spake these words, the Holy Ghost fell on all them which heard the word. And they of the circumcision which believed were amazed, as many as came with Peter, because that on the Gentiles was poured out the gift of the Holy Ghost. For they heard them speak with tongues and magnify God. Then answered Peter, Can any man forbid the water that they should not be baptised which have received the Holy Ghost as well as we?" Of another group of believers, encountered by Paul, we are told, "And he said unto them, Did ye receive the Holy Ghost when ye believed? And they said unto him, Nay, we did not so much as hear whether the Holy Ghost was given. And he said, Into what then were ye baptised? And they said, Into John's baptism. And Paul said, John baptised with the baptism of repentance, saying unto the people that they should believe on him which should come after him, that is, on Jesus. And when they heard this they were baptised into the name of the Lord Jesus. And when Paul laid his hands on them the Holy Ghost came on them: and they spake with tongues and prophesied."

The occasion of the baptism of the eunuch by Philip is remarkable in that Philip was, of the two, the more profoundly moved—so literally moved that he dashed off across country in the familiar Ashanti and Hebrew fashion. "And as they went on the way they came unto a certain water and the eunuch said, Behold, here is water: what doth hinder me to be baptised? And he commanded the chariot to stand still and they both went down into the water, both Philip and the eunuch; and he baptised him. And when they came up out of the water the spirit of the Lord caught away Philip*; and the eunuch saw him no more, for he went on his way rejoicing. But Philip was found at Azotus"—whether after an organised search or not, we are not told.

There can be no doubt about the impetus given to early Christianity by the phenomenon of possession, not only through the excitement,

---

* Philip's aptitude for dissociation was inherited by his "four daughters, virgins, which did prophesy". Acts xxi 9.

the euphoria and the enthusiasm of the possessed, but also by the conviction and authority which this dramatic and supposedly supernatural phenomenon conveyed to the spectator. Jesus had certainly foreseen this. He himself, though traditional enough to begin and end his ministry in the ancestral style, was not, so far as we know, habitually dissociated. Such a relatively cheap and ephemeral form of "comfort" could never have ranked high in his scale of values, but he did not deny its usefulness for those in need of stimulus. But he must also have desired a day when the *content* of his teaching would be valued without such "signs and wonders". And indeed it was not long before Paul declared that there were "greater gifts" and "a more excellent way", and in his immortal psalm, he showed that he had perceived something of the unique beauty and majesty of the already neglected *teaching* of Jesus. *

As has already been said, dissociation is a mental mechanism, a technique, a vehicle for conveying both the convictions of the prophet and the tenets of contemporary thought and ethics. It does not dictate what shall be expressed, any more than a painter's brushes and pigments dictate his pictures. A possessed prophet who proclaims the anger of God, the love of God or the depravity of man is one who has, in conscious thought, reflected upon these topics. The value of Jesus's forty-day sojourn in the wilderness lies not in the dissociated state in which he was "driven" there (dissociation in itself is no more elevating or degrading than are sleep and laughter) but in the quality of his cogitations and the decisions he reached. We know that at the age of twelve he had astonished learned men by his doctrine and no doubt he had continued thinking throughout the next eighteen years. It was those years of reflection, not the emotional crisis of dissociation, that determined the supreme status of Jesus among prophets. The later Christian prophets owed their extinction to the poverty of their understanding and personality and the consequent inanity of their prophesying.†

---

* I Corinthians xii, xiii, xiv.

† Gibbon writes of the primitive Church, "The want of discipline and human learning was supplied by the occasional assistance of the *prophets* who were called to that function without distinction of age, of sex or of natural abilities, and who, as often as they felt the divine impulse, poured forth the effusions of the Spirit in the assembly of the faithful. But these extraordinary gifts were frequently abused or misapplied by the prophetic teachers. They displayed them at an improper season, presumptuously disturbed the service of the assembly and by their pride or mistaken zeal they introduced, particularly into the apostolic Church of Corinth, a long and melancholy train of disorders. As the institution of prophets became useless, and even pernicious, their powers were withdrawn and their office abolished. (*Decline and Fall of the Roman Empire*, chap. xv., Edward Gibbon.)

IV

THE NEW SHRINES

§ 1. INTRODUCTION

Most of the patients described later in this book were found in Ashanti among the pilgrim supplicants at shrines of new or newly revived deities. It is because they are the resort of patients and other anxious people that I deem it meet to turn attention briefly upon the shrines themselves. To explain why the shrines, new in both age and character, are seething with vitality whereas all the ancient supernatural sanctions are moribund is the task of the anthropologist rather than the psychiatrist. The latter accepts the fact of the shrines and the work they do.

In Ashanti, as elsewhere in Ghana, very few of the shrines are ancient tribal establishments but are privately owned and have sprung up in response to a growing sense of insecurity which can be correlated with the expansion of the cocoa industry.

Of the twenty-nine shrines that came within my ambit in Ashanti, only three were ancient; three were established between 1914 and 1919, the influenza pandemic which exterminated whole villages, being a datum-line specifically mentioned by informants; two were founded about fifteen years ago; fifteen were set up less than ten years ago; six were newly established during my two years' sojourn in the district. All the modern ones were privately owned and profit-making.

Mentally ill people comprise only a very small proportion of the pilgrims who flock to these shrines not only from within Ashanti but from distant parts of Akan Ghana. The great majority are healthy people supplicating for "protection". Financially successful men are full of fear lest envious kinsmen should, by means of bad magic or witchcraft, bring about their ruin. Unsuccessful men are convinced that envious malice is the cause of their failure. Thus, a strikingly "paranoid" attitude is normal. Healthy intelligent Africans have some insight into the prevalent distrust and envy, and often refer to it spontaneously as one of the weaknesses of "us black men".

The typical pilgrim comes annually to the shrine, asks the deity for a year's protection and promises a thank-offering of a sheep and a bottle of rum at the end of the year. The deity's protection and blessing is granted conditionally on the supplicant's keeping prescribed rules of ethical conduct. He must not steal, commit adultery, bear false witness, nor curse another person. And above all he must neither possess bad talismans, make bad magic against others, nor engage in witchcraft. If he breaks any of these rules the deity will first "catch hold" of him and then, if he does not promptly confess and obtain pardon, will swiftly kill him or, alternatively, smite him with permanent madness. A similar fate will overtake anyone else who attempts the prohibited offences against the "protected" innocent worshipper.

Two Types of New Shrine

The hundreds of new profit-making shrines which have been set up in Ghana during the past thirty or more year sare of two distinct types:

(1) The *obosom-brafo* type of Ashanti shrine, said to be a revival, in a benign form, of an ancient type of "executioner's" shrine which in the old days dealt out capital punishment to witches and other evil-doers.★ But whereas in the old days death-sentences were executed by human beings, to-day it is held that the deity is able to inflict supernatural death.

(2) The "drinking-medicine" type of shrine, not indigenous, but introduced, with modifications, from the Northern Territories.

(1) The *obosom-brafo* gods of ancient Ashanti co-existed with benign tribal gods—such as the river-gods, Bosom Tano and Bosom Pra—who were concerned mainly with positive blessings—rain, health, fertility, tribal peace and well-being. The priests of the latter gods were not, as a rule, *akomfo* practising spirit-possession, but offered dignified prayer and other rites, not only on behalf of the tribe at annual festivals but also on behalf of individuals who sought help in sickness or trouble. These old benign gods still exist alongside the new *obosom-brafo* shrines, but are considered inadequate for modern needs. One informant, eulogising the new deity Mframa, summed this up by saying, "Mframa is greater

★ This type of shrine is said to have been suppressed by law because of both excessive bloodshed and corruption. The priests abused the privilege of confiscating the property of those sentenced to death. *Brafo* popularly means an executioner or hangman, but at the shrines to-day the *obrafohene* executes all the *obosom's* orders concerning medical treatment, ritual bathing and so on. He is also responsible for the proper conduct of all shrine activity.

than the old ones, because Mframa can *kill*."* The name chosen for
another new deity whose establishment I witnessed was "Kofi the Lion
who Kills Thousands"—a name calculated to attract flocks of customers.

Within the last few years the Ashanti type of *obosom-brafo* shrine has
spread south, outside of Ashanti. The old *obofohene* who "captured"
many new *abosom* in the Mframaso district was recently called as far south
as Akim Kotoku, where he helped to set up a shrine in Abenase, a town
in which I witnessed, in 1938, the work of a then new "drinking-medicine" shrine. A detailed examination of *obosom-brafo* shrines and the
activities associated with them, is reserved for later chapters in this book.

(2) The "drinking-medicine" is rather misleadingly so called, for it
is essentially a deity. The deity does not, however, possess its priest—
except perhaps gratuitously at a festival—and the supplicants carry out
a quick and easy ceremony of putting themselves into the deity's care.
Usually they decapitate a fowl and fling down the headless trunk: if
this, after flapping on the ground, comes to rest breast-upwards, the
deity is assumed to have approved the supplicant: if not, the supplicant
must search his heart and confess his sins and try again. Having been
approved, the supplicant "drinks" the deity's medicine to seal the pact
between them. Usually he does not literally drink but eats a consecrated
kola-nut, but at some shrines he takes a ritual bath and drinks some of
the bath-water. The member's covenant with the deity is the same as
that between a supplicant and an *obosom-brafo*. The commandment forbids stealing, killing, false witness and "bad mind" against another (i.e.,
intent to harm). Marital fidelity is enjoined upon women. Above all,
witchcraft and bad magic are forbidden, as also are cursing and the
possession of bad *suman*. If the member breaks any of these rules the
deity will either kill him or make him permanently mad, but will first
"catch hold of him" by making him either sick or mentally disturbed.
This preliminary "laying hold of" the offender gives him an opportunity for confession and expiation.

It is also in the pact with the deity that if any of these offences are
committed against the supplicant by a third party, the latter will be
punished in the same way.

The "drinking medicine", in the demands it makes and the rewards
it offers, is no different from the *obosom-brafo*.

---

* It is not strictly true that the old gods were regarded as *unable* to kill, rather
were they regarded as preoccupied mainly with blessing. The idea that the wages
of sin is death and the reward of goodness is long life belongs to all the ancient
cults, but in the new shrine cults is the central emphasis.

So far as I know, every shrine of a "drinking-medicine" was fetched from the Northern Territories by a private practitioner who remained under the aegis of the Northern Territory deity and practised in his name. To the forest-country and seaside peoples the drinking-medicines represent an entirely new departure into a non-traditional type of self-insurance.

The most ubiquitous of these "drinking-medicines" is Tigari, whose original home, so far as I can discover, is Ipara on the road to Bole. The oldest imported Tigari shrine that I personally know was set up in north-west Ashanti during the First World War. I estimate that there are now hundreds of Tigari shrines among the Akan peoples, perhaps most thickly strewn in Fanti country. In Akwapim and elsewhere there are annual gatherings of local Tigari priests, and each priest also makes an effort to go annually to Ipara.

In Akim, in the nineteen-thirties, shrines of Senyon Kupo, from Senyon near Wa, were nearly as plentiful as Tigari's, but now seem to have declined.

Another of the "drinking-medicines" is that of Kundi. The oldest of his imported shrines known to me is in north-west Ashanti and was established during the influenza pandemic of 1918. I knew a Kundi shrine in Big Ada in 1938. Another "drinking-medicine" found in Akim in the nineteen-thirties was that of Nana Tongo, from the Tong Hills near Zuarugu, whither some of the most influential literate paramount chiefs in the Gold Coast made pilgrimages at that time. Tongo shrines, however, are seldom seen now that most of the original owners have died. Nangoro, a shrine from Lobi, and Asasi from Kontrobi in the French Ivory Coast, flourished in the same period but have now diminished. Another, Krakyi Dente, said to have come from Kete Krakyi, still has some active shrines in Akim and Kwahu.

The relation between the new shrines—both *obosom-brafo* and drinking-medicine—and the secular authority has always been of some interest. Although it is not unknown for a drinking-medicine shrine to be publicly owned by a town which appoints an official to obtain it, learn the ritual and act as priest, as a general rule the shrines are privately owned.

In the nineteen-thirties chiefs' courts were accustomed to deal with a great variety of disputes and offences. Fines paid into court were a source of revenue. When people formed the habit of settling their inter-personal disputes out of court, at shrines, the chiefs conceived a bitter resentment against the shrines and often made gross misrepresentations against them to the government and the police in an effort to get them suppressed.

At the present day in Ashanti, most paramount chiefs have agreements with all shrines whereby the latter are permitted to practise only on the condition that they pay one-third of their profits to the chief. Some shrines employ a whole-time secretary to keep their accounts. Other shrines pay no fixed sum, but it is understood that they will assist their chiefs generously in time of need.

In the eyes of the new Local Councils all shrine priests rank as private practitioners of native medicine and pay several guineas a year for their licences to practise.* Their methods, however, are as purely religious as those used at Lourdes.

§ 2. AN ASHANTI SHRINE VILLAGE

There are many new villages in Ghana which have grown up each around one new shrine. Some have attained the aspect of considerable townships, but their *raison d'être* is still the shrine.

The village of which I shall attempt a rough sketch is Mframaso, where I lived. The population there was dwindling but was about three hundred souls.

When I first entered the district I had never heard of Mframaso, but hoped to be allowed to stay in another village—Nwase—where there was a shrine so popular that its fame had reached me in Akim, through pilgrims who had made the long journey to it. However, I found the priest at Nwase ill-disposed towards Europeans, but in the hope that he might later relent and allow me access to his huge clientele, I decided to settle within easy reach of him. Although the priest at Mframaso deferred, in most matters, to the judgment of his friend at Nwase, I was nevertheless kindly received in Mframaso—for a reason which will later appear.

The Mframaso shrine was of the *obosom-brafo* type. The general setup, priestly technique, festivals and routine ceremonial, was strictly in accordance with ancient Ashanti practice.

The village of Mframaso was founded, round about ten years ago, by the first priest, by all accounts a man of character so radiant that I have

---

* Through the courtesy of the Minister of Local Government I was enabled to circularise the District Councils and through them the Local Councils. In this way I was able to establish that there are at least ten thousand native practitioners in Ghana, *excluding* the Northern Territories.

seldom deplored anything more than the fact that he had been about a year dead when I arrived. Some of his older friends were still so grief-stricken that they could not speak of him without distress and could contemplate no tolerable future for the village.

The first priest belonged to a local family called the Bokoro people, a kinship group which had a common ancestress about six generations ago. From this group is always chosen the *Krontinhene* (a senior elder) of Wenchi town.

There was already an *okomfo* tradition in the Bokoro, for one member was the priest of the deity Timani, a deity which first "possessed" an ancestress about four generations previously. This ancestress, with her eleventh child, an infant, on her back, was driven into the wilderness for forty days, returning to establish a shrine for Timani. This shrine jogged on in the ancient manner for several generations, and still exists, though it has never become a haunt of pilgrims and strangers.

The founder of Mframaso was an elderly man, quietly farming with his wives and children in a tiny farm camp near a stream when the *obosom* first "came to him" and possessed him. It came in great strength, driving him forth and "shaking him as a great wind shakes the trees of the forest", sometimes flinging him violently to the ground. On one occasion he was driven into the wilderness so swiftly and so far that the pursuers gave up the immediate chase and organised big search-parties from the surrounding country-towns: they eventually found him in the direction opposite from that he had originally taken, exhausted and soaking wet. Though it had not rained, "the *obosom* had bathed him".

Accepting his vocation he went to a very ancient shrine about twenty miles away, where the aged priest—not himself an *okomfo*—guided him through the dangerous early stages of spirit possession, till his behaviour, controlled according to traditional ritual, became automatic and there was no longer danger of his being "taken" irrevocably to bush. He then returned to his farm settlement and built a rough-and-ready thatched sanctuary. The deity was named Mframa* from its resemblance to a rushing mighty wind (*mframa* = wind). The village was named Mframaso—the place of Mframa.

Among the new priest's kinsmen was a retired elephant-hunter, in his active days very intrepid by virtue of the strong "hunting-medicines" that he possessed. He occupied, among the elders of the paramount stool, the post of *obofohene* or Head of the Hunters. He was officially responsible for various outdoor land ritual in remote and

* The name is not a new one among Ashanti *abosom*.

"fearful" places. Since his retirement this old man had established himself as an *adunsini* or medicine-man, and had a roomful of medical insignia, divining apparatus, and countless *suman* for all sorts of purposes. He was not an *okomfo* or priest, but a practitioner of "medicine" (i.e., reputable magic). The long immunity from fatal accident which his "strong" medicines had given him in the presence of "fearful" forces had encouraged him to enter a new field and when new shrines began to appear he made himself into a "catcher of *abosom*". That is to say, he often organised, on behalf of new shrines, nocturnal drumming ceremonies on the forest edge: at the end of every such ceremony he extracted out of the undergrowth, for the edification of the awe-stricken onlookers, coconut-sized lumps of matter encased in gold-leaf and wrapped in white trade calico, ostensibly fallen from heaven in response to the drumming. These fortifying fetishes, by no means essential—indeed foreign—to the theory and practice of *obosom* worship, enhanced the prestige of newly-established *abosom*.

At the time when the new priest's *obosom* started to possess him, his kinsman the *obofohene* had already acquired a widespread reputation as an *obosom*-capturer. He accordingly "caught" one for the simple-hearted and—in this respect—gullible new priest.

Later, additional *abosom*, some of them gentler in manner than the furious Mframa, began to possess the priest from time to time, and the insignia of these were similarly drummed down and captured by the *obofohene* till the sanctuary housed a total of seven, some male, some female, and sharing among them the work of possessing the priest and hearkening to the needs of the supplicants.

From the time of its foundation the shrine of Mframa flourished and leapt into widespread popularity. It soon moved from its first site, and a costly cement and sheet-iron sanctuary and priest's house were built. The new site was two miles from any road, but the priest's helpers soon cleared a rough lorry-track to it.

Various friends and kinsmen of the priest came at his invitation to make a little township. About a dozen were appointed shrine elders, partly to act as trustees in business affairs and partly to be present at every *abisa*, for no *obosom* will hold an *abisa* without a quorum of elders as witnesses. The nominal head of these elders—the "owner" or custodian of the shrine—was a near kinsman of the priest and was already the *odikro* or headman of a country-town some five miles away. He continued to live in his old town but trudged three times a week to Mframaso. He was the twin brother of the man who was driven by the spirit into the bush never to return. The general overseer of the village was the ceremonial head of the priest's family—the *Krontinhene* of the Wenchi stool: he lived in Wenchi and came to Mframaso only on special occasions. The *obofohene* came—with all his *suman*—to live in Mframaso, and later was appointed secular *odikro* or headman. Two of the elders were senior women* kinsfolk of the priest. The *obrafohene* and one of the *akyeame* (spokesmen), the shrine treasurer and various young drummers and shrine attendants were also kinsmen.

Other friends of the priest, some of them immigrant farming "strangers" whose farms neighboured his, came at his invitation and built houses to take in pilgrim lodgers.

The shrine prospered, mainly because of the remarkable personality of the priest. He was full of fire and vitality, and took a warm-hearted personal interest in every supplicant. From those who were needy he would accept no payment, but unstinted free-will thank-offerings poured in from those whose affections he had won. Many stories are told of his paranormal cognition, not only when the spirit was in possession of him but in everyday life. Sometimes he would go out to meet and welcome pilgrims on the road, telling them, before they told him, whence and wherefore they had come.

One story is told of a literate Civil Servant who came to the shrine saying that despite a good salary he did not prosper. Countless calls on his resources kept him always in embarrassment and want. The possessed priest said, "I can see no prosperity for you in your present work; there seems to be good fortune for you only if you became a palm-wine tapper." Now, palm-tapping is one of the lowliest and least lucrative occupations—a degrading come-down for a scholar—and the supplicant went away sorrowful. However, on the way home he reluctantly bought palm-tapper's tools and on arrival gave in his resignation and started the new work. Less than a year later he appeared again at the shrine and jubilantly told his tale, as follows. One day when at work in the forest he was chased by a snake. He ran, at random, towards a nearby lorry-road. Just as he reached it the snake gave up the chase and at that moment a lorry sped past. Out of the back of the lorry, unnoticed by any passenger, fell a large suitcase crammed full of treasury-notes—thousands of pounds-worth.

* The impeccable memory of one of these women, Ekwia Misa, enabled me to construct a detailed genealogical tree of the Bokoro people since the time of the immigration of their founder. The other Bokoro informants could give only vague and inconsistent pieces of information.

This priest's rule of the village was a benevolent despotism: everyone took joy in working with him. The new buildings were put up by the men and youths under the direction of one who had been an army mason, and they still recall their pleasure and enthusiasm. In the *obrafoso* grove where, in the shade of huge trees, *abisa* was often held when the sun was high, a cement-lined pool was made "for the *abosom* to take their baths". The borders of the avenue leading to this grove were planted with red lilies.

No one in trouble or need was ever sent away uncomforted. The stool of the paramount chief—like all stools—was constantly in need of large sums and the priest gave it lavish help. On one occasion some political opponents of the chief suspected that some of this money had been used to further party ends, so some lorry-loads of hooligans— such as all parties contain—invaded Mframaso with the avowed inten-tion of smashing it up and looting. The priest strode out to meet them, armed only with his blazing personal authority, and they slunk home.

Like most other Africans, he saw no incompatibility between Christianity and his own creed. The Christians bothered about only one of God's sons: his own *abosom* were all God's sons. A poor God indeed it would be who could achieve but one son. At any rate the old man proposed to build both a church and a school in Mframaso, and saw no reason why he should not worship God in the church every Sunday after his morning *abisa*. The school he did achieve. He provided the building and the Presbyterians sent a teacher whose salary (if my infor-mation is correct) was paid by the priest. At any rate, when he fell ill, there was trouble with the teacher and the school closed.

When I first visited the village, after the death of this old priest, I suggested staying there to see something of the shrine work. The officials, already feeling insecure under the new regime, were at first suspicious and unfriendly and gave me a not too courteous refusal. However, one of the elders remembered that the old priest had pro-phesied that a European would come and stay in the village. Reminded, they all recalled this dictum, changed their attitude to one of great kindliness and gave me a parcel of land whereon to put up my dwelling. The old priest's friends never tired of telling me that had he been alive he would have insisted on himself building a guest-house and would have visited me every day to see that I had everything a guest could desire.

Another prophecy that he made when the spirit first began to possess him was that he would die after seven years' priesthood, and that his successors would in turn each die after seven years. And indeed, when he had served about six years, it became evident that he had pulmonary tuberculosis. He was not perturbed and refused to spare himself, fasting three whole days in the week and working "like one possessed", which indeed he was. Towards the end, his friends took him to hospital, though he laughed at their foolishness and said no hospital could alter his destiny, even if he wished it. At the hospital his friends were told that nothing could be done for him: he laughed again and thanked the staff courteously for their trouble. He came home and lived longer than the hospital had predicted, for his seven years were not up. Near his end, when he lay weak, wasted and gasping, the spirit continued to come upon him. when he would rise and again be thrashed and shaken like trees in a storm as he uttered his last prophecies. "No one", say the witnesses, "would have believed it possible for a weak and dying man to find so much strength. But the power was from the *obosom*."

When he died, he was buried, in obedience to his own orders, under the spot in front of the sanctuary where the priest stands to conduct *abisa*. His ghost, he said, would there help and sustain his successors.

Asked on his death-bed who was to succeed him, he said that the deity would appoint its own successor by possessing him in great strength.

After his burial there were Pentecostal scenes when a number of people were possessed for the first time in their lives. These were mostly ambitious kinsmen coveting the associated prestige and wealth of priesthood. Finally, the spirit came with unsurpassed violence to the kinsman who had held the post of *obrafohene*. He was with difficulty restrained from dashing off into the wilderness and was sent for training to the same respected old priest who had trained his predecessor. Before he went, one of his rivals made a last bid for the post by bribing his male cook—a priest's wives do not do his cooking—to accept a *dufuaw* and to put it in his food. The cook* was "caught hold of" by the *obosom*, went mad with fear and died within a few days. The rival, a near relative of the new priest and very tough, confessed, made atonement and survived.

When I first visited the village the new priest had been at work about three months. He was a comparatively young man and of a very different clay from his predecessor. He had been known as a freely-drinking, fisticuffing swashbuckler, but under the firm tutelage of his kinsman had been a satisfactory *obrafohene*. As priest there was always at the back of his mind the prophecy that he would die at the end of seven years and

* The cook was a near relative of a chronic schizophrenic whom I knew.

he was the prey of conflict and anxiety. In apologising to me one day
for some trivial breach of faith, he told me that he was always tired, for
akom work was exhausting. And indeed he always seemed reluctant to
start work in the morning and often kept impatient supplicants waiting
outside the locked yard till noon. On shrine working-days when he
fasted till after the evening session and drank only tea, he often flew into
hypoglycaemic indignations, shouting, scolding and rambling from one
topic to another till the elders wondered whether he would ever start
work or, if work was over, go to his house.

Village discipline soon began to suffer. Disagreements which the old
priest would have aborted with one word, not only grew into unseemly
wrangles but were brought to the shrine for settlement before the public
abisa began in the morning. So much *abisa* time was consumed by these
petty disputes that the queues lengthened and pilgrims often waited
days before they got a hearing and sometimes went home disgustedly
without it. Furthermore, the new priest and the new *obrafohene*, neither
with enough foresight to cherish the goose that laid the golden egg,
began to charge supplicants such heavy fees for their ritual baths and
medications that the impoverished wretches never returned again. The
popularity of the shrine plummeted and towards the end of my stay
even the priest's own kinsmen were consulting other shrines.

Nor were the younger men of Mframaso any different from those of
other places in Ghana to-day in their general attitude of grudging envy
towards more fortunate fellow-men. A typical example occurred one
day among the shrine *sinkwafo*. A party of women from a distant
Ashanti town—friends of the late priest—returned to render thanks for
the recovery of one of their number from a severe illness. They stood in
a group at *abisa* and sang thanksgiving songs of their own composition
and brought an unusual number of gifts. One of these was a length of
cloth and a special song for the shrine assistant who had carried out
most of the patient's daily treatment. This attendant, a most good-
natured and happy individual, was the only one of the attendants who
never scamped his work and was always cheerful and friendly. No
sooner was his name mentioned in praise than the brows of the other
sinkwafo blackened. Five minutes later, when the *obosom* "went to sleep"
and drumming began, the favoured attendant took up his drumsticks
light-heartedly as usual, but to his hurt bewilderment they were
snatched from him and he was elbowed savagely aside. He protested,
"But don't I always drum?" They answered sardonically, "You have
become senior now: you can't mix with us any more." He quickly

became resigned, for his colleagues' attitude was a familiar one: he regretted only the inconsiderateness of the visitors who had singled him out for praise.

Another typical instance of the same attitude occurred when the senior elder's lorry, which plied between Mframaso and Kumasi with pilgrims, was found to be losing money through the peculations of the driver, who, by some oversight, had never been put into precautionary fealty to the *obosom*. He was dismissed and his post was offered to a young literate who had driven the priest's private car in palmier days. This driver, a sober and pleasant person, badly in need of a job, found some excuse to decline. He told me later, quite matter-of-factly, that his life, even if safe, would have been intolerable under the barrage of hatred, had he accepted.

§ 3. ROUTINE SHRINE PROCEDURE

No two shrines are alike in details of ritual and priestly technique. The following is an account of procedure at Mframaso, the village in which I lived.

After dark on the evening before a shrine working-day, of which there are three every week—Sunday, Wednesday and Friday—the drums are briefly beaten to remind the village to prepare for the morrow. This means that the elders, shrine officials, *sinkwafo*, and *Apo* women are to eschew sexual intercourse till after the day of worship.

Soon after dawn the next morning the drums are beaten again and the women *Apo* singers beat their rattles and sing cheerfully and tunefully. The women are apt to be slack about turning out for this, and from time to time the possessed priest reproves them and fines them a fowl.

About nine o'clock—it was earlier, I was told, in the zestful days of the first priest—the talking-drums shout, "*Mommra, mommra*" (Come ye, come ye). The elders, other drummers, shrine officials and the priest's wives then assemble in the big walled yard, the gates being as yet unopened to the populace.

Within the big yard is the circular sanctuary with its door opening on to a fenced dais which juts out like an apron-stage. The elders take their seats under a sheet-iron awning looking towards the side of the dais. Between them and the sanctuary stands the smaller of the two orchestras consisting of two calabash drums, two thonged under-arm tonal drums and one stumpy wooden drum. The other, and major, orchestra under a sheet-iron awning in another corner of the yard consists of two of those huge tall *fontomfrom* drums which send out impressive deep booming notes, a pair of "talking drums", a couple of smaller drums and a clamorous iron gong-gong. Sitting on the ground to one side of the sanctuary door with his back leaning against the sanctuary wall is the horn-blower with his ivory horn, reiterating a little motif said to be, "*Mmere dane, dane*" (Times change, change.) Around the steps to one side of the dais the priest's eight wives, picturesquely wrapped in white calico shawls, sit on low stools or squat on the steps.

Then the *obrafohene*, two *akyeame* and various attendant youths bring out of the sanctuary the *dua*. This is a heavy cylindrical wooden block, like a chopping-block, encircled with a binding of white calico which holds in place a close-set circle of knives and daggers, hilts upwards. In front of the *dua* they place a large wooden cradle, with open ends, holding a collection of variously shaped wooden clubs. These are the *nkotoba* clubs with which transgressors of *obosom* law invariably dream that they are being beaten.

Lastly the priest emerges from his own house—which has a private door into the yard—and strides, often wearily, across the yard to the sanctuary. He is a tall, lean, dignified figure without any pompous self-consciousness. He is austerely clad in commonplace khaki shorts and a short-sleeved thigh-length tunic of white calico. He wears no beads, decorations or *suman* of any kind: only his uncut hair and his white calico mark him out from other people. At the foot of the steps he kicks off his sandals; then he mounts, hands the key of his private living-room to the *okyeame* and holds out his hand to receive an egg. This he flings on to the flat top of the *dua*. If it breaks unpropitiously (with the concavities of the shell fragments downwards) he looks worried, if satisfactorily he looks pleased and bows in reverent gratification over it. Then, stooping, he enters the low door of the sanctuary and immediately both orchestras play furiously to call the *obosom* to come and possess him.

After a few minutes of mounting expectancy the calico curtain at the sanctuary door is suddenly flung aside and out dart the attendants, the *obrafohene* and the two *akyeame*, and lastly the possessed and quivering priest. The latter takes his stand with his back to the sanctuary door and facing the *dua*. He never varies his style: he stands upright on one spot with folded arms but with his head shaking unceasingly from side to side in furious agitation, his long tassels of *mpese-mpese* hair flicking like whips round his head, his face mask-like, but his expressionless eyes rolling from side to side and his eyebrows flickering up and down as though worked by machinery. The drums redouble their frenzied beating, the gong-gong its iron clatter and the horn its piercing cries. After another minute or two the priest holds out his hand for an egg and smashes it on the *dua*. Then after a further minute or so he raises a hand to silence the drums.

Then, before work begins, is held the *Akyima* ceremony, an exchange of greetings between the deity and his children. The possessed priest mutters to the spokesman, who shouts to the various groups in turn. "Elders! Grandfather says he gives you Good-morning." The elders then rise and come to the edge of the dais and bow, calling, "Good-morning, Grandfather." The possessed priest turns towards them in acknowledgment. Then the wives are greeted. "Wives! Grandfather says he gives you Good-morning." The white-draped women prostrate themselves on the steps. Turning to the first orchestra the greeting is repeated. "Drummers! Grandfather says he gives you Good-morning." One drum beats out in reply the five syllables, "*Makye, Apiaow!*" The other orchestra in turn is greeted and the drummed response comes back, "*Makye, Apiaow!*"

After this pleasant little ceremony the wives shamble off to their domestic duties and *abisa* begins. If there is any family or village quarrel this is dealt with before the public is admitted. These private hearings are unbearably tedious, and sometimes keep the pilgrims impatiently waiting all day. The deity, in the course of these, often employs the licence of divinity and reviles the elders, calls them fools and insults them freely—to the delight of the young *sinkwafo*. On one occasion, when the priest had already endured some weeks of wrangle and petty dispute, the private *abisa* went on, with brief pauses, till early evening, when the deity—through the possessed priest as mouthpiece—expressed his disgust and despair at his children's behaviour by weeping aloud —a succession of keening wails which froze the audience into spellbound silence—and threatened to desert the shrine and depart for ever from their unworthy midst.

When the private *abisa* is over, the assistant *obrafohene* flings open the yard gates and admits the flood of supplicants, each holding two eggs. They crowd round the low parapet of the dais, each trying to catch the eye of the *obrafohene*, who, when one has succeeded, takes the two eggs and hands them to one of the two spokesmen who stand right and left of the possessed priest. The spokesman says to the supplicant, "Speak!" and the latter tells his tale. From time to time the possessed priest, his head in perpetual motion, asks questions. He speaks in a low muttering monotone and only the nearest spokesman by bending intently towards him can pick up what he says. The spokesman repeats his dicta in a ringing shout, rocking with laughter if the deity calls a stupid person a fool or says his face is a sheep's. With especial relish does he bellow, "You will die!" This somewhat shocked me till I noticed that the supplicant usually took this utterance in good part, smiled politely, placed his hands in the gesture of self-abasement and reiterated, "*Dawuruma*" (Grace and mercy), after which formality the deity, ceremonially relenting, said, "I will do my best for you", and gave appropriate instructions.

If the deity still insists that the supplicant will die—which he does when witchcraft, bad medicine or other grave sin has been committed —an elder called the *Gwantoahene* (the Chief Implorer) comes forward and begs the deity to relent. For this service the *Gwantoahene* takes a fee from the supplicant. In the days of the old priest there was no *Gwantoahene*.

The deity's usual instructions to a commonplace supplicant are, "Bring me a fowl and state your need when you bring it", or, "The *obrafohene* will give you medicine from the Seven Pots [or from the Three Pots]. Use some of it to drink, some to wash and [occasionally] some as an enema."

At the end of each supplicant's *abisa* the possessed priest takes one of the eggs and smashes it on the *dua*. If the shell fragments lie concave towards the sky the deity's co-operation is assured, but if not, the deity may have reservations.

Every hour or so the deity leaves the priest and "goes to sleep". The priest suddenly turns on his heel, rushes at the sanctuary, flings himself at the wall—his head striking a leather-covered cushion hung there to receive it—slides limply downwards and disappears into the sanctuary. He quickly emerges again, unpossessed, goes and has a drink of tea (apart from which he fasts all day) or sits around chatting. After a few minutes he resumes work, always going first into the sanctuary while the drums call the deity to come again and possess him.

At midday the shrine closes down, and opens again in the late afternoon.

When the day's last *abisa* is over, the supplicants who have been instructed, "Bring me a fowl", do so. They usually buy a very small chick from a keenly business-like little girl of about eight who scours the surrounding villages for chicks and sells them at a profit of several hundred per cent. The chick is brought to the edge of the dais and handed over the railing to the *okyeame*. He places it on its feet on the *dua* and leaves it standing there while the supplicant repeats his request to the deity. If the chick puts down its head and pecks (the upper surface of the *dua* is always covered by a thick film of nourishing paste left by the day's smashed eggs) the deity has accepted the sacrifice and will help the supplicant. The *okyeame* then wrings off the bird's head and drips a little blood on the *dua*, on the cradleful of clubs and on the small conical stone permanently embedded in the cement floor of the dais. He then flings the decapitated bird into the yard, where it flaps convulsively till the watching vultures swoop down and seize it. If it happens to be a large fowl, small boys forestall the vultures and gleefully run off with it for their supper.

If the fowl, when placed on the *dua*, declines to peck, the *okyeame* hands it back to the supplicant, who then sometimes goes away and communes with his own soul, returning when he is ready to unburden it, or perhaps simply comes back with another chick hoping to find the deity more gracious or the chick hungrier.

Occasionally the priest varies his practice of standing before the door of the sanctuary during *abisa*. He may stay inside out of sight. The spokesman then sits on the ground in the doorway and repeats what the supplicant says and what the priest says. This method is the invariable practice at some other shrines, but it can never impress the supplicant so forcibly as the sight of the priest with the spirit upon him.

There are occasions when, for no apparent reason, dissociation fails to occur. The priest goes into the sanctuary as usual: there is a long wait, the drummers work themselves into a lather, but "the *obosom* does not come". The priest at last emerges, shrugging and with a slight rueful smile. He told me on one of these occasions, with an air of righteousness, that some priests would have put on a mock possession act,* but this was very wrong and he never did it.

Another "possession" technique invariably practised at some shrines but never at Mframa's consists of "carrying the *obosom*". The priest stands before the door of the sanctuary holding on his head the sacred receptacle which the *obosom* is believed to inhabit. This is a hollow cylindrical object with one end flat and the other a rounded cone. Its capacity is about that of a bucket and it is usually encased in the hide of some wild animal. It contains the object believed to have fallen from heaven when the *obosom* was "captured". The act of placing the sacred insignia on the *obosomfo's* head is held to send the *obosom* immediately

---

* This, no doubt, has always been the practice of "false prophets".

into possession of him, but to me this type of "possession" does not carry the same conviction that the priest is dissociated as does Mframa's type of dissociation.

But despite a good deal of variation in detail, all the *obosom-brafo* shrines have the essentials in common. The priest either stands outside or remains within the tabernacle of testimony and the supplicants come up to a fenced-off area in front of the door. There is always an *okyeame* or spokesman, and there are always elders to act as witnesses in case of any dispute concerning what took place on any given occasion. There are always drums to assemble the elders and to call the *obosom* to possess its priest.

At every shrine, festivals are held from time to time for the *obosom*. These vary in number and grandeur from shrine to shrine. At Mframaso the first priest had laid it down that all the traditional religious festivals of old Ashanti should be fully observed.* These included not only the annual festivals but the *Addae* festivals recurring every forty days. These latter were an interruption of the work and tiresome to pilgrims, since *abisa*, if held at all on these days, was not till late evening when very little work could be done.

On these forty-day occasions a good deal of dancing and *Apo* singing took place in the street, and the possessed priest, followed by a lively congregation, made a circuit of the village visiting various houses. If I was at home he always visited mine and smashed an egg before the door, and sometimes very kindly instructed the villagers to clear the weeds from around the building. When I was a newcomer he was wont to say, rolling his eyes balefully, "You are a stranger: nobody knows why you have come, but if you have a bad mind against me I will kill you." Towards the end of my stay he usually said, "If you had had a bad mind against me I would have killed you." On these tours round the village various people were admonished concerning those peccadilloes of which other neighbours might only whisper. A promiscuous young girl, the daughter of an elder, was told to marry and keep to one man or she would catch *babaso* disease and die. An elder's wife who had fallen out with her husband and threatened to go back to her own kinsmen was told that if she did so she would die. Another elder's wife, barren, but light of heart and of virtue, who had been absent from the village without taking leave of the *obosom* and had presumably been engaging in illicit pleasures, was ordered to sacrifice a big fowl and was

* These have been described in detail by other writers, notably R. S. Rattray, *Ashanti*. Oxford, 1923. E. L. Meyerowitz, *The Sacred State of the Akan*. Faber, 1951.

warned that next time it would be a sheep. A couple whom everyone knew to be casually cohabiting were told to carry out the proper marriage rites or else desist. In short, the *obosom* always reproved those who erred and strayed from traditional morality.

At one special annual festival the *obosom's* fetishes, imprisoned in their hallowed receptacles, were brought out and carried in palanquins to the *ebem* grove in the forest, with great tumult and rejoicing. All sorts of people besides recognised *akomfo* were possessed on this occasion. On the way back from the grove the carriers of the palanquin became possessed and appeared to be propelled by their portentous burden. They went butting and plunging dangerously round the town with their heavy load. One rather unpopular official, amid the derisive joy of the populace, had to shed his dignity, dodging and scuttling, as the charging carriers—personally exonerated by the circumstance of spirit-possession —made a dead set at him.

Annually the deity "went on leave to his town". The shrine closed down, the walls of the sanctuary and yard were whitewashed and, lastly, the priest washed his own *kra*.

There were also various untraditional breaks in the work when the priest's smouldering anxiety concerning his allotted seven years' lease of life would flare up and he would leave the village to consult various other *abosom* about the possibility of their co-operating with his own to change his destiny.

At only one of the *obosom-brafo* shrines of Ashanti was it permitted to take photographs of either a possessed priest or any of the sacred insignia. The ancient Ashanti deities—such as the one at Traa—whose priests are not *akomfo*, had no objection. This is because photography is held to extract some modicum of "being" or virtue out of the photographed object. The priests of the new shrines are never so completely "sure of themselves" as the ancient ones, and feel that they cannot risk the extraction of even a particle of "power". Some think that even one attempt at such extraction would cause the deity to desert the shrine in displeasure.

V

THE TROUBLES AND DESIRES
OF ORDINARY PEOPLE

§ 1. INTRODUCTION

Most shrines are open two or three days a week for *abisa*. Ordinary people then come to make known their troubles and requests to the deity or to return routine thanks. A popular hard-working shrine may deal with upwards of a hundred commonplace cases in a day: some of the newest shrines and some of those declining through the old age of their priests may see only half a dozen.

Usually the supplicant does his business briskly and hurries off towards the lorry-road. It was therefore seldom possible for me to have private interviews with these supplicants. The gravely ill patients, however, the witches and others "caught hold of" for their sins, always took lodgings in the village for investigation and treatment at the shrine. From these latter I was able to take the full case-histories which appear in Part II of this book. The present chapter deals only with the humdrum cases which are the bread-and-butter of the shrines.

§ 2. ANALYSIS OF COMPLAINTS AND REQUESTS
MADE AT ROUTINE ABISA

Complaints of "not prospering" (including 31 lorry-drivers)	397
Routine thanks for a year's protection	350
Unspecified sickness	151
Sick children	123
Requests for the birth of a child	112
Requests from pregnant women for safe delivery	110
Thanks for the birth of a child	107
Complaints of long childlessness	100
Requests by new supplicants for unspecified protection	94
Requests for help in new enterprises	93

Marital problems, including requests for divorce	59
Thanks for cure of sickness	57
Money urgently needed	55
Protection requested from specified dangers	53
Complaint that children born always die	51
Consultation on behalf of absent sick people	47
Complaint of money and valuables lost or stolen	44
Reporting the death of a child	34
Thanks for miscellaneous blessings	31
Complaints of impotence	28
Complaints of miscarriage or threatened miscarriage	28
Requests for help in lawsuits	27
Complaints of worrying dreams	26
Women in want of husbands	25
Pregnant women in fear of maliciously caused abortion	24
Children refusing to go to school or doing badly	23
Voluntary (prudential) confessions	22
New wives brought for protection	22
Drunkards requesting rescue	19
Complaints of venereal disease	19
Thanks for the death of an enemy	19
Complaints of eye-trouble	15
Complaints of fits	14
Children brought for protection	14
Reporting the death of a protected adult	13
Men in want of wives	11
Thanks for victory in lawsuits	11
Complaint that the "pregnancy does not grow"	9
Thanks for success in obtaining a husband	8
Complaint of bad *suman* found	6
Explanation sought of encounters with snakes	6
Consultation concerning a doubtful *suman*	5
Complaint of unaccountable insomnia	5
Complaint of amenorrhea	5
Complaint of "seeing fire" (migraine?)	3
Miscellaneous unclassified consultations	48
Total	2,537

The above cases were recorded at more than one shrine and at unselected times whenever I happened to be present during *abisa*. If I was engaged elsewhere during *abisa* my field-assistant carried out routine recording but made a note of anything out of the commonplace for me to pursue in person later.

§ 3. UNPROSPERITY

Of all the supplicants who bring their troubles to shrines the most frequent is the frustrated, unhappy, despairing man whose complaint is, "I am not prospering."

Sometimes such a supplicant has only one trouble, such as, "My lorry ran into the ditch", or, "I have a cement-block house in a big town and I cannot get a tenant for it," or, "I am a hunter and when I fire my gun I always miss." But often he brings a string of misfortunes. Sometimes he says, "I have never been happy in my life."

Most of those with a sea of troubles include the plaint, "I am also sick all the time." Though it could well be asked whether some chronic indolent ailment were not the root of the matter, the answer is probably no, for most people have such and endure it with fortitude so long as they are stably adjusted. The sicknesses of these unprosperous people are usually of the anxiety-begotten kind—palpitations, tremblings, pains all over and so on.

At the shrine the possessed priest questions the supplicant as he does those who complain simply of physical sickness, and if he elicits family strife and anxiety he advises concerning it. If the supplicant is on good terms with his wife, he usually brings her with him. If she is absent the priest asks why. A goldsmith whose wife had refused to come with him was told, after answering leading questions about her, "She is the cause of your plight. Leave her and take a better woman." When the supplicant is paranoid and says, "People envy me and want to keep me down", or, "Please kill the person who is doing this to me", or, "Witches have caused people to dislike me", the priest usually falls into step, diagnoses witchcraft or bad medicine and gives a reassuring promise of protection. He makes no identification of the witch or medicine-maker, but simply says, "The cause is among your own kinsmen", or, "There are witches in your house."

It is not usually possible, at an ordinary *abisa*, to know whether the supplicant is literate or illiterate unless he mentions it when he tells his tale, but quite a high proportion do mention that they are literate. Most of these have taken employment or embarked on modern ventures without any appreciation of the type of self-organisation and discipline called for by the work. When trouble follows they feel that sinister forces are after them. For instance, an able store-keeper in charge of one of a chain of bookshops had not calculated that the cost of living for himself and his wife and child in a strange town would be higher than in his native village, and he soon found himself living beyond his means. To mitigate this he put a few extra pence on the price of each school text-book. The travelling overseer of the chain of stores discovered this by questioning school-children and then blackmailed the store-keeper, demanding an annual heavy Christmas "dash" of crippling size. The store-keeper appeared to bear no more personal animosity to the overseer than he would have borne towards a slug which devoured his seedlings: it was the creature's nature and his own misfortune. What he worried about was the bad medicine by which, he felt certain, envious illiterates among his kinsmen had sent this trouble.

Among the literates who reported their failures were: men sacked from job after job, including one man who was never retained for more than a month; a dismissed teacher; a time-keeper at a mine; various literates, including teachers who could obtain no work at all; an auctioneer in debt; a sacked store-keeper; a Government clerk; a tailor; several cocoa-buyers; two policemen asking protection from their colleagues; several carpenters; several store-clerks aware of "hatred" among their fellow-clerks; a cocoa-buyer who said he was always in debt; a cocoa-grader; a Government Agricultural Officer; various schoolboys who failed in their examinations; a bar-keeper who complained that the police came and beat him up in his bar simply to spoil his work.

Of the modern callings the one whose followers most often come in trouble to the shrines are the lorry-drivers. So eager is the would-be driver to become one of these lordly beings, that he never stops to work out whether his takings on a projected run can exceed his running costs, still less whether he can make enough profit to pay off his initial debt. When it becomes only too clear that he is losing, he hastens anxiously to a shrine to inquire whether envious kinsmen have made bad medicine or whether witches have "made his hand into a sieve". Often he begins his *abisa* truculently: "I want help in destroying my enemies", or, "I am not prospering because of the bad mind of my envious brother."

Among those who came with more than one affliction were: a haggard and despairing teacher, who said he felt sure that witches in his house were spoiling his teaching and making his wife both barren and unfaithful; a transport owner who said that he made no profits and that his wives were all unfruitful; a man whose food-farm was ravaged by an antelope and whose kinsfolk made insatiable demands on his bounty; a man whose wives always died and whose son was unsuccessful at school; a woman whose trading never paid and whose husband neglected her for a new wife; a man whose business brought no profit and whose wife and child were both sick; a man whose five children had all died and whose cocoa was dying; a man who prospered at no kind of work, was always sick and whose wife wanted a divorce; a teacher on the staff of a prominent training college whom witches, he thought, had brought into debt and whose mother was incapacitated by illness; a tailor and a literate carpenter, each of whom said that his work went badly and that no woman would accept him as either lover or husband; a man to whom no one ever repaid loans and whose schoolboy son had begun refusing to go to school; a literate diamond-miner who was failing in business, whose wives were barren and who had lately become impotent; a literate unable to get work and whose brothers, who supported him, had all died; a lorry-driver who said that his wife had bought him a lorry but his kinsmen had by bad medicine turned her mind against him and also caused the lorry to run at a loss; a carpenter whose wife was refusing intercourse and whose son had run away.

A special group of unprosperous people are the drunkards. A drunkard is regarded as a man impelled by a force; something evil has got into him and "spoilt" him. Invariably he himself deems his plight to be the work of witches. One man came complaining that he could not take even a taste of drink without becoming uncontrollably "mad", doing damage and running into disgrace and debt. Witches had thus ruined him.

I recall another occasion when I was walking through a strange town with an unemployed literate as guide. I asked him to take me to greet his kinsmen. The house was tumble-down and neglected, and as we approached it he burst out, "You see how my house is spoilt. Witches have done that. My house is full of witches and they have made me a drunkard."

Drunkards are the only people—in my experience—who ever make point-blank accusations of witchcraft, though as a rule they are content, like the man just mentioned, to blame vaguely rather than pin-pointing an individual. Thus the *face-saving* rôle of witchcraft is perhaps its most welcome "social function".

Another well-defined sub-group of those who do not prosper are those who cannot look after money. They complain, "My hand has become a sieve. Money does not stay with me: it becomes *basaa* (disorderly) and I do not know how it goes." A workman came saying that he earned very high wages but witches had made his hand into a sieve and every week the money "got finished" with nothing to show for it, and he remained in poverty. The priest not only promised him the deity's protection from witches, but told him to lock half his wage in a box every week as soon as he received it. He told a woman who complained of trading losses that she would never make a trader and had better go back to farming. No doubt she had already considered doing this, but after instructions from the shrine, she could do it without loss of face.

Farmers on the whole complain less of not prospering than do people following newer callings. The cocoa virus-disease which first struck at Akim in the nineteen-thirties and has now devastated the cocoa of that region has only recently begun to invade Ashanti, sending the farmers to the shrines with their tales of woe. Farmers of other crops come complaining of antelopes, grass-cutters and other pests. The commonest cause of all agricultural mishap is, according to the shrine dicta, witchcraft and bad medicine, though sometimes the farmer is told that the land itself or a neighbouring stream requires the sacrifice of a fowl and a bowl of yam-and-egg mash.

Though witchcraft and bad medicine are the commonest causes assigned to failure, there are a few others. Farmers forget to propitiate land, rivers and trees; family ghosts and family *obosom* may be neglected; a venerated wild animal may have been shot; a wife may have been ill-treated; or a person may have displeased his own *kra*.

To complete the picture of the anxious man's reaction to adversity he should be viewed alongside the stable man who meets a succession of gratuitous disasters with uncomplaining fortitude. Such a man was Kofi P., one of the shrine officials in my village. He was quiet, kindly and not very intelligent: he never took part in the unceasing acrimonious wrangles of the village. He was not very robust or well nourished, and had a good many wives and swarms of young children which he found it hard to feed. One morning when he was away camping in his own farm settlement he rose at daybreak and went out hunting with his gun—a muzzle-loader using black gunpowder and home-made lead pellets. In the half-light he saw what he took for a bush-pig drinking from a stream, fired, hit it and then found it to be a Northern Territories migrant labourer setting a fish-trap. He sent his neighbours to succour the wounded man and then borrowed a bicycle and hastened to report himself at the nearest police-station, some twenty miles away. It was about noon when I heard this news and also that the police had made no move to bring in the wounded man, but were having private financial discussions with Kofi P. By the time I reached the police station with my Land Rover to demand a constable, some bearers, and Kofi as guide, the unhappy Kofi had already pledged his cocoa-farms to raise the sum necessary—as he believed—to persuade the police to charge him with manslaughter or wounding rather than with murder, or attempted murder. We got the wounded man to hospital where, in spite of a pellet in the abdomen, he recovered. Kofi P. was fined £5 for carelessness and £5 as compensation to the victim. Nevertheless, the episode cost him £150 which, in spite of a generous gift from his own shrine and another from a shrine whose priest was a kinsman of one of his wives, left him with two future cocoa crops in pledge. Some months after this, one of his sons died and a little later a bush fire demolished a number of people's cocoa-trees, including his. He took all this with imperturbable patience and good temper, though he looked thin and worn. Then a few months before I left the district, some children, playing near his house one day when all the inmates and neighbours were out on their farms, made a bonfire which set the thatch alight and destroyed the house, together with a store of maize just prepared for the market. At the sight of the burnt-out ruins the unlucky man gave way to tears, but they were soon over and he doggedly started to rebuild. The work was already in hand when he went to the shrine and asked, as one seeking information, the cause of his disasters. The deity said they were the work of a remote witch kinswoman of one of his wives, but the malefactor would soon die. Meanwhile, the deity said, because the sufferer was a good man and a shrine servant he was to be given some shrine monies towards rebuilding. When I last saw him the new house was nearly finished and he remarked: "I think it is now better than the old house."

The point here to be stressed is that if ever anyone could justly complain of "not prospering" this man was he, but knowing neither animosity nor self-pity, he neither railed, wailed nor sat down with "pains all over".

§ 4. THANKSGIVING

The staple income of every shrine is derived from the sheep—or the money equivalent of sheep—which supplicants bring at the end of each year in return for the year's protection from death and misfortune. A strikingly "paranoid" attitude is normal. Financially successful men are just as certain that envious kinsmen will do their best, by means of bad medicines, to "bring them down" to ruin and death as are unsuccessful men that envious malice is the cause of their failure. A well-adjusted and serene man of Akwapim said to me, "It is only since Tigari and the other protectors came that rich men in Akwapim have dared to show their riches by building big houses. Before that, if they did anything to show their wealth, they were sure to be killed. I remember thirty or forty men in Akwapim who started building big houses, but they died before they were finished." At no shrine session is there no pilgrim with a yearly routine thank-offering; after the cocoa seasons there are long strings of such pilgrims.

Next in number are those rendering thanks for the birth of a child, and next again those who have recovered from illness or whose children have done so.

The next biggest batch are those whom come, not perfunctorily but with every appearance of satisfaction, to thank the deity for either killing or "catching" hold of an enemy. A Fanti said, "Thank you for killing my sister; she never liked me."

Several wives "caught hold of" by the deity had confessed to adultery, and the husbands—after duly collecting adultery compensation—returned thanks.

One supplicant, in gratitude to the deity for smiting down an enemy, asked, and was granted, permission to carry out the reverent ritual of washing one of the deity's knives.*

About equal in number are those who bring thanks for help in building a house, winning a court case, prospering in trade and having good farm crops.

Finally there are a host of miscellaneous mercies for which the deity is thanked—for procuring a driving licence, for sending a son to Europe, for acquiring a husband or a wife, for finding a lost relative or some lost property, for enabling a son to complete his apprenticeship, for healing a marital quarrel, for frightening a thief into bringing back stolen property, or for preserving the worshipper's life in a lorry accident.

§ 5. SICKNESS

According to African dogma sickness and health are ultimately of supernatural origin. Even food does not act physiologically but by

---

* I am uncertain whether these knives simply symbolise the deity's destructive power, or whether the deity uses the invisible destructive essence of the knives to kill evil-doers. The ancient type of deity's knife is shaped like those carved on the stones of Stonehenge.

pleasing or displeasing the patient's spirit. Apart from influences external
to the patient—malicious magic and witchcraft from other people, un-
propitiated ghosts, offended deities and so forth—the patient himself
has a *kra* and a *sunsum* (spiritual components of his make-up) of whose
wishes he is not always aware but whose co-operation is essential for
health and prosperity. Further, a bad conscience and ill-will towards
others are held to disturb the peace of the indwelling spirit which in turn
disturbs the owner's health. Some tribes (though not of modern
Ashanti) begin their annual festival with a day of peace-making on
which people seek out their friends and relatives and confess not only
their misdeeds but also any secret resentments they have harboured,
holding it useless to ask the gods for health and prosperity when un-
spoken rancour is gnawing at their vitals.

The majority of these who come to the shrines complaining of sickness
do not appear to have anything organically wrong, but they are in
anxiety. They complain of palpitations, pains all over, headache,
trembling, giddiness, and darkness in front of the eyes. The priest is
quick to recognise these patients and comments, "There are troubles in
your sickness", or "You are sick because you are keeping things in your
head." Often he elicits confessions and fears by employing shock tactics.
"What about a certain man? What about a certain woman? What about
a certain quarrel?" If the patient looks genuinely blank he tries another
tack, but if there is any hesitation or embarrassment, he presses the point
till he has elicited either confession or specific anxiety. Adultery on the
part of women is one of the commonest causes of palpitations and
"pains all over". If the patient is reticent, he says, "Go away and come
back when you are ready to lay bare what is in your mind."

Often the patient does not wait to have his misdeed or his apprehension wormed out of him, but he tells of it together with his symptoms.
One said, "I have had pains all over ever since the day I cursed my
nephew." Another man with pains all over came with his wife confessing that they had together been to a Kramu and made bad magic
against the wife's mother. For this they were fined a cow each, the wife
also being ordered to give a sheep to her mother. Another uneasy man
said, "I bought a bad *suman* to use against my uncle, and I have been
sick and miserable ever since the day I bought it." Another said, "I have
been sick ever since I did my kinsmen out of their share in a cocoa-
farm", and yet another said, "I used a bad *suman* to protect my cocoa-
farm against my neighbours." A woman who had not reached the point
of bad magic against her husband said that she had felt ill ever since she

made up her mind to injure him. Among other sick people who came bringing their own diagnoses one said he had reviled the *obosom*, another that he had eaten tabooed food, several that they had omitted to bring their promised thank-offering and another that he had flouted the *obosom's* advice.

But concerning "bad mind" against others, conscience in pure culture is relatively rare: usually there is also fear of the adversary's counterattack or fear that he may be, unknown to the aggressor, under the protection of a deity who will exact retribution. A literate came saying that he had had pains all over ever since he quarrelled with his sister and that he thought she had "given him to a Kramu". A man who confessed to deserting his wife without due cause and a woman who similarly left her husband were both found to be in fear of the deserted partner's supernatural revenge. An electrician's sick apprentice admitted that he had cheated his master out of a good deal of money and was in fear of discovery and dismissal. A Local Council clerk complained of a sickness sent to him by those from whom he had extorted money: he asked for protection from *their* malice, but neither expressed contrition nor was given any censure.

Simple folly is sometimes regarded as an outrage on the perpetrator's own spirit and, as such, likely to cause sickness. A young girl with headache and palpitations was told to stop being promiscuous and two other ailing young women were admonished because they were making no attempt to procure husbands. Straightforward quarrels and estrangements are often thought sufficient cause for aches and pains. "You have offended your wife." "You have disobeyed your husband." A woman said she had had pains all over since she had declined to sleep with her husband, and a man suffering all over his body admitted that he had been planning to divorce a good wife.

Simple-hearted people are prone to fall sick when dismayed at finding they have misplaced their trust. Several men came, sick and worrying, because wives whom they liked wanted to leave them. One man, a neighbour of mine whom I knew very well as a guileless, kindly, happy and hearty clown, went off his food and became unrecognisably cadaverous and languid within a week of discovering that he had long been —as everyone else in the village knew—an unsuspecting cuckold. He went to the shrine complaining of headache, weakness and inability to eat. The deity said, "Stop worrying about your wife's adultery. There are plenty of better women in the world." He did, in fact, soon become resigned, and fattened accordingly.

Such instances of illness engendered by pure distress of spirit are relatively rare: there is usually an interwoven fear of malicious machinations even when the patient's own conscience is clear. One woman whose palpitations began seven days after marrying a man who had three other wives said she thought one of them had designs on her life. The deity, though confirming this, reassured her and foretold for her a long life. Again, a man said that he had married a widow who he thought had engineered her first husband's death. A literate Christian government servant came complaining of "giddiness in his eyes" and said that he knew his wife had consulted a bad medicine-man when the patient neglected her for a concubine.

Sometimes palpitations or pains accompany pre-marital apprehensions. One woman, a widow, was sought in marriage by a man whom she liked but whose first wife, still with him, she thought to be a witch. A man patient had similar misgivings about his affianced bride. The *obosom* advised both these patients to abandon their plans.

Kinship dispute even more than marital disharmony emerges as a potent cause of that anxiety which destroys the sense of physical well-being. Needless to say, money and cocoa-farm inheritance are the commonest bones of contention. One sick man admitted to having given his son £450 to buy a lorry and so incurred the resentment of his own kinship group. Another who came complaining of his belly said that his young kinsmen would do no work for him though it was he who fed them. Yet another had lent money to a kinsman and, though needing it, could not recover it. Another, embroiled in family dispute, was told that his kinsmen had "given him to a river" (i.e., implored the river-god to destroy him). In a number of cases where it seemed that the patient was going his own way in selfish disregard of family obligations he was told to remember his duties to them and to make an apologetic sacrifice to his family ghosts and to his ancient family gods. One was told, "Make a sacrifice to your dead brother's ghost, but also keep an eye on your envious sister."

Another familiar figure among the nervous patients is the one who, without admitting any misdemeanour of his own or being able to produce any concrete evidence of ill-will on the part of others, reports sick saying, "My kinsmen envy me and have sent me a sickness." School-boys with such complaints as giddiness are wont to say that they are envied because of their cleverness. These people with a vague sense of malice all around them are much more disturbed than those fundamentally healthy people who come saying, "I have had a headache ever since the day I found that someone had put a bad *suman* under my pillow", or one righteously indignant woman, not sick at all, who announced with sturdy matter-of-factness that she had found a bad *suman* in her fireplace and wanted to know what to do about it.

An outstanding case of fear of malicious magic-making, probably well founded, was exhibited by a very wealthy illiterate money lender, whose relentless avarice had doubtless caused many a victim to writhe in hatred. He suffered endlessly from his belly, went to hospital after hospital for full investigation with the invariable verdict that nothing was wrong. He at length came to a shrine village, stayed a few weeks, felt secure and was well. He went back to his town, only to succumb again to belly pains, in the atmosphere of menace. He returned to the shrine and was again cured. The cycle was repeated till he decided that his life would be safe only if he came to live in the shrine village under the close shelter of its deity. This he did, bringing his wives, his Cresta car and its driver, his wireless set, and other luxuries. A house was lavishly made over for him and a garage built. A junior partner came by lorry to fetch him when business called him to town, but his stomach was not at peace except in the village. He was a fat man who ate heartily and had probably nothing wrong with his stomach but fear.

The anxious, maladjusted and paranoid people who flock in such great numbers to shrines, throw into bold relief the few well-balanced successful people who are able to accept calmly the indubitable fact that less successful people do bear them ill-will.

One such successful man, a village elder whom I knew well, was an excellent personality who had become wealthy enough, through sheer hard farmwork, to support several young kinsmen in university courses overseas. He was somewhat prone to malaria and often came to me for quinine, but never complained and never went off work. One day I had a message from him, saying that he had gone down with fever in another village and would like some quinine. I sent some but it never reached him. I afterwards learnt that a band of relatives had descended on him as he lay sleeping and carried him forcibly off in a lorry to a yet further village, ostensibly to give him treatment. However, he managed to escape to his home and when he had shaken off the fever he appeared unperturbed and uncomplaining before the shrine, saying simply that he had been sick and had come to thank the deity for his recovery. The *obosom* said, "Everybody envies you because you are clever. You must walk very carefully. Never accept a drink from anyone." He nodded, and said, " I have heard and thank you. I will do what you say", and went off serenely to plant a new yam-farm.

§ 6. ORGANIC ILLNESS

Organic illness is almost always attributed to either witchcraft, bad medicine or sin, seldom to worry and stress. Where witchcraft is invoked it may be that witches have taken and are eating the patient's *kra*; it may be that witches, desiring the patient to become one of them, have given him, without his knowledge, an *obayi* which, being repugnant to his own spirit, has thrown the latter into turmoil and distress: or it may be that the patient has, albeit unwittingly, accepted an *obayi* and used it to do harm, for which sin the *obosom* has laid a punitive hand on him.

Although the shrine therapists recognise their limitations and frequently tell patients with pneumonia, cardiac failure or pulmonary distress with blood-coughing, to go to hospital, they stand firmly on the theory that the primary vulnerability of the patient to the disease is of supernatural origin and until redemptive ritual has been performed the hospital efforts are futile. When a patient who is already under the *obosom's* protection comes asking permission to go to hospital this is always given.

When the patient seems to be beyond all aid he is told, "Not even God has any medicine for that sickness," or, "You are dead already: the witches have already eaten your *kra*", but there is always, "Nevertheless, I will ask the *obosom* to do his best for you."

A few examples will illuminate the attitude of both Christians and non-Christians towards illness.

A very sensible and hard-working woman farmer, a friend of mine, who lived near my village and was one of the shrine's leading *Apo* singers, had several strapping sons, all literate, highly intelligent Roman Catholics. One of these youths—a clerk—fell ill and threw up his job. His mother asked me to see him. I found him coughing, febrile, wasted and profusely sweating at night. I told his mother to take him to a Mission hospital some twenty miles away for a chest X-ray. She did this and was advised to send him to the tuberculosis unit at Kumasi for inpatient treatment. She was an enterprising and resolute woman and consented. But the question first to be solved was, "Who had sent the illness?" The youth remembered that he had attended a funeral in a neighbouring town, had there accepted a drink from a fellow clerk and the following day had begun sickening. The clerk, he decided, was envious and had conveyed to him in the drink, not physical poison as Europeans understand it, but an evil influence to break him down. His mother brought him to the shrine, where the deity confirmed his conjecture, ordered ritual to nullify the existing evil and took him under protection. He then went to hospital with a quiet mind, made a good recovery and after a few months returned looking fat and well to thank the deity for making his cure possible. I discussed the situation with one of his Roman Catholic brothers. The latter referred to all *abosom* as "the little gods" and took the usual view that they were all sons of God and very hard-working in the matter of their children's needs and dangers. He said, gleefully gloating on what would happen to the patient's envious fellow clerk if he tried his tricks again now that the patient was under the *obosom's* protection, "Let him try now, and Bang! the *obosom* will kill him."

Again I found at another shrine an exceedingly sick woman whose husband—a teacher—had taken her first to hospital where she was admitted with a diagnosis of cerebro-spinal meningitis. "But", said the husband, "she had injections there every day for a week, but she was still sick, so I could see that the trouble was something spiritual [i.e., supernatural] so I brought her here."

Many hospital patients who discourage their doctors by "not settling down" and then by discharging themselves after a day or two of treatment are to be found the next day at the shrines, either confessing sins or asking delivery from malicious evil. The deity is then wont to say, "Why did you send the patient *first* to hospital. Give me a sheep for his sin and then take him back."

The illness which more consistently than any other is held to be the work of witches is *babaso* (usually gonorrhea, though syphilis is not unknown). "I got it from a strange woman: I think she was a witch." If a woman says she took the illness from her husband, the explanation is that a witch gave it to him. Though everyone is aware that the disease, as such, can be treated at hospital for a few shillings, the ordinary patient still feels it imperative to travel perhaps some hundreds of miles to a shrine where the primary cause of his vulnerability can be established.

Few patients come to the shrines in the early stages of this infection, some not till complications produce impotence or an infected wife has become sterile. Sometimes a urethral stricture is their earliest protest. One man with a classical aortic aneurism said he had never been well since he consorted with a witch prostitute years before, but had recently begun to feel himself choking to death.

Another organic illness which, as might be expected, arouses the conviction of evil forces at work, is epilepsy. Most small children wear a talisman against convulsions, which at their age are commonly caused by round-worms. A boy of ten had frequent fits which stopped when he was cleared of worms but recurred months later when a new infestation had grown up. A girl of sixteen with an apparent idiopathic epilepsy had several fits a week before her worms were cleared but only a fit every few months afterwards.

One of the most memorable scenes I ever witnessed at a shrine concerned a young man in his twenties who came to stay in the shrine village to have treatment for fits. These were of recent onset and he thought they were sent by someone in his house jealous of his success as a building contractor. He asked for sanctuary in the village till the illness had gone. He managed to do enough work for the elders to earn his keep and settled down, fairly happy, though still having occasional fits. After a few months his father came to the shrine asking permission to take him home. The patient then stood forward and made an impassioned speech saying that nothing would induce him to go home to the people who had sent him such an illness. The father departed and the patient settled down again. The fits, however, began to increase, he became dissatisfied with the *obosom's* protection and said he might as well go home. The *obosom* warned him not to go, but he went. A few months later a messenger came to report that he had gone raving mad and died.

§ 7. SICK CHILDREN

When a sick child is brought to the shrine the priest invariably seeks first for strife between the parents, a circumstance in which, it is held, no young child can thrive. One mother came spontaneously confessing that she had been planning to divorce her husband without due cause and therefore, she said, her child had fallen sick. The father of a sick child came admitting many offences against his family.

Though the commonest reason assigned for the sickness of a child is open quarrelling between the parents, a number of mothers were blamed for adultery, refusal of intercourse with the father, and plain neglect of the child. Several times a mother was told that her child was grieving for the father whom the mother left.

On the latter point, African fathers of small children are indulgent paediolators and in my village one such child separated from its father adopted my cook *in loco parentis* and followed him about with dog-like devotion.

Again a child may be a bone of contention between its father and its mother's brother (the latter being, in a matrilineal system, its next-of-kin and sometimes over-possessive), and this again is held to spoil the child's well-being.

Though witches commonly confess to killing children, this cause is comparatively seldom invoked to explain a child's illness. More often the parents were told that family ghosts had not received their rightful ritual, that the child had eaten tabooed food, that family gods had been neglected and that rivers and other deities to whom the parents were under obligation had not been satisfied.

§8. REQUESTS FOR CHILDREN, HUSBANDS AND WIVES

The commonest specific request made at any shrine is for a child. The majority of people making it are young, newly married and healthy, with every chance of a quick fulfilment of their desire.

The request that a woman may bear a child is frequently made by her brother or maternal uncle, for the Akan child belongs to its mother's kinship group. Female children through whom the group can alone be perpetuated are particularly desired. (I knew one man who hauled his neighbour before the elders' court for having disparagingly flung it in his teeth that he had no sisters.)

An infant born in answer to prayer is brought to the shrine* together with a sheep or other promised thank-offering and is named after the *obosom* who was implored to send it. For the first three or four years the hair of such a child is not cut for "its head is in the *obosom*". At the end of that time the parent pays another sheep to have the head "taken out", and the *obrafohene's* assistant shears off the shaggy mat of hair.

Similarly, people come requesting husbands or wives. Most of those wanting husbands are young girls or comely young widows with no reason to suppose they will need supernatural assistance.

"Unprosperous", stupid, unattractive or drinking men, who are

---

* On my very first visit to an Ashanti shrine the *obrafohene* came up carrying a new-born infant to show me and remarking, "You see, this is what the *obosom* can do. What do you think of it?" A literate bystander remarked condescendingly, "I think it is very decent."

clearly unlikely to make satisfactory husbands, have a poorer prognosis and indeed often come complaining that witches or bad-medicine makers are obstructing their efforts.

§ 9. CHILDLESSNESS

Barren women, childless couples and infertile men leave no stone unturned in their earnest search for the cause and cure of their privation and often go from shrine to shrine offering extravagant gifts in exchange for a child.

Most commonly the deity diagnoses witchcraft. The witches have stolen away the supplicant's womb or penis—that is the spiritual counterpart of the organ—and have either eaten it (in which case there is no hope) or broken it in pieces, or hidden it in a river. The supplicant is told to lay his need before the deity, make a sacrifice to the river in which the damaged organ is hidden, and the deity will do his best to repair and restore it. Sometimes the sufferer is told that no evil has been at work: his childlessness is "from God" and is his destiny (*nkrabea*). Occasionally, but not often, the supplicant is told to carry out some unusual ritual, such as bringing the *obosom* a live cat-fish, or a live cat or a doll whose calico wrapping is taken into the sanctuary for special rites: it is then hoped that the *obosom* will intercede with his father, the Supreme God, and get the supplicant's destiny changed.

It is believed that women conceive only with difficulty in an atmosphere of kinship strife and marital disharmony. One quarrelsome couple were asked, "Which do you prefer, quarrels or children?" A guilty woman is also held to be one to whom unborn children only reluctantly come.

A number of barren women confessed to adultery and one to intercourse with her mother's husband.

Miscarriages

These are usually assigned to the same causes as barrenness—witchcraft, bad medicine, infidelity and quarrelling—with the additional common diagnosis of neglect to propitiate family ghosts and family gods.

§ 10. PREGNANCY

The commonest specified danger requiring the *obosom's* protection and help is pregnancy. Here again the supplicant may simply feel that she is taking an ordinary wise precaution. On the other hand, there may be guilt on her mind or dispute between herself and her husband. Particularly is it held that "adultery spoils pregnancy" and in such cases the deity seldom gives any hope that the woman will be safely delivered of a live child.

I recall the case of a young primipara—a Christian, not under the aegis of Mframa—in a village a few miles away from Mframaso. She had an obstructed labour and was taken to the nearest hospital. There a diagnosis was made of contracted pelvis (an affliction common among rural women and all too often killing them at their first pregnancy). The hospital doctor offered to carry out surgical delivery. This was declined, the patient was brought home, confessed to adultery and died in the odour of horror and terror. To be buried with an undelivered child is an ancient and widespread taboo, whose violation is held to inhibit the dead woman's ghost from entering the place of the dead and to convert it into an abominable and savage enemy of its survivors on earth. The funeral, which I witnessed, was in two parts. The first was a procession to the cemetery, led by the local catechist, followed by the mourners with slow steps and clasped hands making the droning sounds which among rural Christians pass for singing. Under a tree in the cemetery was waiting an *odunsini*—old, experienced and very brave—holding a calabash of magical herbal lotion. The body, wrapped in white calico, was lowered into the grave round which the young men held up screens of cloth. The medicine-man muttered an incantation, got into the grave, washed his knife and his hands in the protective concoction and carried out an upper-segment Caesarian operation. Then he brought forward the foetus and showed it to the grateful mourners, standing around with their prayer-books and rosaries. He then purified the congregation by sprinkling them from a bunch of herbs dipped in the magical liquor. The foetus was then buried with the mother. The operator charged £10 for his work.

§ 11. REQUESTS FOR PROTECTION

When a supplicant comes asking for the deity's protection the priest usually finds out first whether this is simply a prudent precaution—an insurance policy, as it were—or whether the supplicant is in specific anxiety. When the supplicant offers a cow or any more valuable gift than the usual sheep in return for a year's protection, he is certain to be unusually worried. If the supplicant comes alone he is asked why the husband or wife is absent. The questioning technique is the same as that employed in investigating anxiety-begotten illnesses and the same kind of fears are laid bare. Where there is family or marital disharmony and suspicion the supplicant usually fears that the adversary will employ bad medicine against him. The priest generally discovers who started any such dispute and if the supplicant himself is at fault he is told he will get protection conditionally on making amends.

Among those who came for protection impelled by a specified event were a clerk who had been promoted above the heads of his peers and feared their vengeance; a man whose good *suman* had been stolen by another who had long desired his death; a man whose brother and nephew had unaccountably died, presumably through witchcraft; a woman whose grown-up children had become dangerously embroiled in modern politics; a man whose sister had fallen ill and confessed to witchcraft, and numbers of men afraid that unfaithful wives were conspiring with illicit paramours.

Newly married men often bring their wives for protection, but this is also a prudential measure, for a protected wife cannot be unfaithful with impunity. One man requested in so many words that his new wife might not bring evil with her, and another, having some misgivings about his bride, asked whether she was a good choice and was told that she was unlikely to stay with him long.

§ 12. HELP IN NEW ENTERPRISES

A familiar figure at the shrine is the man or woman embarking on a new enterprise. Heading the list of these are people sending their children to school and hoping they will do well and prove a profitable investment. Next in number are the lorry-drivers bringing their new lorries and themselves for protection from accidents, enemies and financial ruin. "There is death and life in lorry work." Almost equal to the lorry-drivers in number are the farmers clearing new farms.

Among the rest are people starting trading ventures, literates applying for jobs or promotion and school-children and college students sitting for examinations. One man wanted protection for his brother who had gone to England on a scholarship to study medicine.

One modest-mannered but quietly business-like woman said she was a prostitute in Kumasi and asked for success in her work. As she was not married, approval was readily given to her enterprise. When I sought to know the general climate of opinion concerning this I was told matter-of-factly, "It is her work. When a man has to stay in a town like Kumasi one of the things he may need is a woman. Also travellers need somewhere to stay the night."

§ 13. MARITAL TROUBLES

Marital troubles take up a fair amount of shrine time.

When a couple have put themselves jointly under the *obosom's* protection they may not separate without his leave. Sometimes when they come seeking this he brings about a reconciliation.

A number of married people come alone reporting that the partner now refuses intercourse, usually because of a new object of affection. A woman sometimes complains that her husband, having too many other wives and being an irresponsible fellow, is neglecting to provide her with due subsistence for herself and her children. Such a complainant usually comes asking the deity to reform the errant partner, but if the latter does not thereafter mend his ways the divorce goes through and the offender is put outside the pale of the deity's protection.

Fear of witchcraft or bad medicine is often the impulse which sends the complainant to the shrine. If any other woman in a wife's family confesses to witchcraft the men married to her sisters and other kinswomen may begin to shun them.

One man whose wealthy trader-wife had bought him a lorry came complaining that her family had made medicine to spoil her friendly attitude towards him.

One woman came complaining that her husband would not allow her to visit her mother. She had left the husband once, but her father, who had "drunk the head money" and did not want to return it, made a magic to change her mind and send her back. Having got her back the husband was, she thought, unreasonably possessive. Another woman said that her husband never slept with her, and as twenty other men were desirous of sleeping with her she wished for freedom.

The most usual fear is of magical machinations by the partner's extra-marital consorts.

§ 14. REQUESTS FOR MONEY

Most of the people who come imploring the *obosom* to help them to acquire money are deeply in debt. The commonest of these are lorry-drivers, some of whom have had their lorries or their relatives' farms seized.

Others ask the deity to help them in borrowing capital. An Akwapim wanted £1,000 to buy farm-land. Others wanted several hundred pounds to start trading, to learn a trade, to go to Europe, to build town houses to let to strangers, and of course to buy lorries.

One smooth-spoken literate from Accra said that he sold petrol for a firm on a small commission, which would never enable him to save enough to build a large house in the commercial part of Accra. He asked the deity to help him to mislay and juggle with invoices in such a way that he might cheat his firm out of the price of several whole consignments of petrol. He promised the deity £100 if he succeeded. The deity gave no promise, but said, "If I help you and you succeed and don't keep your promise, I shall pluck you like a paw-paw from a tree." Successful cheating is not regarded as stealing, for if the defrauded party is unaware of his loss he is clearly not suffering.

§ 15. LOST OR STOLEN PROPERTY

Though a great many cocoa-farmers and others who handle several hundred pounds at a time now use the Post Office Savings Bank, a good many more keep money in locked boxes in their bedrooms. Sums ranging from £4 to £1,000 were stolen from people who came asking the deity to "catch hold of" the malefactor. If the latter knows that the sufferer has been to a shrine he may indeed return the money.

People who borrow capital seldom have either the desire or the intention to repay it: consequently the shrines see many disconsolate lenders. Like cheating, the failure to repay a loan does not rank with stealing as a sin, and the deity can only undertake to "trouble" the debtor with unrest and ill-luck; he cannot "catch hold" of him and kill him.

§ 16. DEATHS OF CHILDREN

When children die and the parents come to ask why, the reasons given are the same ones invoked when children fall sick, but occasionally the parent is told, "There is nothing bad; the child did not intend to stay. It will come again."

The people who come complaining that all their children die—one couple had lost eight—are more than those who report the loss of one. Where such people are mentally stable, they bear their losses with surprising fortitude. Though self-accusations of witchcraft do occur in depressed women who have lost children, not one of the fifty-one repeatedly bereaved women in this sample of *abisa* cases accused herself. One would, however, predict with fair confidence that not all of them will go through the involutional age without doing so.

§ 17. "THE PREGNANCY DOESN'T GROW"

Frequently a woman comes saying, "I have been pregnant a long time but the pregnancy doesn't grow." Sometimes she claims to have been pregnant for several years. Though occasionally the patient is a young woman with amenorrhea accompanying obvious wasting disease, she is usually a woman who has just reached the menopause and is reluctant to confess it, knowing that the husband to whom she has given years of faithful service will probably take a young additional wife.

§ 18. IMPOTENCE

In no patient is the influence of fear and anxiety more marked than in the impotent. In half a dozen shrine cases the patient had two wives, an "old" and a new young one, and was impotent only with the new, fearing that the other, out of either jealousy or just resentment of neglect and ill-treatment, would make bad magic against him. Another patient had left an earlier wife because she had been "caught" for bad medicine-making. Another had on his conscience a first wife who had died in the distress and want occasioned by his neglect and he feared her ghost. Another widower, dejected and forlorn, was ordered by the deity to propitiate his late wife's ghost because "the love is not yet finished". One admitted intercourse with a married woman whose justly resentful husband he believed to have consulted a bad Kramu medicine-man. One became impotent after dreaming of intercourse with "a certain woman", but gave no further details. In several instances the patient had a wife who had become reluctant, from which the patient inferred that her affections were elsewhere and that the rival was making bad medicine. In two instances the patient dated his trouble from the day he had intercourse with a "strange woman" who, he afterwards decided, was a witch.

In only three cases the patient reported an infection caught from a prostitute and in two of these he reported disabling swellings. Although most patients know that such infection can be treated at hospital with little trouble and expense, they are still convinced that without witchcraft or bad magic they would not have succumbed, and they hold the hospital efforts futile till the ultimate malevolent power has been broken.

§ 19. ABSENT PATIENTS

Often a supplicant comes on behalf of an exceedingly sick relative who is either too ill to travel, too uncooperative or unable to find the money. Several cases of "madness" were thus reported and five others of dumbness—the latter being sometimes the result of a hemiplegia and sometimes of a mental illness. One man reported that his son, a young carpenter, could no longer keep his mind on carpentry and just sat around. Various recurrences of witchcraft guilt were reported by proxy. One absent patient coughing blood sent to say that his opponent in a land dispute had made bad medicine against him, and others sent confessions of adultery and other offences.

Other vicarious supplicants appeared to be simply well-disposed people, wishing to leave no stone unturned to help a sick parent, uncle, sister, husband or wife but not possessing any authority to bring the patient away from home.

§ 20. SCHOOL-CHILDREN

A common disappointment among ambitious people is to send children to school and then see them doing badly. It should be stressed that few parents send *all* their children to school. They select the most able and as a rule they are shrewd in their assessment. When the child does not do well, they are usually right when they judge that something untoward is preventing him from doing his best. In addition to the obvious stresses, the child may be fearing the magical machinations of rival class-mates or of siblings and cousins doomed to illiteracy. When the parents say that at first the child did well but, towards the end of primary school, "his mind become unsteady on his work", or "he no longer liked learning", or "his mind became *basaa* at school", or "he felt too lazy to go to school any more", then all too often there are other signs of incipient schizophrenia.

When the reason for a schoolchild's failure is obvious, the parent comes asking the deity to change the child's attitude. For instance, one schoolboy had decided to throw up school and become a soldier, several adolescent schoolgirls had become interested in lucrative prostitution, and one boy from a coastal town had become the inseparable playmate of the illiterate and wealthy children of an illiterate but very wealthy building-contractor.

§ 21. LAWSUITS

Although I have included lawsuits among the troubles from which people ask deliverance, litigation is perhaps the national sport, albeit an expensive one, and some litigants come to the shrines in much the same spirit as does the occasional captain of a football team asking for a season's success.

§ 22. PRUDENTIAL CONFESSIONS

Of the sinners who come confessing to the shrines only a small proportion come "caught" in a mad frenzy of fear. To see *only* these fear-crazed cases would give an unbalanced picture of a reign of terror. As we shall see later, the persons specially prone to exaggerated fear reactions are the potential schizophrenics and sometimes people in such fevers as malaria, pneumonia and influenza. But when the everyday work of the shrines is watched, it is seen that a number of those in fealty to the deity come quite quietly and in full command of themselves and confess that they have transgressed the rules and so laid themselves open to divine wrath and retribution. Some of them report palpitations and other anxiety-bred bodily discomfort; indeed, a considerable number of these we have already met, presenting as minor illnesses but very ready, when pressed, to confess their adultery or other sin. But some of those bringing voluntary confession of major sins are no more perturbed than one of ourselves who, observing a small defect in a tooth, goes promptly to his dentist. Others are not worried till a coincidental minor ailment "shakes" them. One man who lived in a village around which lurked a seemingly psychotic footpad, one day became, under the influence of too much palm-wine, unwontedly presumptuous and cursed the marauder to the guardian deity—a forbidden act, for the deity guards his children without being specifically ordered about. A few days later the offender took diarrhoea, remembered his offence and came promptly to the shrine, his demeanour calmly matter-of-fact.

But now and again a voluntary confession is made by a person in fairly severe distress of mind and appears to abort a psychotic attack. For instance, a pregnant woman came from a nearby village, pacing about unceasingly in anxious restlessness saying that she had eaten corn out of due season—a taboo often broken without misgiving. This woman calmed down immediately and went home. She did not return, so presumably all went well, but I thought her unduly vulnerable and should not have been surprised had she appeared again with a major mental illness.

Again the prognosis seemed to me very poor in the case of a man who came confessing that he had stolen money from his mother and sisters, had ill-treated his wife and then, when the latter refused to sleep with him, had made bad magic against her, using for the purpose some of her pubic hairs. The man was brought complaining of pains all over and was not able to state his own case. He did not remain in the village for treatment, so I could not take his history, but he was clearly a grossly ill-adjusted person and the bad medicine against his wife was of ominous import.

§ 23. REPORTS OF DEATH

When the death occurs of anyone who has been under the protection of the *obosom* the family send a report of this.

Sometimes the priest says that the deity killed him for breaking rules, sometimes quite trivial—such as forgetting to come back and thank for a year's protection. Sometimes the deceased by forgetting, as it were, to renew his insurance, carelessly lays himself open to the bad magic of enemies. But now and then the priest says, "He was killed because he had taken up witchcraft again", or, "She was a witch, though no one but the *obosom* knew it."

In such circumstances the next-of-kin is expected to thank the deity for killing the evil person. Sometimes the thanks are perfunctory, the mourner being in real grief, but even so the attitude is usually, "Who would have thought it? What a narrow escape for us. So the death was all for the best after all." Only once have I seen a grief-stricken man re- fuse to return thanks. He had come reporting the death of his daughter in childbirth. The priest said the deity had killed her for witchcraft. The man stood dazed and dumb. The *okyeame* said, "Why do you not thank the deity for delivering your family from this bad thing?" He made no reply but turned and staggered out of the yard.

§ 24. SUMAN

Magical apparatus has no part in the work of shrines. The principle enunciated by the early anthropologists, that religion involves a deity whom the worshipper implores while magic involves impersonal forces which the operator commands, holds good, and, as might be expected, the strictly consistent priests of deities do not look favourably on magic and the possession of *suman*. To use or even possess bad *suman* or bad medicine is, of course, a major sin and punishable by the deity with death. The possession of good *suman*, though not encouraged, is not forbidden and a certain amount of consultation takes place at the shrines concerning the nature and strength of doubtful *suman*.

It may be remembered that the dogma of witchcraft provides that the *obayi* which imparts the power of becoming a witch can only be given to a person in some concrete object, usually food, but often in gifts and legacies of small chattels, and above all in small *suman*. A person who possesses a supposedly innocuous *suman* often, when in fever or anxiety, begins to have misgivings about it and to wonder whether it is bad and has made the possessor into a witch.

Sometimes people bring to the shrine a *suman* or medicines that they have found on their premises. One woman found a dead owl and cowries in her fireplace, an elder found an old inverted tortoise-shell containing mysterious oddments, placed in his farm. Another supplicant brought a *suman* she had found under her pillow and another a *suman* found under his doorstep. In each case the deity confirmed suspicions that an enemy had planted the evil thing and told the supplicant what purification rites to carry out. One woman found that a snippet of her cover-cloth had been cut off and taken away, presumably by an enemy to use in magic against her. A Lobi medicine-man who brought a *suman* complaining that it was not working was told to kill a fowl for it.

Several *suman* were pronounced harmless but not of much use. Occasionally men brought their gun medicines and so on, suspecting that the proximity of a menstruous woman in the house had spoilt them. One man brought a *suman* which he thought his wife had deliberately spoilt when she was thus ceremonially unclean.

§ 25. SNAKES

In a region where snakes are not psychoanalysts' symbols but a cause of sudden and most unpleasant death, anyone who has a narrow escape from a snake comes to ask who sent it and why.

One woman came asking why a snake had fallen out of a tree on her granddaughter's neck while the girl was standing in a river washing clothes. She was told that witches in her own house had sent it. Witches are indeed believed to transform themselves at times into snakes.

A man on whom a snake fell while he was asleep was told that he had offended the land which he farmed and must propitiate it.

One day the priest himself sent to me post haste asking treatment for his daughter who had just been bitten. I found her with a very rapidly swelling leg, but she responded well to anti-venin and recovered. Later her mother took her to the shrine and was told that the shrine deity had sent the snake to warn her, and all the village people, not to break his rules by going to farm on his day of worship. The next person thus to offend would die.

§ 26. DISORDERS OF SLEEP

Insomnia is sometimes the only trouble a supplicant complains of, but, as might be expected, other troubles emerge on questioning. One man said he could not sleep for thinking of his unsatisfactory wives whose bad behaviour, he felt sure, had been induced by witchcraft.

Another patient said she slept but her spirit was always "flogged" in her sleep so that she woke up aching and her life had become very unhappy.

Patients often complain not of any clear-cut dream but of their dreams having become chaotic. They cannot remember what they dreamt of, it was too confused, but it left them worried and miserable.

One elderly woman complained that whenever she dreamt of her children, who were all grown up, she felt worried and upset. This was not surprising, for her sons, all except one, were ne'er-do-wells, and the only one who was a good personality and had been an asset had just resigned from his job. He pleased his employers so well that his fellow employees became enviously resentful and, he thought, dangerous.

Dreams are regarded as highly important and when vivid or frightening give the dreamer great anxiety till a satisfying interpretation is found. Such interpretation is a part of the work of shrines.

Different persons in similar situations often dream identical stereotyped dreams. For instance, people in fear of retribution for sin commonly dream that the deity, in the guise of a long-haired priest, is chasing them with a club and sometimes knocks them down.

Most of the dreams brought to everyday *abisa* at the shrines have a manifest content very little removed from the latent content. An ageing woman came saying that she often dreamt that her son was dead. On inquiry she revealed that the son was virtually dead *to her*, for he had long disregarded her feelings and wishes and had just gone away and left her, disclaiming any responsibility for her welfare. Another elderly widow who said, "I dream that someone is dead" also revealed that she had had a bitter quarrel with her brother, since when she had become very lonely and miserable. A little girl of ten who was sick and afraid of dying dreamt that she saw the ghost of her dead grandmother and some other ghosts, one of whom spat in her mouth. A man who had had a run of ill-luck dreamt that his good talisman was damaged. Another man who had recently seen the death of a number of his hopes and ambitions dreamt that he saw people making grave-mounds. An ex-witch, who at intervals was afraid that her illness might return dreamt that she was eating *kyim*—a food made of sheep's blood and red palm oil and commonly believed to be the vehicle by which the new *obayi* is carried for implantation.

The mother of a long family, pregnant again, dreamt that a barren woman in her house was stealing the foetus out of her womb. This was attributed by the priest to the pregnant woman's fear of the jealousy of the barren woman. Towards the end of her time the dreamer came back in considerable mental upset and guilt and it then became clear that the dream symbolised her own envy of the barren woman, for she confessed that she had not wanted another child because of estrangement from her husband and kinsfolk.

We shall return, however, to the structure of dreams as this is illustrated from time to time in the case-histories of patients making longer stays in town.

§ 27. MISCELLANEOUS *ABISA*

A number of cases fall into no special category. Those I saw included a woman who was under the *obosom's* protection but came asking permission to join a Christian Church. She would continue, she said, to send the *obosom* a yearly sheep and she wished also to put her children under his protection.

One supplicant came saying that he had been offered a legacy but did not know whether, in view of the envy it would provoke, it would be safe to accept it.

A couple came and said they had twelve children and did not want any more. A gasp of astonished horror went up from the bystanders, and the priest said that the deity would never listen to such a depraved request.

Another request was by a literate Government official who wanted the deity to soften his daughter's heart towards the man he desired her to marry. Another supplicant was a woman whose mad son had wandered off and got lost. Another came to give thanks for the return of her son, who had been driven by the spirit into the wilderness and had turned up again after being several days lost. A man came complaining of ill-treatment by a woman who broke her promise to marry him.

Another man wanted his uncle to give him a cocoa-farm. Another brought his motherless new-born child. A woman brought an infant whose twin had died and said that the survivor called the departed in the night and wanted to follow him. The relatives of a dying woman came complaining that she had refused to tell them where she had hidden her money and valuables.

Various chiefs, literate and illiterate, came desiring protection from assassination. A man complained that someone had cursed him to another *obosom*.

Several parents brought backward children, either retarded in growth or late in talking or walking. A few very aged people, feeling their sands running out, asked for renewed tenure of life. A married couple complained that their seven children were all of one sex.

Another asked to have no more children because they always died: the *obosom* refused to consider this request but said he would help future children to survive. The headman of a village complained that though the village was on a main road, it did not prosper: people died, others went away and left their houses to fall down and no one built new houses.

A man who complained that a woman who had promised to marry him had run off with £30 he had given her for trading was told by the deity that he was a fool and deserved to lose the money.

APPENDIX TO CHAPTER V

A NOTE ON LORRY-DRIVERS

Ordinary Ghana people, in passenger lorries, probably travel more often, faster, farther and lighter than any other people in the world. The drivers of passenger lorries, as has been said, are often seen as supplicants at shrines. Although I do not think their general attitude to success and failure is basically different from that of their countrymen in other occupations, they have one peculiar method of proclaiming that attitude. This we shall now briefly examine.

In Ghana, as elsewhere, drivers of fast vehicles experience an enjoyable "inflation of the ego". Among young men, particularly illiterates, there is no more widespread ambition, nor one more often achieved, than to drive, and if possible own, one of the thousands of passenger lorries that raven about the roads.

Having achieved this ambition, the driver is acutely conscious of himself as an object of envy, and has much anxiety lest those seeking his humiliation should bring it about by bad magic designed either to wreck his lorry or to bring it financial disaster. Therefore he seldom neglects to take his new lorry to a shrine for protection.

Financially, the lorry-driver's calling is highly hazardous. He usually acquires his vehicle only by running into debt to a trading-firm with a kinsman's cocoa-farm as security. If he is extremely lucky a bountiful uncle, father, mother, or even wife, will advance the whole purchase price at the outset. Indeed, the buying of lorries is one of the major outlets for rural wealth. In raising what Europeans call "the standard of living" such wealth is seldom used.

Even the most casual tourist to Ghana has noticed the fashion of decorating lorries with mottoes, proverbs, epigraphs and other strange devices, painted in bold letters on the backs, sides and front.

In the choice of these inscriptions the driver unconsciously reveals his dominant attitude, and preoccupations, sentiments and character-traits. Many of the same inscriptions that are painted on lorries are also painted on the outsides of houses, particularly new or newly inherited ones. The lorry-drivers' attitudes are in fact the normal ones, enunciated with rather more than normal clarity and trenchancy.

Some of the lorry and house inscriptions, however, are so cryptic in meaning that it is only by questioning the driver or house-owner that one can discover what he means to convey. In the following collection from lorries, where many were recorded on the roads, it was of course possible to question only a small proportion of drivers, but when they could be so questioned a remarkable correspondence was found between their interpretations and those given by ordinary people.

The collected inscriptions were found to express sentiments falling into several well-defined categories.

1. Paranoid apprehension and paranoid boast.
2. Financial anxiety.
3. Adulation of financially generous kinsmen.
4. Confidence in supernatural protection against enemies.
5. Miscellaneous, including simple gratification, meaningless verbiage, the advertising boast, the pious platitude, the waggish quip, etc.

In the following list, (a) is the exact transcription of what was written on the lorry; (b) is the English translation, if called for; (c) is the meaning as explained by the driver or other informant.

1. (a) "Ebi resu na ebi reserew."
   (b) Some are crying and some are laughing.
   (c) I am laughing because I have been able to buy a lorry, but other people are crying because they can't.

2. (a) "Mongye nkontabu."
   (b) Don't do any arithmetic.
   (c) If anyone knew what a lot of money I was making he would envy me.

3. (a) "Afi sem."
   (b) Domestic affair.
   (c) Those who envy me are those of my own house.

4. (a) "All in vain."
   (c) I am well protected, so if envious people plot my downfall, they won't succeed.

5. (a) "Too good."
   (c) Things have gone well with me and I have a lorry.

6. (a) "Obi mpe."
   (b) No one likes it.
   (c) No one likes me to have this lorry: they envy me.

7. (a) "He who wishes my downfall shall never prosper."

8. (a) "Monka nea mo pe."
   (b) Say what you like.
   (c) Whatever you say about me, I am not afraid, because my lorry is protected and you can't hurt it.

9. (a) "Mind your own [business]."
   (c) People have been wondering how I got the money to pay for this lorry.

10. (a) "Adom ne Nyame."
    (b) Help is God.
    (c) God has helped me to get this lorry: human beings haven't.

11. (a) "Wofa/Agya/Yere/Panyim pa ye."
    (b) There is a good uncle/father/wife/elder.
    (c) A good uncle/father/wife/elder has helped me to get this lorry.

12. (a) "Aboa a onni dua."
    (b) [God looks after] an animal that has no tail. (Proverb.)
    (c) I have no father or mother, but God will help me to pay for this lorry.

13. (a) "O God help me."
    (c) Oh God, help me to pay for this lorry.

14. (a) "Ade akye abia."
    (b) Now the day has dawned.
    (c) I have many enemies who start to talk about me as soon as the sun gets up, but let them talk and envy me as much as they like, for I have an *obosom's* protection.

15. (a) "Enemies all about me."

16. (a) "Otamfo ka ko na odofo akyere me mmere bi be du na."
    (b) An enemy speaks and goes on his way, but a friend will tell me when the time has arrived.
    (c) In spite of my enemies I shall have help when I need it.

17. (a) "Na mompe mode."
    (b) Now you don't like your own things.
    (c) You are coveting this of mine.

22. (a) "I am sure."
    (c) I am sure that some day I shall be able to pay for this lorry.

23. (a) "He who wishes my downfall shall never prosper."

24. (a) "Yehowa ye me nkwagye."
    (b) Jehovah is my salvation.
    (c) No envious person can hurt me.
25. (a) "Obi mpe obi yiye."
    (b) Nobody likes another's good.
    (c) No one likes me to have this lorry.
26. (a) "Life is war."
    (c) I fought to get this lorry.
27. (a) "Wo susu se wa awie."
    (b) Do you think you have finished?
    (c) I still have difficulties to face.
28. (a) "Samson too can fly."
    (c) I am a fine fellow.
29. (a) "A day will come."
    (c) Alternative meanings:
        (i) Some day I shall be able to pay for this lorry.
        (ii) Some day my enemies may overthrow me.
30. (a) "Kill me and fly."
    (c) If you do me any harm you won't escape.
31. (a) "Konkonsani bebere."
    (b) A double-dealer will be tired.
    (c) If you are secretly plotting against me you will suffer.
32. (a) "Agoro ye de."
    (b) Play [sexual dalliance] is sweet.
33. (a) "Obi anku wo a obi aku wo."
    (b) If someone has not seen you someone has seen you.
    (c) If you are plotting against me secretly you will be found out.
34. (a) "Mede masem ama Nyame."
    (b) I have handed over my affair to God.
    (c) Alternative meanings:
        (i) God will help me to pay for my lorry.
        (ii) God will save me from my enemies.
35. (a) "Woye papa a woye ma woko."
    (b) If you do good you do it for yourself.
    (c) I did good, so someone helped me to get this lorry.
36. (a) "Otamfo nnim aye yi."
    (b) An enemy does not know praise.
    (c) If you hate me you don't praise me whatever good I do.
37. (a) "Su nkwa na nsu ade."
    (b) Cry for life but not for things.
    (c) Envious people are after nothing less than my life.

38. (a) "Stop hating me."
    (c) You hate me because I have a lorry, but you'd better stop because I have supernatural protection against you.

39. (a) "Onyame nti menka koraa."
    (b) Because of God I will say nothing.
    (c) God will prevent people from harming me.

40. (a) "O abotare ye."
    (b) O, Humility is good.
    (c) Humility towards kinsmen got me my lorry.

41. (a) "Onipa behwe yie."
    (b) A man will look out.
    (c) I am wary of enemies.

42. (a) "Obi resu."
    (b) Someone is crying.
    (c) Someone is chagrined that I have a lorry.

43. (a) "Ade nyinaa yiye."
    (b) Everything is good.
    (c) Good and bad is all the same to me.

44. (a) "Mahu ma awie."
    (b) I have seen my end.
    (c) I see my way to pay my debts.

45. (a) "Adru ye."
    (b) Medicine is good.
    (c) I have medicined my lorry against all harm.

46. (a) "Ade nyinaa ne adwene."
    (b) Everything needs brains.
    (c) If I hadn't brains I could not have got this lorry.

47. (a) "Obiara bewu."
    (b) Everyone will die.
    (c) You will all die whether you envy me or not.

48. (a) "Eye wose wa awie?"
    (b) Did you say you had finished?
    (c) I have achieved a lorry but I have still to pay for it.

49. (a) "All is well."
    (c) It is gratifying to have a lorry.

50. (a) "Wages of sin is death."
    (b) If you practise bad medicines against me you will die.

51. (a) "Fear the man and leave the ghosts."
    (c) People, but not ghosts, will try to harm me for having a lorry.

52. (a) "Fear women."
    (c) Women will waste your money and give you sickness.

53. (a) "Enam obi so."
    (b) It comes from someone.
    (c) My lorry came through someone's help.

54. (a) "Onyame wo ho."
    (b) God is there.
    (c) God will punish you if you try to harm me.

55. (a) "Eka obi nko a."
    (b) If it rested with somebody.
    (c) If somebody had his way, I shouldn't have this lorry.

56. (a) "Etire nyinaa nse."
    (b) All heads are not equal.
    (c) If I weren't cleverer than most I wouldn't have got this lorry

57. (a) "Din pa ye sen ahonya."
    (b) A good name is better than wealth.
    (c) Because I was well thought of someone helped me to get this lorry.

58. (a) "Boafo ye na."
    (b) Helpers are scarce.
    (c) I have not yet paid for this lorry.

59. (a) "People will talk of you."
    (c) They are talking maliciously of me because they envy me.

60. (a) "Show your love."
    (c) Help me to pay for my lorry.

61. (a) "Obre twa owuo."
    (b) The end of being tired is death.
    (c) I have suffered in getting this lorry, and whether I die with it or whether I get profit from it, I am past caring.

62. (a) "Onyame kai me."
    (b) God remember me.
    (c) God help me to pay for this lorry.

63. (a) "Two shadows."
    (c) I have an extra spirit, I am under supernatural protection.

64. (a) "Suro nnipa."
    (b) Fear people.
    (c) Be wary. People will do you harm if they can.

65. (a) "Suro nea oben wo."
    (b) Fear the one who is near to you.
    (c) Someone in my own family dislikes my success and seeks my downfall.

66. (a) "Otan hunu ye yaw."
    (b) It is painful to be hated for no reason.
    (c) I am hated just because I own a lorry.

67. (a) "Ei! wiase ye hu."
    (b) Oh, how fearful is the world.
    (c) I have overcome fearful things in acquiring this lorry, but there are more ahead.

68. (a) "Otamfo ani awu."
    (b) The enemy is abashed.
    (c) My enemy looks silly now that I have achieved my ambition.

69. (a) "Ennam Onyame nti."
    (b) It comes through God.
    (c) No human being gave me any help in getting this lorry.

70. (a) "Obra wo rebo afa."
    (b) The character you are making you have to take.
    (c) If anyone hates me for having a lorry it will come back to himself.

71. (a) "Watch and pray."
    (c) Because I am a prayerful and circumspect Christian, I have been able to get this lorry.

72. (a) Who knows?
    (c) I don't know who can be trusted.

73. (a) "Boafo ho ye na."
    (b) Helpers are scarce.
    (c) I have few friends so it will be hard to pay for this lorry.

74. (a) "Asikafo, mon dwene."
    (b) Rich people, consider.
    (c) You rich people refused to help me, consider now how I have succeeded without you.

75. (a) "Nyame do."
    (b) God's love.
    (c) Through God's love I have this lorry, though people have refused to help me.

76. (a) "Baako nua ne odo."
    (b) One man's brother is love.
    (c) If you have no brother, love is your brother. I am an orphan, but people who love me have helped me to get this lorry.

77. (a) When shall I?
    (c) When shall I be able to pay for this lorry?

78. (a) "Baanu ye."
    (b) It is good to be two.
    (c) Someone helped me to get this lorry.

79. (a) "Su nkwa."
    (b) Cry for life.
    (c) I have got a lorry, but now I cry to get a living out of it.

80. (a) "Eka obi nko."
    (b) If it were someone.
    (c) If my enemy had his way I shouldn't have this lorry.

81. (a) "Not yet."
    (c) Two alternative meanings:
        (i) I am well protected; therefore it will be a long time before anyone can bring about my downfall.
        (ii) I am not yet able to pay for this lorry.

82. (a) "Otan nni adru."
    (b) Hatred has no medicine.
    (c) People hate me, but it can't be helped.

83. (a) "The beginning of life is not hard, but the end."
    (c) I have got this lorry without much trouble, but shall I ever be able to pay for it?

84. (a) "Aka m'ani."
    (b) I have experienced it.
    (c) I had a lorry and was bankrupt, but have learnt by my mistakes.

85. (a) "Nyamprani."
    (b) Nyamprani [a shade-tree of the *obosom*].
    (c) An *obosom* helped me to get this lorry and is sheltering me from envious people.

86. (a) "Otan firi fie."
    (b) Hatred comes from home.
    (c) My kinsmen hate me.

87. (a) "Onipa befwe yie."
    (b) A man should take care.
    (c) I must look out, because people envy me.

88. (a) "Women are woe to men."
    (c) If you spend your money on women you won't be able to pay for your lorry.

89. (a) "Travel and see."
    (c) I have seen the world and am now wary of it.

90. (a) "Eka obi nkoa anka mawu."
    (b) On account of someone I might have died.
    (c) If my envious enemies had their way, I should be dead.
91. (a) "Mahu ma awie."
    (b) I have seen my end.
    (c) The *obosom* has foretold a long and prosperous life for me.
92. (a) "Because of money."
    (c) If I hadn't money I couldn't have got this lorry.
93. (a) "Fine boy."
    (c) What a fine fellow I am.
94. (a) "Eye ahonya."
    (b) There is abundance.
    (c) This lorry is a small thing to me who have cocoa, buildings and other wealth.
95. (a) "Ade nyinaa nse."
    (b) All things are not alike.
    (c) I have been able to buy a lorry but most people couldn't.
96. (a) "Happiness."
    (c) I am happy because I have a lorry.
97. (a) "Biribi nsuro biribi."
    (b) Something doesn't fear something. [Like doesn't fear like.]
    (c) If you make a strong medicine against me I also have a strong medicine.
98. (a) "Afei na ato adwene."
    (b) It is now a matter of brains.
    (c) Now I have a lorry I shall use my brains to keep it.
99. (a) "Still wonderful morocco."
100. (a) "God is."
    (c) Through God I have a lorry.
101. (a) "Remember the judgment."
    (c) If you plot my downfall you will pay for it.
102. (a) "Obi nkyen ye tra na."
    (b) It is difficult to live as a guest.
    (c) It is useless to depend on others: I had no help in getting this lorry.
103. (a) "Ahoanya."
    (b) Wealth.
104. (a) "Monka neamope."
    (b) Say ye what you like.
    (c) People talk about me with spiteful jealousy but I don't care because I am protected.

105. (a) "Onipa sunsum ne sika."
     (b) The spirit of man is money.
     (c) I have enough to have obtained this lorry.

106. (a) "Ebia."
     (b) Perhaps.
     (c) Perhaps I shall be able to pay for this lorry.

107. (a) "Su wo ho na nsu me."
     (b) Cry for yourself but not for me.
     (c) If you try to injure me it will rebound on you for I have a
         powerful protection.

108. (a) "Ahobrease."
     (b) Humility.
     (c) I had to humble myself before I got this lorry.

109. (a) "Nnipa ahooden ne kunim."
     (b) Man's strength is victorious.
     (c) I have achieved my lorry through strength.

110. (a) "Obi do bi."
     (b) Someone loves someone.
     (c) Because someone loved me I was able to get this lorry.

111. (a) "Enye m'asem."
     (b) It is not my business.
     (c) I don't mind what you want to do to me.

112. (a) "Onyame ne me boafo."
     (b) God is my helper.
     (c) No human being helped me to get this lorry.

113. (a) "Aware pa ye."
     (b) A good marriage is all right.
     (c) Through making a good marriage I got this lorry.

114. (a) "Atomicity."

115. (a) "God bless me."
     (c) May God help me to pay for this lorry.

116. (a) "Bo wo ho mmoden."
     (b) Try for yourself.
     (c) I had to help myself to get this lorry.

117. (a) "Mframa see dua."
     (b) The wind spoils the tree.
     (c) I won't boast of my splendour because even trees have some-
         thing to bring them down.

118. (a) "Odo na eye fe."
     (b) Love is pleasant.
     (c) It would be better if you loved me instead of hating me be-
         cause I have a lorry.

119. (a) "Leniency."
     (c) God is generous, man isn't.

120. (a) "Nso Nyame ye."
     (b) But yet there is God.
     (c) God will protect me.

121. (a) "It is easy for God."
     (c) It is easy for God to punish my ill-wishers.

122. (a) "Seniority."
     (c) I am senior because I possess something my kinsmen don't.

123. (a) "Kumasi Night Sports."
     (c) Sexual dalliance in Kumasi.

124. (a) "Odo wo yonko."
     (b) Love your fellow.
     (c) Give me love rather than hate even though I have a lorry.

125. (a) "Mereye bi afwe."
     (b) I am having a try and will see.
     (c) I am taking a chance. I may fail in this venture.

126. (a) "Hama bedu soro a, na efi dua."
     (b) If a liana will reach up it comes from the tree.
     (c) Before you can buy a lorry you must have someone richer to
         help you.

127. (a) "Obiara wo ne tamfo wo wiase."
     (b) Everyone in the world has his enemies.
     (c) People covet my lorry.

128. (a) "Friends to-day, enemies to-morrow."
     (c) Those who were my friends became my enemies when I got
         this lorry.

129. (a) "Obedience good boy."
     (c) I had to humble myself before I got this lorry.

130. (a) "Akomam boafo ne Nyame."
     (b) The only helper is God.
     (c) Nobody but God helped me to get this lorry.

131. (a) "Sister girl."

132. (a) "Obi ada woroma."
     (b) By the grace of someone.
     (c) Someone helped me to get this lorry.

133. (a) "Bere no nsoe."
     (b) The time has not yet come.
     (c) Alternatives:
         (i) The time has not yet come for my enemies to overthrow me.
         (ii) I have not yet paid for this lorry.

134. (a) "Odo ye wu."
     (b) Love is death.
     (c) If you love a woman and she doesn't love you it will kill you because you waste your money on her.

135. (a) "Ohia ma nnipa te nkwasia."
     (b) Poverty makes people hear foolishness.
     (c) If you go for money to a rich man you will hear nothing satisfying, so depend on yourself like me.

136. (a) "Sunny boy."

137. (a) "America boy on road."

138. (a) "A woman never boast on me."
     (c) No woman can sneer that I have no money.

139. (a) "Onipa susuw ne sika."
     (b) A person thinks of his money.
     (c) I didn't buy a lorry till I could afford it, so now I can crow over those whose lorries will be seized.

140. (a) "Death takes no bribe."
     (c) Your money will not protect you from death if you do me any harm.

141. (a) "Nkrabea."
     (b) Destiny.

142. (a) "Sharp sharp."
     (c) I am very clever indeed.

143. (a) "Nnipa dee nse."
     (b) People are all alike.
     (c) Everybody is bound to envy me.

144. (a) "Still New Boy."

Part 2
THE PATIENTS

INTRODUCTION TO PART 2

Most of the cases described in the following pages were of acute illness and, with very few exceptions, were found at shrines. The last section only, on Chronic Schizophrenia, concerns patients who were sought out in their own homes in a circumscribed area around my own dwelling.

Since this is a book about mental illness in only a part of rural Ghana —a very small corner of a continent racially and culturally heterogeneous even before the white man came to it—I must resist my friends' urgings to discourse here and now on the reiterated question, "Do primitive* people have the same mental illnesses as ourselves?" In so far as rural Ghana can contribute to an answer, my case-histories must speak for themselves.†

A part of the answer, however, is implicit in the classification of cases which I have been forced to adopt. The first problem of classification— whether to adopt an ethnological or a psychiatric basis—was easily disposed of. Had I chosen the former, each category would have remained hopelessly heterogeneous. For instance, a heading "Witchcraft cases" would have been found to embrace depressive delusions, physical illnesses supposedly sent as punishment for sin, febrile fears of children, epileptic sensations of swinging through the air, migrainous experience of quivering lights, the obsessive impulse to attack children with a cutlass, and divers other ills with nothing in common except that the patients thought themselves witches.

Most of the cases can be classified in commonplace psychiatric terms without any misgiving. Where others could be given no well-worn diagnostic label, I have found it expedient to classify them in terms of such universal entities as fear and anxiety.

The case histories in the following pages are a representative selection from my notebooks.

---

* I would define "primitive" people as self-sufficient people. There are still to be found in Ghana people who are quite self-sufficient except in the matter of iron-smelting and fire-making, which two arts have been lost.

† In general terms I would go no further than saying that there are probably as many different kinds of healthy mentality among primitive peoples as there are among advanced peoples, and consequently as many types of mental illness.

I

DEPRESSION

§ 1. GENERAL REMARKS ON DEPRESSION

Depression is the commonest mental illness of Akan rural women and nearly all such patients come to the shrines with spontaneous self-accusations of witchcraft—that is, of having caused harm without concrete act or conscious will.

A depressed patient is not considered mentally ill, for she is correctly orientated, accessible, and says nothing which is—in the ideological setting—irrational. She is taken at her word when she says she has done harm. If she is restless, agitated, sleepless, unable to do her work and so on, this is taken to mean, as she says, that the *obosom* has caught hold of her and is troubling her. The depressive personality is, in sickness and health, self-effacing and is seldom a disturbing nuisance. She is therefore the last type of patient who would ever find her way to any kind of European hospital unless she had some concurrent and conspicuous physical trouble—such as a retained placenta or a pneumonia. It is not surprising therefore that psychiatrists and other doctors who see patients only in hospitals and clinics should have the idea that depression in Africa hardly exists.

§ 2. INVOLUTIONAL DEPRESSION

In rural Ghana, Involutional Depression with agitation is (as in our own society) one of the commonest and most clearly defined of mental illnesses. The majority of patients are conscientious women of good personality who have worked hard and launched a fleet of well-brought-up children. Many of them have paid for their children's schooling with money earned by diligent trading, market-gardening or cocoa-farming. Asked to describe the onset of their symptoms they use the phrases familiar in the admission wards of our own mental hospitals. "I became useless. I couldn't do any work but neither could I sit still and rest. At night I couldn't sleep because my mind was restless and I often got up and walked about." Then they add, "Soon I knew that I was no good and had become a witch. I have done so much evil that I ought to be killed."

In Ghana the patient often has the additional stress of seeing her husband take an extra and younger wife so that he may continue to beget children. Flighty young girls in their teens are particularly attractive to men who are past their own prime, and the man frequently lavishes on the young woman money and luxuries which are among the fruits of his older wife's years of labour. Most women, quite apart from the depressives, are worried by these social hazards of the menopause, and many of them, when they first become aware of amenorrhea, go from shrine to shrine over several years with the plaint, "I am pregnant, but the pregnancy doesn't grow."

Although illiterate Africans never know how old they are, I think there is little doubt that the menopause of rural women seldom occurs before the age of fifty. Rural Africans of both sexes seem to carry their years remarkably well, remaining smooth-skinned, black-haired and supple into old age.

CASE 1. AMA A. of Offuman district, Ashanti. F. *c.* 50.

Shrine
   Oboo at Offuman.

Reason for referral
   Self-accusations of witchcraft.

Family History
   Father: Dead. A native of Offuman. An illiterate, non-Christian farmer. He had some cocoa. His marriage was not cross-cousin.
   Mother: A native of Techiman, Ashanti, where she still lives. She was quite well till a few months ago when she was injured in a lorry accident and was a week in hospital.
   Siblings: Several, including two sisters in the mother's house at Techiman. All well.

Personal History
   Childhood: N.a.d. She was brought up in Offuman, but family ties and obligations are mostly in Techiman with her mother's people.
   Schooling: Nil. Non-Christian.
   Work: Koko-yam farmer and trader. No cocoa.

Marriage: Her first husband was a native of Offuman and died about twenty years ago. On his death she was given to his younger brother. Both marriages were happy. There were no co-wives.

Children: Twelve live births. Seven died, some in infancy, some after growing up. Of the five survivors, two are grown-up and married. One son, aged sixteen, has a mental illness (see Kofi A., Case 80), one child goes to school (Standard IV) and the youngest child is about eight.

Previous Illnesses: Nil.

Home

The house is owned by the husband's uncle and contains the husband and his maternal uncles and their wives and children, the husband's sister and her grown-up daughter and the latter's children.

Previous Personality

Universally respected and leant upon. Talkative, brisk and hard-working, meticulously clean and tidy.

Katamenia

Cessation of menstruation at about the time of the onset of the present illness.

Present Illness

Several months ago, the patient's son and mother were both in a lorry accident. They were taken to Techiman hospital where they remained a week. The patient was sent for to care for them after their discharge to the family house in Techiman.

About three months ago, while still in Techiman, the patient dreamt one night that she had gone to her mother's town, was frightened, wanted to shout but could not. The next day she found that she was "no good" and that "the world was no good". She had "burnings" all over her scalp and in her belly and was restless, "going here and there". She felt weak, tired and "useless", could not do her work and could not sleep. Later she began to feel that she had caused the lorry accident, was a witch and had been "caught" by the *obosom* at Offuman for her sins. She was brought to the shrine, where she said she had killed her children and caused the lorry accident and her son's illness. She had also planned to kill her mother and her two sisters.

Interview: 16.8.56

I did not see her till the day after her confession at the shrine. Physically normal, though having the non-toxic goitre very prevalent in the Techiman district.

She was depressed and dejected but rational, and she smiled an appropriate but watery smile. She said she was not feeling better for having confessed her sins. She denied weeping but looked on the verge of tears. She was silent unless addressed, restless, anxious, slow and a poor witness. She said that the night after going to the *obosom* she dreamt she was in an unpainted, shabby lorry which was running away with her and that she was frightened and jumped out.

21.3.57. I did not see her for some months, as she went away to a "village" and has only just returned. Witnesses say there was not much change till recently when a relative who usually stopped on his way to Kumasi to leave her a gift one day went past without calling. She resented his neglect, but her own self-reproach soon magnified her criticism of him and she said she had attempted to kill him by witchcraft. One day she was walking to farm when she was overcome with remorse and sat down on the path, becoming almost mute. She has hardly moved and hardly spoken since. Witnesses say, "She hears what you say when you speak to her, but sometimes she doesn't answer till you have forgotten what you said, but she has not forgotten. Sometimes she won't eat at all and sometimes she won't be washed. She lies down most of the time, but sometimes gets up very slowly. If you give her something to launder she will go on washing it all day until the bar of soap is finished."

I do not think this washing is obsessive, but simply inertia.*

I found her lying down. She replied in a monosyllable to my greeting but was otherwise mute. She very slowly put out a hand to shake mine.

16.6.57. No change. She spends most of her time lying down. The relatives agree that "she is not mad, only very slow".

1.8.57. No change. Much retarded, but she exchanged greetings after long pauses. She eats rather a lot, absent-mindedly going on when once started.

16.12.57. They said she was better and had gone to her village. I went there but she had gone to farm.

2.1.58. Much better. I saw her working hard repairing the walls of a room with new clay. Her speech is still slow, her smile is reluctant, but warm.

COMMENTARY

Involutional depression in a good, conscientious personality. Her son may be regarded as an additional reactive factor.

The dream of saving herself by jumping out of the runaway lorry is

* Not inertness, but inertia in the exact sense of the word as used in Physics.

quite commonly dreamt by people immediately after going to the shrine when they feel that they have taken active steps to get out of their troubles. It imparts a happy effect.

CASE 2. AMA F. of Bekwai district, Ashanti. F. *c.* 55.

Shrine
Mframa at Mframaso.

Reason for referral
Self-accusations of witchcraft. She came alone to the shrine.

Family History
Parents: Cross-cousins. Both are dead. They were illiterate, non-Christian cocoa-farmers.

Mother's brother: He was shunned by the patient's mother and other relatives and they never visited him. When he died he was buried by "a grandfather and some young men in the town" and no funeral custom was made. This implies a "bad death" concerning which the patient is reticent, though she asserts that she probably got her own witchcraft from this uncle.

Siblings: Seven born: only the patient and one other—now a cocoa-farmer—survived.

Personal History
Childhood home: The father owned the house and lived there with all his wives and children and also his brother and sister. The house was in town and they farmed from there.

Schooling: Nil. Non-Christian.

Marriage: She married her cross-cousin. He has two other wives. The patient is on excellent terms with them: they go to farm together and share one another's food. (This implies genuine harmony.) She says that she has not killed any of her co-wives' children and they do not suspect her of it but she is afraid she might unwittingly kill some of her husband's sisters' children. The husband has recently drunk at Mframa's shrine because he is afraid of the patient's witchcraft.

Children: Nine born, six died. One died when grown-up, about ten years ago. The others died all in infancy. The survivors are all daughters, all married except the youngest, aged fifteen.

Household: The husband, the husband's wives, the husband's brother, husband's sisters and their children. One of the husband's wives has lost three children out of six, the other three out of nine.

Previous Personality: She says she "was always laughing and playing".

Katamenia: Menopause about six years ago.

Present Illness

About ten years ago her uncle (*vide supra*) fell sick and died. The relatives were sent for during his last illness, but the patient was the only one who obeyed the summons. Just before dying he gave her some gold trinkets. The patient thinks that an *obayi* was in these trinkets because she began to feel herself a witch shortly after. About that time her son died and she felt that she had killed him. She went to Tigari whose medicine she had drunk and surrendered her evil trinkets, but Tigari did not succeed in removing her feeling that she was a witch.

Her sensations were of giddiness, headache and blackness before her eyes. Sometimes bright, flickering lights appeared before her eyes and stayed only a few minutes. (Migraine scotomata?)

Now she often dreams that someone is dead and that she is crying at the funeral. She has other dreams that she cannot remember, but in them she is often frightened and often cries. Often she cannot sleep at all. When she lies down and closes her eyes she often has the feeling that she is swinging and flying. She says she can still take pleasure in her work.

Interview: 22.6.56

At the shrine she stood anxious, agitated and weeping. She talked loudly, anxiously and protestingly, saying that although she had killed her brother and several of her children she had no desire to be a witch. When she knelt to implore that the evil power might be taken from her, four other women also knelt and interceded for her. These were not relatives but women she had made friends with on the lorry. The *obosom* said he would require a cow from her and she asked permission to go home and raise the money to buy it. At private interview she was less agitated and gave a clear, ready account of herself. She did not appear so much distressed as frightened into an anxiety by her physical symptoms.

23.6.56. She has gone home to find money for her cow.

29.9.56. She has been away three months. She returned and appeared at the shrine with her cow. She told the *obosom* that she had a further confession to make. Before her first appearance at the shrine she went one day to her farm and there found a dead antelope. She brought it home and sold the meat in the market. Recently she realised that the carcass was the corpse of the son she had killed and turned into an antelope. She knew it was an "evil antelope" because its decaying smell was what led her to find it in the farm.

At the shrine she told this tale quite cheerfully and went through her ritual dance and purification as if she enjoyed it.

At private interview later she seemed very well, cheerful and brisk—

in fact, rather exuberant. She says she now feels quite well and is very happy about it.

10.10.56. Though now at liberty to go home in peace she says she will stay for a few weeks to confirm her cure. She is now rather over-active, always sweeping, washing, cooking and doing farm-work, for the old elder in whose house she lodges. She often comes to see me, talks and laughs noisily and heartily and is rather difficult to get rid of. She is popular in the village and can always raise a laugh in the typical warm hypomanic fashion.

31.12.56. She is still staying in Mframaso, saying that she wants to be sure that her illness is not coming back. When asked whether there was anything in her home she was afraid to return to, she laughed heartily, made a crack and would disclose nothing. Probably someone at home is afraid of her and has expressed ill-will, whereas in Mframaso she is very popular and happy.

31.1.57. She is still in Mframaso. Now rather subdued. Maybe she is going into a depressive phase.

20.2.57. She is silent unless addressed. Unsmiling. Looks unhappy.

10.8.57. She has spent several months looking rather oppressed and sitting in the yard, but has now brightened up.

COMMENTARY

Long, depressive episode with self-accusations at the involutional age in a manic-depressive personality.

The sensation of swinging on lying down is familiar to psychiatrists as a complaint made by epileptics, though it may be associated with a normal E.E.G.

CASE 3. AKOSUA T. of Kwahu. F. 50+.

Shrine

Mframa at Mframaso.

Reason for referral

She came alone on her own initiative, complaining that she felt completely miserable and was sure that she had been made into a witch against her will.

Family History

Parents: Not cross-cousins. Illiterate, non-Christian cocoa-farmers. They are both dead. The mother died about seven years ago. One year before her death she became miserable and weeping and could not sleep. She complained that whenever she slept she had frightening dreams of being chased by a cow, of walking into a stream and catching cat-fish and of crossing a river and being swept away by it. Then she said it was the *obosom* Tigari who had caught her for being a witch. When told that she must therefore go to Tigari and confess or she would die, she said that she wanted to die so would not confess. After about a year she did die.

Personal History

Childhood: N.a.d. Happy. Home contained parents and father's sister.

Work: Hair-dyer. Cocoa, corn and cassava market-gardener. Is financially prosperous, has built her own house and educated two sons.

Marriages: Her first husband was an illiterate Christian lorry-driver. The patient became a Christian because of him. He drank a little and never aspired to have a lorry of his own. When the children were small (about twenty years ago) he became lean and died. The second husband was unsatisfactory and the patient terminated the marriage at the instigation of her children. A lover now lives with her and wants to marry her, her children think for her money.

Children

First marriage

1. Daughter. Illiterate. She is married and lives in Kyibi with her husband. She has children and one grandchild.

2. Son. Illiterate. He is a lorry-driver. He drinks heavily and once said he would kill his mother for making him a drunkard by witchcraft. (Drunkards are virtually the only people who ever make direct accusations of witchcraft and they always blame the witch for making them drunkards.) He consulted an *obosom* who, however, exonerated the patient. He had two big lorries, but since he started drinking has lost them both. He has three times ditched his lorry; the first time he was fined lightly, the second heavily, the patient contributing £27. He now drives for a European. He is married and has children. He lived in his mother's house till he began to blame her for his drunkenness.

3. Son. Literate. He was a driver, but is now a dispenser-in-training at a Mission hospital. He is married and has children. He is kind to his mother, is upset because she is miserable and wants her to go and live with him.

4. Son. He went to school but did not reach top class and became a motor-mechanic. He is married with children. He also is kind to his mother.

5. Died in infancy.

Second marriage

1. Died in infancy.

2. Four-month abortion.

Previous Illnesses

About twenty years ago (?) one day when she was isolated outside the back of the house because of menstruation, she was given a meal cooked by her mother. While eating this, her mouth suddenly became crooked and she became unconscious. She remained so for four days and was restored to consciousness after her brother had made medicine over her. She was unable to talk for a month. She denies any residual weakness in any limb but felt "something like needles walking" in her feet and coming up her legs. For this she had outpatient hospital treatment, consisting of "many injections". She is sure that her mother gave her this illness in the food* she was eating when it started.

Shortly after this stroke she became pregnant but had a four-month miscarriage.

Katamenia

Still menstruates, but intervals have lately become long.

Previous Personality

Always a hard worker and successful money-maker. A regular church-goer. She never joined the choir or women's class, but the minister admired her industry and made her the leader of the women who cleaned and cared for the church buildings.

Household

She lives in her own house with her weaver "husband" and grand-daughter, aged eight, who does not go to school. The drunken son lived there but he has now left.

Present Illness

Onset about ten years ago. She seldom slept but lay on her mat, thinking. She was utterly miserable and often wept. When she slept she dreamt the same dreams that later troubled her mother except that she (the patient) often dreamt of being chased not only by a cow but by the police and by Europeans. She always woke up terrified. She became thin, sometimes giddy and had pains all over. She thought she was "caught" by Tigari at whose shrine she had drunk about a year previously, so she went to Tigari and said she had been "caught" for being a witch.

She added that she had never used her witchcraft or done any harm or wrong, but could not explain her misery on any other ground than that of being "caught".

* Not, of course, as a direct poison but as a magical influence.

When she went to Tigari's shrine, they said, "Say what you have done and you will be cured", so she said she had done every wrong she could think of, but felt no better after it. She has been to Tigari twice more since then, complaining that she is not cured and she has confessed to everything she thinks her *obayi* might have done without her knowledge but feels no better. She has not lost her ability to work but takes no pleasure in it. She is sure that her mother gave her some kind of witchcraft and that she is "caught" for possessing it. She came to Mframa for help because Tigari was unsuccessful. She had never drunk at Mframa's shrine.

First interview: 8.12.56

Well-nourished, briskly walking, resolute woman, seemingly full of well-directed vigour and drive. There is a slight asymmetry of her face. She looks exceedingly worried and unhappy. Her face is deeply lined and anxious. She talks fluently and rather indignantly but gives a clear trenchant account of herself. She says she does not feel physically ill or weak, just miserable, troubled and sleepless. Unlike other witches, she has no ideas of unworthiness. She stoutly denies that she has ever done anything wrong with her witchcraft but bases her belief in its existence on the evidence and insists that she has been wronged by having it thrust upon her by her mother.

She is intelligent, friendly, forthright, capable and self-reliant.

15.12.56. She was alone to-day and I was able to do a neurological examination. The pupils were equal and reactive and everything was quite normal. Now that the excitement of coming and making her *abisa*, etc., has worn off and she has settled down, she is much less brisk, though far from being slow. She now says she sleeps fairly well, but the thing that worries her most in her illness are the danger-dreams. She insists that she has never done anything wrong.

20.2.57. She has been in Mframaso ever since. Unchanged.

20.6.57. Unchanged.

COMMENTARY

This is an atypical anxious depression of spirits without any depression of energy and drive, and without protestations of unworthiness.

Her stroke twenty years ago may have been caused by a malarial cerebral embolus or perhaps a syphilitic endarteritis. The subsequent sensations in her feet and legs suggest tabies as does the course of "many injections". The deaths and abortion of her last three children are consistent with this, as also is the fact that her husband was a lorry-driver who would travel to ports and other urban centres.

The police and Europeans who chase her in dreams are no doubt symbols of Authority.

Case 4. YAA N. of Konongo district, Ashanti. F. *c.* 55.

Shrine
Mframa at Mframaso.

Reason for referral

She was brought by a family party (two older brothers, three sisters, sister's son and her own son), all wishing to clear themselves of suspicion of having caused the illness (sleeplessness) of the younger brother (see Kwabena A., Case No. 63). The patient was especially under suspicion because she had proclaimed herself a witch "caught" by Tigari five years earlier.

Family History

Parents: Both are dead. They were not cross-cousins. N.a.d. disclosed.

Siblings: (1) Elder brother, about sixty. Head of the family. He came to Mframaso with the party. (2) Brother. (Kwabena A.)

Several other brothers and three sisters—n.a.d. All are illiterate, non-Christian cocoa-farmers.

Personal History

Childhood: N.a.d. disclosed.

Work: She was industrious before her first illness. She had her own cocoa-farms.

Marriage: She separated from her husband fifteen years ago. She had wanted to divorce him earlier for neglecting to give her necessities, but he refused to go, so she committed adultery. She has not married again.

Children: Seven born, five died. The survivors are a son and daughter, both grown-up. The daughter has two children. The son is a lorry-driver's mate. He has spent about £30 (so he says) in bribes to the police, but still cannot pass his driving-test. He now blames his mother's witchcraft for this. The son and daughter live with their father, presumably for fear of their mother.

Household: The patient, the sleepless brother, a sister and her thirteen children and some grandchildren.

Previous Illness (from patient): Five years ago she began to feel "changed" and miserable. She "couldn't go anywhere", could do no work, take no interest in anything, nor sleep. Sometimes she shed tears. Then she knew that she was a witch and was "caught" by Tigari at whose shrine she had drunk. She developed pains all over, palpitations, and blackness before her eyes. Then she realised that her mother must have given her the *obayi* when she was about fourteen. Her mother, who was a heavy pipe-smoker, one day handed her the pipe and told her to take a few whiffs. She did so and felt giddy and had blackness before her eyes, but never recalled the incident till blackness and giddiness recurred years later.

She confessed to Tigari and was cleansed, but says, "Since then I have never been happy."

Present Illness

At the shrine the sleepless brother made his complaint. The *obosom* said his *kra* had been taken away by witches and that he would soon die if it was not returned. The patient then placed herself in the sinners' dock and said that she was the witch. She added a long string of the usual stereotyped confessions, claiming to have brought about every death in the family for the previous twenty years. She also said that because she was feeling miserable and useless she went to a medicine-man about eighteen months ago and he told her that someone in her household had often insulted her ever since Tigari "caught" her. She told the medicine-man, "Yes, indeed"—her brother had never stopped insulting her and she wished the medicine-man would "tie" him "to return some of my humiliation to him." A few days later the brother's bed fell down and his sleeplessness began.

She was told that she must go back to the medicine-man to have her brother "untied", after which she could come back with a cow for her ritual cleansing. She replied that if she failed to do everything in her power, then might the *obosom* kill her like a sheep.

Interview: 13.5.56

Agitated and depressed. No retardation. She walked and spoke briskly. Her face was deeply marked with anxious lines confirming her story of long-standing misery. At interview she answered all questions readily and clearly and was grateful for friendly overtures. She was co-operative and anxious to fall in with the *obosom's* instructions.

15.5.56. After her appearance at the shrine she walked anxiously up and down the street and then went to the *obosom's* clerk and asked him to take down further confessions—all of the stereotyped kind. After these had been read at the shrine she left Mframaso and went home to see the medicine-man who had "tied" her brother. After this she will be at liberty to return with a cow for her purification.

30.12.56. Up to date the patient has not returned. The inference is that her sleepless brother, who is now, together with the rest of the family, under the protection of Mframa, is not willing to pay for a cow and is prepared to let her die in her sin at the hand of the deity.

COMMENTARY

Involutional depression with self-blame in a previously industrious woman.

CASE 5. AFUA F. of Kwahu. F. *c.* 50.

Shrine
Amfemfri, at Asuoyi.

Reason for referral
Self-accusations of witchcraft.

Family History
No information except that they all farm cocoa and are illiterate non-Christians. Brother is an elder of the town.

Personal History
Marriage: The husband is an illiterate, non-Christian cocoa-farmer.
Children: Eight alive, some dead. The eldest son was seen—a strapping, healthy, pleasant man of about twenty-five, an illiterate Christian. The youngest child is only a year old.
Katamenia: Menopause not yet reached.
Household: The patient lives with her brother and other siblings in a house which belonged to their maternal uncle. The brother says it is a happy household. The patient's husband lives in his own people's house.

Previous Illness
The patient was "caught" by Tigari ten years ago, because someone had done her wrong and she "kept it in her head", resentfully brooding instead of "speaking it out". She was smitten with pains, went to Tigari and confessed, and was cured.

Present Illness
She came to the shrine at Asuoyi with her son, brother and husband, all four as ordinary suppliants, simply seeking protection and prosperity. Immediately after the customary presentation of eggs to the *obosom* the patient began to shake and tremble before the shrine. Asked what ailed her she said she was "caught" for her sins. She said she had killed her uncle and his children and had intended to kill a brother. The name of her *obayi* was Bayi Kofi, and her "flying-song" was "O, Bayi Kofi, take me away and bring me back".

Interview: 9.8.56
She was seen a week after confessing at the shrine. Though she had calmed down immediately after her confession, her purification ceremony was not performed till a week later when I first saw her dancing to the *obosom's* drums with the smashed egg still plastered on her head. Later on the same day I had a brief opportunity of talking to her. She

was tired by the dancing and very irritable and cross, with alternate sulks and outbursts of petulance. She was thin, anxious and miserable, in contrast to her relatives who were well-nourished and healthy.

20.8.56. Depressed and languid, not agitated, but slow and dejected. She was perfectly accessible but too listless to talk. She said perfunctorily that she was better but could not interest herself in anything. She said it was more than three months since she had felt any pleasure in her work. She was thin but said she had been fat till she became uninterested in eating.

30.8.56. Still sitting huddled, dejected, slow and forlorn.

4.9.56. She has gone home, they say recovered, but I doubt the latter.

COMMENTARY

Depression with self-reproach in an anxious, elderly woman whose child-bearing has extended over at least twenty-five years. One anxiety episode ten years ago.

CASE 6. EKWIA S. of Techiman district. F. *c.* 50.

Shrine
Amfemfi, Asueyi.

Reason for referral
Fear of becoming a witch.

Family History
Parents: Not cross-cousins. Non-Christian, illiterate yam-farmers. No cocoa. They died when the patient was newly married.

Siblings: Four born, two died.

Mother's sisters: Three of these were "caught", talked "basa-basa" and after about a year died.

Personal History
Childhood: N.a.d.

Schooling: Nil. Non-Christian.

Marriage: Husband is still alive. Non-Christian, illiterate cocoa-farmer. Patient is the second in rank of four wives. One of these lives in her own house: patient and two others with the husband. There are occasional transient wrangles between the wives but no jealousy.

Children: Seven born, three died. The survivors are all married with children, except the youngest who is in his teens and at school. The patient's eldest grandchild is about ten.

Work: Farmer.

Katamenia: Menopause about a year ago.

Present Illness

About a year ago the patient became unable either to sleep or work and wept both day and night. When she lay down she was troubled by the pounding of her heart. If she slept a little she dreamt that she was chased by a cow and fell down in running from it. She also often dreamt that people called out her name and urged her, "Let's go, let's go!" She always refused to go and woke up protesting. She thought that her mother's sisters—confessed witches—had probably given some of their witchcraft to her without her knowledge and for this the *obosom* had "caught" her. She went to the *obosom*, was cleansed and felt better, but in a very short time the trouble returned, and has plagued her ever since. Recently she dreamt that someone brought her some red firewood and asked her to help light it, but she was frightened by its redness and refused. This dream sent her again to the *obosom*.

Interview

A pleasant, intelligent, good personality. She is depressed but can smile if need be and speaks freely. There is no obvious agitation or mental retardation (tests well done). She is not paranoid: says only casually that her three witch aunts must have given her witchcraft when she lived with them, basing this on the evidence.

Physically she is thin and has a nodular goitre and a pulse-rate of 104. No exophthalmos.

COMMENTARY

Involutional depression with some thyrotoxicosis in a good personality.

CASE 7. EKWIA B. of Kumasi. F. *c*. 45.

Shrine

Mframa at Mframaso.

Reason for referral

Frightening dreams. Fear of becoming a witch.

Family History

Incomplete. (Patient was in Mframaso only a few hours and I could talk to her privately for only a few minutes.) She came with her aged mother, who seemed a very good personality.

Personal History

    Childhood: N.a.d.
    Schooling: Nil, Non-Christian.

Work: Trader in Kumasi.

Marriage: She left her husband many years ago and has not been able to procure another. (This may mean that casual unions are no longer financially satisfactory. She was reticent on the subject of marriage.)

Children: Three born, only one survived. He is an electrician in Accra, is married and has children. He complains of dreams in which wild animals chase him.

Katamenia: Menopause not yet reached.

First interview: 10.5.57

Obese, urban type. She looks very wretched and anxious. She says she sleeps very little and dreams that a *sasa bonsam* is raping her. She says she often weeps, cannot do her work and goes from task to task accomplishing nothing.

COMMENTARY

Depression, probably partly involutional and partly reactive to frustration. I should not be surprised to see her here again with self-accusations of witchcraft. Other patients with involutional depression have dreamt of being raped by a *sasa bonsam*—perhaps the ultimate Nemesis.

CASE 8. AKOSUA B. of Techiman district, Ashanti. F. *c.* 60.

Shrine
Amfemfi, at Asueyi.

Reason for referral
"Caught" by *obosom* for cocoa-stealing.

Family History
    Parents: Both long dead. Illiterate, non-Christian cocoa-farmers.
    Siblings: Three sisters, one brother.

Personal History
    Childhood: N.a.d. disclosed.
    Marriage: Husband cocoa-farmer. He left her a long time ago and now lives in his "village". There was one other wife.
    Children: Seven born, one died. All survivors have children.
    Home: Patient lives in town with her son, whose three wives and twelve children are in their own homes elsewhere.
    Katamenia: Menopause about ten years ago.
    Previous Illness: About ten years ago the patient was very miserable, could not do her work, could not eat, and dreamt that a cow was chasing her. Then two of her children (the "policeman" and one other),

who were already grown up, fell sick and the patient became more miserable and began drinking. The children recovered. The patient has never left off drinking and now admits to taking a half-bottle—about a pint—of *akpateshi* (illicitly distilled neat spirit that will catch fire) every day. She eats very little.

Present Illness

About a year ago someone—believed to be the patient's brother—made a sorcery against the patient's son, who then fell suddenly sick and became mad, throwing away his clothes and talking "*basa-basa*". He was sent to the shrine at Asueyi where he completely recovered in two weeks. Ever since then he has stayed on in Asueyi as the *obosom's* "policeman". (He is a strapping, healthy-looking, cheerful fellow.) The patient comes to visit him every week, but last week sent a message that she was sick. She reported pains all over, headache, shivering, sleeplessness, "*basa-basa*" dreams, but chiefly trouble in her belly. She said she was "caught" for evil-doing and was brought to the *obosom*. She confessed to having lately stolen some of her son's cocoa.

Interview

Lean, miserable, weeping, bleary-eyed. Typical alcoholic tremor, peripheral neuritis in feet, enlarged liver. Mentally surprisingly well preserved: arithmetic, etc., very well done. She gave a straightforward account of herself with no undue self-reproach. She freely admitted that she drank, saying she knew it was the cause of all her troubles. She started it, she said, because she was miserable and then couldn't stop. She seemed to be the wreck of a very good personality.

COMMENTARY

Chronic alcoholism beginning with involutional depression. Unlike all the male alcoholics I have so far met, she does not blame other people for making her a drunkard by witchcraft.

CASE 9. ADWOWA N. Native of Kwahu. F. *c.* 45–50.

Shrine
Amfemfi, at Asueyi.

Reason for referral
Incomplete recovery from previous illness.

Family History
Parents: Not cross-cousins. Illiterate, Christian cocoa-farmers. The mother is dead but the father is alive and well.

Mother's brother: This man, my informant, is a non-Christian illiterate and a very intelligent, good personality. He brought the patient to Asueyi because she is his responsibility in spite of her illustrious husband.

Siblings: The patient is an only child.

Personal History

Childhood: N.a.d. disclosed. No schooling. Non-Christian.

Marriage: The husband is literate. He is a very successful cocoa-farmer and cocoa-buyer who has become wealthy and built four large business-houses in the heart of Kumasi where the average rent for such houses is £50–£70 a month. He had four wives, of whom two remain, and has about forty children. The patient and the other wife and children live with him in a two-storey house together with all those of his children who have not left home. The husband has sent many of his children to school.

Children: The patient has ten children, all alive, the youngest being about three. Nearly all have been to school and have done or are doing well. Five are now in England studying Law and Medicine. One son has had a mental illness (*vide infra*).

Katamenia: Menopause not yet reached.

Previous Personality: Happy, hardworking. Trader.

Present Illness

About seven months ago one of the patient's sons—a literate who had been through Secondary School and was employed in Kumasi—had an illness "like madness" and jumped down from the first-floor verandah into the yard below. He was brought to the Asueyi shrine by his mother (the present patient) and her maternal uncle. The *obosom* said that some-one in the household had caused the illness. Thereupon, on the same day, the mother was "caught" with violent pains all over, especially in the head, but said she had not done any harm to her son.

She was purified at the shrine, and her uncle took her home, leaving the sick son for treatment. When they reached home (at Kwahu not Kumasi), they found that four other women, two of the patient's sisters and two of their daughters, in the house had also been "caught" in their absence, all with severe pains especially in their heads. One of them "nearly died" but they were brought to Asueyi where they all recovered.

The patient's sick son remained five months in Asueyi, made a complete recovery and is now back at work as a clerk in Kumasi.

Though all the other women "caught" at the same time as the patient recovered quickly and completely, she did not. She has felt miserable and useless ever since and has been unable to do any work except a little cooking.

Three weeks ago she became restless and unable to stay in one place.

She is always worried and anxious, often weeps, cannot sleep, but walks about in the night, cannot do her work but sits with her head bowed in her hands. She has never talked incoherently and has always appeared clear-headed.

Interview

Socially competent. Superficially, she shows neither depression of energy nor agitation, but looks exceedingly anxious. But in conversation she became suddenly irritable and walked away weeping. She insists that she has not done anything wrong and does not deserve to feel so wretched.

Physically she is much better nourished than the rural people, but she said she had lost weight because she was not interested in eating.

Four months later

There is no change. She is reticent and says she is quite well, but she looks unhappy and shows no sign of wanting to get back to her work.

COMMENTARY

Involutional depression in a good personality.

CASE 10. EKWIA Z. of Takoradi district. F. *c.* 48.

Shrine

Mframa at Mframaso.

Reason for referral

Patient complains that her husband's family think she is a witch and blame her when anyone dies.

Family History

Parents not cross-cousins. Father, now dead, was a fisherman. Mother is alive and well.

Siblings. The patient is the eldest of eight. Others well.

Personal History

Schooling: Nil, but was a Christian. She has given this up.

Marriage: She left her first husband because he took a second wife. Four years ago she married an illiterate carpenter who has no other wives. He has four children by an earlier marriage.

Children: Six children by the first husband. Her eldest daughter has children.

Work: Cloth seller.

Katamenia: Menopause not reached.

Present Illness

About a year ago she began to feel tired, sleepless and not interested in her trading. The work stopped paying so she gave it up and sold fish: this too did not pay. She has steadily become worse and sits about weeping. Her husband's family have commented that she is behaving as if "caught", and on this evidence now blame her for deaths.

Interview

I saw her only once as she was going home forthwith. She was an overweight urban type. She looked extremely miserable, anxious and restless, but denied that she was a witch, though she said she had begun to feel something "catching" her before the idea of witchcraft occurred to others.

COMMENTARY

This is an involutional depression of the common type. The only uncommon feature is that the relatives have forestalled the patient's claim to be "caught" for witchcraft.

§ 3. DEPRESSION PRECIPITATED BY CONVERGING FACTORS

When I was a medical student it was taught* that "everyone has his cracking point" and that the mode of his cracking was determined by his own constitution. Experience in the bush has in no wise undermined this axiom. There are innately unstable people who crack on little or no provocation: there are others who sustain an assortment of crippling burdens simultaneously till broken by some last straw.

This is most often seen in the depressions of rural women in the younger age-group, where one can often find half-a-dozen "causes" converging upon one patient. In the field I called this phenomenon, in my own mind, "convergent depression". Vast numbers of ordinary rural people have subclinical vitamin deficiencies which become acute when any unusual call, such as pregnancy or debilitating illness, is made upon vitamin reserves. As is well known, the classical features of beri-beri, pellagra, kwashiokor and scurvy include mental symptoms. Furthermore, hookworm and malaria are able to produce severe anaemia. Many rural women have a long string of pregnancies without any cessation of lactation over a number of years, and finally a point is reached when childbirth, particularly if accompanied by any sepsis, precipitates a depression. If the new-born child is sickly and dies, there

* By Professor D. K. Henderson.

is an added element of reactive depression, and the patient, tormented by irrational guilt, says that it was she herself who, by witchcraft, killed it.

CASE 11. EKWIA A. of Wenchi district, Ashanti. F. *c.* 30.

Shrine
Abonsam Kwesi, at Anyinabirim.

Reason for referral
Self-accusation of killing her children by witchcraft.

Family History
Parents: Not cross-cousins. Both alive (both seen). They are extremely sensible, quiet, friendly people. They are non-Christian, illiterate cocoa-farmers. The father is a town elder.
Maternal uncle: He is also an elder. He has Parkinson's Disease but is active as an elder in spite of it.
Siblings: The mother has a "long family": the youngest child is one year old.

Personal History
Childhood: She was a biddable and happy child. She had no schooling but became a baptised Christian. The parents and the patient's siblings all lived in one house.
Marriage: Evidently unhappy. The husband is a farmer, but is also a catechist. He cannot read English but reads vernacular Gospels. I have seen him three times: on two of those occasions he had been drinking and was arrogant and self-important. He insisted that his name was not John but *Saint* John.
Children: The patient has had nine pregnancies, but only two live births. A son, aged thirteen is at school, a daughter, aged nine, is not at school. A seven-month miscarriage occurred four months ago.
Household: She lives with her husband, partly in his mother's house in a country town with his mother and her other children and her daughters' children, partly in her husband's father's "village", five miles away. She and her husband are alone there except for the father's cocoa-labourers, the father himself being in his home-town.
Previous Personality: She has always been hard-working, conscientious and well liked. The children are well-dressed, well cared for, and well behaved.

Present Illness
Ever since the miscarriage four months ago, she has been in her husband's village brooding over her lost children. The onset of the

illness was six days ago with headache, shivering, pains in the belly and behind the eyes, aching all over, seeing double and seeing zigzag. She took no notice of these symptoms but went to her husband's father and complained that her husband was always reading the vernacular Gospels aloud and saying, "Humm, humm", throughout the reading. The "Humm, humm" noise got on her nerves so that she wanted to end the marriage. She said she wanted no more of marriage because marriage was "no good" when the children always died.

Three days later she suddenly became noisy and disturbed in the middle of the night, wept, talked wildly and said she had killed her dead children, and would have killed the remaining two had her husband's religion (their baptism?) not been strong enough to prevent this.

Interview: 15.10.56

When first seen, an *abisa* session was going on before the shrine. The patient had already made her confession and said she had killed seven people, had intended evil against her husband, had resolved to kill her young sister (aged one) and her uncle (the elder with Parkinson's Disease). I found her writhing and rolling on the ground in much mental distress, shouting, crying and singing. However, she got up to shake hands with me and allowed herself to be led to a nearby shade where she sat with fair co-operativeness, though very restless, anxious and apprehensive. She gave an adequate though disjointed account of herself, interrupted by anxious side-issues and protestations of guilt—e.g., "God has taken away my *kra* (soul) already, so I am as good as dead." She described her symptoms quite well—the prodromal physical symptoms and the inability to sit still, sleep or work. She said that whenever she sat down she felt startled and frightened, she knew not of what, and that she "saw darkness" and saw "two or three people instead of one". She said she often dreamt that she saw many people cooking, making soup and pounding fufu and when they had finished she went to eat with them. Asked what made her think the *obosom's* medicine had "caught" her, she said that she had wickedly resolved not to stay with her husband any longer and that she had done him harm which she could not define.

Towards the end of the interview she became restless, got up and waved her arms and cried out, "Now you too know all my guilt and will judge me and punish me. I have done evil. I am guilty." She then resumed the overactivity in which I found her.

23.10.56. She has been brought to her husband's mother's country-town because it was decided that it was the *obosom* at Akrofrom and not the one at Anyinabirim who had "caught" her. Her own mother is with her. She is mute and retarded, but restless, moving slowly and hesitatingly about and looking distraught. She would not shake hands but made the gesture recognised as supplicating for forgiveness and help. The family say she sleeps quietly during the first part of the night but wakes in the small hours and walks miserably about.

30.10.56. Quite mute. Lying down in a semi-stupor. She eats and drinks a little with great persuasion, but will not get up and allow herself to be washed.

9.11.56. Much better. Moving slowly about cooking. She slowly moves up her hand to shake hands. She speaks a little in a very low mutter. She looks rather bewildered but shows no confusion in speech or behaviour.

14.11.56. Still improving. Brisker, speaks more freely.

26.11.56. When I called at the house they said she was quite well and had gone with her parents to a place near Kumasi to help them harvest cocoa as she is now able to work hard. Informant was the catechist husband's grandmother, a charming, wise and vigorous woman, looking only about half her age.

COMMENTARY

Reactive depression with acute exacerbation precipitated by febrile illness (probably cerebral malaria). Her stressful marital situation is strikingly similar to that of Akosua N. (Case No. 19).

CASE 12. AFUA N. of Akwapim. F. *c.* 30.

Shrine
Mframa at Mframaso.

Reason for referral
Self-accusations of witchcraft. She was brought to the shrine by her mother. (See Ama K., Case No. 71.)

Personal History
Childhood: N.a.d. She drank at Tigari's shrine in childhood.
Schooling: Nil. Non-Christian.
Marriage: Twice married. Her first husband died. The second belongs to an Akwapim chief's family. The marriage was happy but since her illness the husband has not taken her away from her mother: he would resume the marriage if she recovered.
Children: A son, aged twelve, by the first marriage: a daughter, aged eight.

Present Illness
Onset eleven years ago when the mother's illness began. She was in her mother's house with her infant child at the time. Before the illness

began she often dreamt she was being chased by a person she could not see and sometimes by a cow. She had had this dream often even before she had borne any children. Since her illness she dreams that she is in a river and is being swept away.

The illness began with fever, giddiness, belly-pains, and talking "*basa-basa*". She took quinine and recovered but felt "changed". She thought Tigari had "caught" her, and her mother fostered this idea and has fostered it ever since, taking the patient with her to all the medicine-men she herself visits. The patient says she is always miserable and some-times cries. She does what work she must but feels no interest in it or in anything else. "If I buy new clothes I don't feel any pleasure in putting them on."

Interview: 21.11.56

Thin, languid and apathetic. No extravagant self-reproach or delu-sions but she says she would not be so miserable if she were not a witch and "caught" for it. She smiles reluctantly but appropriately and is a pleasant, intelligent person.

COMMENTARY

Long-standing mild depression, first precipitated by febrile illness when lactating, now mainly reactive to the neurotic tyranny of her mother.

CASE 13. ADWOWA S. of Akwapim. F. *c.* 18.

Shrine
Mframa at Mframaso.

Reason for referral
Self-accusations of witchcraft.

Family History
Parents: Both dead. Illiterate non-Christian farmers. The mother was the younger sister of Ama K.'s mother. The patient is therefore known as the younger sister of Ama K. (See Ama K., Case No. 71.)
Siblings: The patient is the second of six, all surviving except one of a pair of twins. The elder brother is a farmer, married with children.

Personal History
Childhood: She started school at about seven and left two years later when her father died. She was clever at school and distressed at leaving.
Work: She has a farm bequeathed by her mother.
Marriage: She was thinking of marriage when she was "caught", and has abandoned the idea for the present.

Present Illness

Onset about a year ago. She dreamt that cows and many people with sticks and cutlasses were chasing her and she always woke up terrified. She often cried, could not do her work but slept fairly well. No physical symptoms except pain in the thighs and "the same kind of burnings as Ama K.". She thought she was "caught" for witchcraft. Ama K. encouraged this idea and said the sickness was just like her own. The patient told her that she (patient) had made up her mind to kill a member of the family, not Ama K. but another woman who bore her no ill-will. Ama K. took her to Tigari and several other minor deities, and brought her to Mframaso together with her daughter.

Interview

Pleasant and co-operative. She smiles appropriately. Her memory and concentration are good. Good intelligence. She is pale, thin, walks languidly and is dispirited, but less depressed than Ama K.'s daughter. She does her work, but without zest.

Progress

She remained patiently with her "mother", helping to plant crops, etc., and was still there when I left.

COMMENTARY

Mild depression, possibly related to hookworm or other infestation, certainly in some degree reactive to frustration and neurotic tyranny of an older woman.

CASE 14. EKWIA M. of Techiman district, Ashanti. F. *c.* 25.

Shrine

Dimankoma at Akrofrom.

Reason for referral

Self-accusations of witchcraft.

Family History

Parents: Not cross-cousins. Non-Christian, illiterate cocoa-farmers. The father is dead; mother is alive and well.

Siblings: Three brothers, two sisters, all grown-up except one brother who is at school and wants to be a teacher. The others are all non-Christian illiterates. All these live in one house in the country-town where the patient was born with the mother and the sisters' children. The sisters' husbands and the brother's wife are elsewhere. One of the brothers is a drunkard and is unmarried because he cannot procure a wife. Ten years ago a marriage was arranged and the ceremonial completed, but the wife left him before the marriage was consummated —probably on account of impotence though this was not explicitly stated. This brother looks quite as depressed as the patient.

Personal History

Childhood: N.a.d. disclosed.

Work: Successful farmer and trader.

Marriage: The husband is an extremely pleasant, intelligent cocoa-farmer, about the patient's own age.

Children: Five born, four died and the survivor is about five, healthy and well-cared for. The last child died about three months ago aged fifteen days. The patient became pregnant again immediately after.

Home: She lives with her husband in his home-town together with his parents and several grown-up brothers and sisters. All are non-Christian illiterates, and pleasant, friendly people. The husband's father has a small shrine of Tigari on the premises, brought from Ipara many years ago. It has gone out of fashion and no one comes to it now.

Previous Personality: Quiet, industrious and well-liked. She was exceptionally tidy and clean.

Present Illness

The patient has been miserable and weeping ever since the death of her new-born child three months ago, but she has kept going and done her work.

A few days ago she went normally to bed at night, but about midnight rose and began washing clothes in the yard. After washing them she tore them up and remained restless and agitated all night. In the morning her husband took her to Techiman hospital out-patient department, reporting restlessness. She was given some medicine to take home and drink. On reaching home she refused to take it, saying that it could not help her because she was a witch, had killed her children, plotted to kill one of her brothers and five other people and was the cause of her brother's drunkenness and inability to get a wife. She demanded to be taken to the *obosom*—at whose shrine she had drunk— to confess her sins and be cleansed. The husband says she has not slept since the onset of her illness but has walked about in agitated misery and self-reproach.

Interview: 9.11.56

She is a healthy-looking, adequately nourished, young woman. She is miserable, oppressed, anxious, agitated and frowning but not retarded and can smile in greeting. At the shrine she gave a ready account of herself, repeating the self-accusations made at home. She became calmer immediately after stating her case.

13.11.56. Much improved. No longer agitated but miserable and unsmiling. She replies in a flat monotone when addressed, but does not spontaneously talk. She was sitting in the yard threading beads—her old ones having been left at the shrine as a part of the purification ritual.

26.11.56. The patient was alone in the husband's family house when I called, everyone else having gone to farm. She was busily washing clothes in the yard. She smiled pleasantly, said she was much better and certainly looked much happier and brisker.

10.12.56. Seen having a meal with two other women. She now seems quite well. Noticeably cleaner and neater than the others—clothes apparently freshly washed.

2.2.57. She has gone back to her kinsman's house. She looks well and contented.

7.4.57. She delivered a child nine days ago. She looks very happy but the child is a wretched, sickly specimen in respiratory distress and looks unlikely to survive.

14.4.57. The child is still alive and is attending the hospital out-patient department where it had some injections. The patient complains that she has no milk.

25.4.57. The child is improving but wails unceasingly. Still going to hospital. Lactation improved.

20.9.57. The child has done extremely well and became fat and contented. The patient was very happy till she took influenza (during the epidemic) and died a few days ago. The *obosomfo* said she must have resumed witchcraft and been killed for it by the *obosom*. I arrived in the middle of the obsequies when the yard was thronged with mourners. All the nursing mothers of the town were co-operating to keep the child breast-fed till a permanent plan could be made for it. The child seemed to be horror-stricken: it was not wailing and its eyes were bulging.

COMMENTARY

Depression, probably reactive, though starting in the puerperium.

CASE 15. AFUA T. of Techiman district, Ashanti. F. *c.* 35.

Shrine

Dimankoma, Akrofrom.

Reason for referral

Self-accusations of witchcraft.

Family History

Maternal grandmother: Queen-mother of a small country-town.
Parents: Cross-cousins. Non-Christian, illiterate cocoa-farmers.
Father died when the patient was about ten. Mother is a very good personality.
Siblings: Ten born, eight survived. The youngest is about twenty The patient is the eldest. One brother and one sister are literate. The latter is a clerk in a hospital office.

Personal History

Childhood: N.a.d.
Schooling: Nil. Non-Christian.
Work: Food farming and helps her husband with his cocoa. A good worker.
Marriage: Satisfactory. The husband is not a cross-cousin. There is no other wife.
Children: Seven born, three died. The eldest survivor is thirteen, the youngest three. One child died, aged ten months, about two months ago.
Household: Husband's own house with his sister and her children.

Present Illness

A year ago, shortly after the birth of her last child, she became miserable, weeping and unable to do her work. Two months ago she became worse, had fever, "pains in the eyes", "burnings all over", photophobia and sleeplessness. She denies headache. A fortnight later the child died and she became more distressed and said she had killed by witchcraft not only it but the other two. Sometimes she talked "*basa-basa*", though she never behaved strangely and always lay quietly. She said that when she lay sleepless she thought only of having killed her child. When she slept she dreamt she was about to kill her mother and her son with a cutlass and was then chased by a chameleon, black cows and an *obosom* who hit her with his *nkotoba* clubs. She went to the *obosom*, confessed and was purified, since when she has slept better and improved a little though her mother says she still talks "*basa-basa*" at siesta-time when the sun is high.

Interview: 19.2.57

I did not see her till four days after her confession. She was thin and anaemic, languid and weak. She was anxious and depressed but not extravagantly and was pleasant and friendly. Mental tests were all satisfactory except money sums, but the mother said "she was never clever at counting". She herself joined in the laughter when she gave

Aburokyeri (Europe) as one of the towns in Ghana and said, "I can't think well since the *obosom* caught me."

21.2.57. She still looks pale, ill, weary and miserable, but is composed and sociable. She seems a very good personality. When I suggested hospital investigation for hookworm, etc., she asked for a letter.

10.3.57. No change. She has not been to hospital.

20.4.57. Feeling better although she has not been to hospital. She says she was pregnant at the time she was "caught", having become so immediately after the death of her last child.

10.10.57. Almost full term now. Quite content. She goes to work on her farm regularly.

31.10.57. Relapsed five days ago and said she was "caught" for witchcraft again. She says she feels that witches have taken away her *kra* (soul). She hears them saying, "Let us go!", and, "Come along", both in her dreams and when she is awake. She did not, however, look hallucinated and was quite clear-headed. She looked anxious, apprehensive and depressed, but physically in good condition. She says she weeps, cannot work and does not sleep at all.

4.11.57. No change. She is still able to be actively kindly. Last time I visited her I remarked on a woven grass bag and said it was well made. To-day she gave me one she had specially procured.

18.12.57. Delivered a healthy child three days ago. She looks quite well and is happier but says she still does not sleep.

COMMENTARY

This depression in a good personality began in the puerperium and later was reinforced by a reactive element. I think she had also some chronic low fever, and possibly a hookworm or other debilitating infestation.

CASE 16. AKOSUA S. of Bekwai district, Ashanti. F. *c.* 40.

Shrine
Kyinaman at Bredi.

Reason for referral
Self-accusations of witchcraft.

Family History
Mother: Illiterate, non-Christian. Alive and well.
Father: A Moslem Nigerian. An illiterate, he came to this country to trade and later took up cocoa. He is also a medicine-man and specialises in medicines for barren women. He left the patient's mother for another

woman before the patient reached puberty, but appears to be still friendly with the patient's family, though not with the patient and her mother. When the patient goes to see him there are always hard words.

Siblings: Six born, one died. All illiterate, non-Christians.

Maternal uncle (seen twice): He supports the patient's mother and the patient. He is a literate, licensed surveyor, lorry-owner, etc., but "his hand has become a sieve" and he has had several operations, apparently for two inguinal hernias and a peptic ulcer. He looks extremely thin, care-worn and sour. He and another maternal uncle quarrel concerning the support of the patient and her children. On the second occasion of seeing him he had taken drink and said that although he was a Christian he had found that only the *obosom* had any power.

Other relatives: Another uncle was "caught" by an *obosom* and died. A cross-cousin of the patient was "caught" but recovered.

Personal History

Childhood: Patient's mother and children have always lived with the mother's family.

Schooling: Nil. Non-Christian.

Work: Farmer.

Marriage: The husband is a cocoa-farmer. One other wife, with whom the patient says she was on good terms. The husband left the patient five years ago and she returned to her mother and uncle.

Children: Five born, four survived. The eldest is a daughter who married this year. The youngest is three to four but is still suckling. This child was born of casual intercourse.

Home: Maternal uncle's house with her mother and various others. Another uncle is not far away.

Present Illness

About four months ago the patient had a cough, and pains in her left ribs. She went to a clinic, was treated with injections and recovered, but has felt tired, sleepless and miserable ever since, has not been able to do any work and has had pains all over. She began to feel that she was responsible for her uncle's illness and lack of prosperity and "thought that the *obosom* was against her". She felt as if she had given her uncle an invisible *suman* to make him acquire money to support her children. So she got up one night to go to the uncle's house to take the *suman* away, but on the path she saw an *obosom* with a stick to hit her. (She became much agitated and distressed at this point in her story.)

She became convinced she was a witch and that the *obayi* had been given her by her father who wanted her to kill people and give him their flesh, and in particular he wanted her to give him the spirit of her womb so that he might give it to another daughter who was barren.

This conviction followed a dream in which three Moslems came from her father bringing her a wrapped-up gift which she refused. Her other dreams have supported her conviction of witchcraft. She dreamt that she had gone into the bush alone to catch game: there she met a friend who wanted to take her to a market. She resisted, but the friend compelled her. When they reached the market there was a lot of fresh human meat. She refused to take any, saying that she had her own meat in the bush. The people in the market, however, forced her to accept some dried meat, and though she refused to eat any of it she set out to carry it home. On the way she met an *obosom* who asked what she was carrying. She replied human flesh, whereupon he knocked it out of her hand and also hit her, but not very hard.

In another dream some friends came to take her to the bush. She refused to go, but they carried off her son Kodzo, not to kill him but to make him a witch like themselves. She ran after them to rescue him: then they saw the *obosom* coming and ran away.

Interview: 17.10.57

The patient is thin, miserable and anxious. She denies weeping but looks on the verge of it. She is more indignant than self-reproachful. The uncle was looking on sulkily while she told her tale.

31.10.57. The uncle has gone home and the patient has immeasurably improved, being now rather pert and saucy.

5.11.57. The patient has gone home.

COMMENTARY

This is not quite a typical depression with wholly irrational self-reproach, for the depressive fantasies following the physical illness mainly embellished the genuine ill-will that exists between the patient and her uncle and her father.

Concerning the uncle, his was the second operated peptic ulcer I had met among harassed lorry-owners at that particular shrine.

CASE 17. YAA K. of Techiman district, Ashanti. F. *c* 22.

Shrine

Abiri at Awuruwa.

Reason for referral

Self-accusations of witchcraft.

Family History

Parents: Not cross-cousins. Alive and well. Non-Christian, illiterate cocoa-farmers. The mother is a petty trader. She has recently left the father because he neglected her, and has come back, with the patient, to her own father's house which is a large compound built with cocoa-money.

Siblings: Thirteen born. Eight died. All farmers. One has an ambitious son aged about sixteen at a training-school. This son makes poor progress and when he fails an examination blames family witchcraft.

Personal History

Childhood: N.a.d.

Schooling: Nil, but she is a Christian.

Work: Farmer.

Marriage: Happy. The husband is a Christian. He has no other wives and lives in his own kinsfolk's house, not with his wife.

Children: Three born, all died, the last a week ago at the age of two weeks.

Household: The patient is with her mother in the latter's father's house.

Present Illness

The patient's last child was very sickly and the patient became increasingly worried, depressed, sleepless and weeping as it grew worse. She had "*basa-basa*" dreams in which she was chased by a cow and by someone with *mpese-mpese* hair, and had nowhere to run for refuge. She also dreamt she was in a swift river being swept away. As the child became moribund the patient developed severe pains in her head, belly and chest and asked to be taken to the *obosom*. She was trembling and unable to stand, and approached the shrine on hands and knees saying that she was a witch, had killed two children and was about to kill the third. The *obosom* commented, "You have killed it already." Asked what other evil she had done, she said she had brought about the separation between her parents; that she had taken the money-power out of her mother's hand so that she traded at a loss; that she had killed eight siblings and that she was causing the scholastic failure of her brother's son. After confession she was able to walk home. When she reached home the child was dead, but the patient began to make a steady recovery.

Interview

I did not see the patient till about a week after the death of the child. She was well nourished and seemed in good physical condition. She looked languid and depressed, but not agitated or anxious. She said she often wept and could not do her work. She was brooding alone in the house, everyone else having gone to the farm.

Progress

A few days later she too had gone to the farm. About a week later she looked quite well.

COMMENTARY

Brief reactive depression with self-reproach but no psychotic fantasies—i.e., the untoward events which she claimed to have caused had all in fact taken place.

CASE 18. YAA A. of Techiman district, Ashanti. F. *c.* 20.

Shrine

Dimankoma, Akrofrom.

Reason for referral

Self-accusation of witchcraft.

Family History

No information. Mother's brother seen: a pleasant, good personality.

Personal History

Childhood: N.a.d. disclosed.

Work: Farming.

Marriage: She was married when a young girl to Kwesi B. (Case No. 41), being then probably too shy to say that she found him unattractive. She was divorced after her witchcraft episode. She is now married to an extremely pleasant kindly young man of good personality and roughly her own age.

Children: None alive. She had two pregnancies by Kwesi B. The first ended in a seven-month abortion. The second child was born alive but lived only a week. She is three months pregnant now.

Previous Illness

This occurred two years ago. (I sought her out in her "village" after hearing about her in connection with Kwesi B.) The onset coincided with the death of her child. It began with weeping, then self-reproach and self-accusations of having killed both it, the first foetus and various other relatives by witchcraft. The uncle said that during her illness she talked *"basa-basa"* and also said she was "caught" by the *obosom* for her sins. She was taken to the shrine, where she confessed, was purified and improved immediately. At the end of a month she was quite well.

Interview

A healthy-looking but exceedingly shy, nervous girl who looked so frightened when I mentioned her last illness that I hastily dropped the subject, fearing to arouse apprehensions concerning her present pregnancy.

COMMENTARY

Depression, chiefly reactive, in the puerperium.

CASE 19. AKOSUA N. of Begoro district. F. *c* 26.

Shrine

Mframa at Mframaso.

Reason for referral

Weeping, sleeplessness, self-accusations of guilt and witchcraft.

Family History

Parents: Cross-cousins. Illiterate, Christian farmers. The mother is alive and well: the father died two years ago.

Mother's elder sister: This woman brought up the patient from the age of two. She was "caught" by the *obosom* Tigari nine years ago (involutional depression?), volunteered that she was a witch and had furthermore given an *obayi* to the patient. The patient was feeling well at the time, so took no notice. This aunt was energetic and popular before she was "caught".

Siblings: Four brothers, all grown-up and married. The patient is the third child. Only the youngest is literate and is a teacher. All the others are farmers. One is a Seventh Day Adventist.

Personal History

Childhood: Before the age of two the patient used to scream in the night that a fire was coming to burn her. The parents suspected witchcraft and took her to a medicine-man to be cleansed.

When the patient was about two she was given to her mother's elder sister who was barren and wanted her. This aunt lived in the maternal grandmother's house (about twenty miles away) with other maternal aunts and uncles and the aunts' children. The aunts' husbands lived elsewhere in their own mothers' compounds. When the patient was about ten the aunt was divorced for barrenness and came back to town bringing the patient, but not to the patient's mother's house. The patient continued to regard this aunt's house as her home and always stayed there when visiting town after her marriage. When the present illness began, both the patient and the aunt moved into the patient's mother's house.

Marriage: The patient is married to a catechist who is a native of her own home-town but is stationed at a distance. He is unfaithful to her and has contracted "*babaso*" (i.e., either gonorrhea or syphilis). He also fails to give maintenance money for her and the children. Other Christians give her food from their farms. The patient left him and returned to her mother about a year ago on becoming pregnant, making this her excuse and without having made up her mind to leave him permanently. Her mother considers that the marriage is very unhappy and should be ended.

Children: Four born, three survive. The eldest is eight, the youngest two. She had a miscarriage eight months ago.

Previous personality: Shy and timid. Very intelligent. She would have been sent to school had there been the money. A very conscientious Church member and anxious to uphold her husband's prestige in spite of his behaviour. All the members of the Women's Class wept when she left.

Previous Mental Illness

She had a similar illness when her first child was a few weeks old. She volunteered that she was a witch and said the *obosom* Nangoro, at whose shrine she had drunk, had "caught" her for this sin.

Present Illness

The onset was eight months ago immediately after a four-month miscarriage with heavy blood-loss. When she walked about she felt darkness coming over her and something crawling up from her feet. She attended a hospital out-patient department and was given "injections and medicine". She improved physically but continued to brood. Four months ago she started strange behaviour. She sat about weeping and refusing food, was sleepless and walked about at night. She said she had seen people on the wall at night. One night she said she had seen someone with *mpese-mpese* hair (i.e., *obosomfo's* hair) standing in the yard and that it meant that the *obosom* under whose protection her brother had put himself had come to "catch" her because she was a witch and had planned to kill the brother. She said she had done a great many other evil things. When she saw people talking in the street she thought they were talking about her.

The teacher-brother wrote down her "confessions". Her mother and another brother came to Mframaso with her, bringing the written confession which the *obosom's* clerk read before the shrine. This included most of the stereotyped misdeeds of witches—killing her own and her relatives' children and various other people; causing accidents, illness, barrenness, poverty and the blighting of crops; night-flying; harbouring big snakes in her belly, head and vagina; planning further deaths not yet achieved. But she added a few original and revealing misdemeanours of her own. She said she had made her husband impotent when he went to other women and that she had planned to kill him because he kept her short of necessities. She had planned that her brothers should never have children so that they might be free to support *her* children. She had made up her mind to purify herself of her *obayi* by sacrificing her daughter's *kra* (soul, life) to a river called Akuroma. She also said that she had sometimes maliciously prepared her husband's soup with the filthy water she had used for washing her perineal cloth. (Such a cloth is ceremonially unclean and destructive of good influence: her act was equivalent to making a bad medicine against her husband.)

In spite of all these misdemeanours the *obosom* said she had more to confess and must come back again another day.

The next day I saw the patient, the mother and brother privately. They were nagging at her to confess more, and she, with equal heat, was refusing, saying that she had no more to confess. The mother asked me if I could help, as the *obosom* would do no more without more confession, and had washed his hands of the case.

Interview

Extremely thin, but otherwise in good physical condition (Hb. 90%: E.S.R. first hour—16 mm.). Clean and well-groomed. No retardation. Fully accessible. Replies were terse and to the point. A much better witness than her brother or her mother. No abnormalities of manner except anxious tension, worried gloom and irritability. Her smile was reluctant but appropriate.

Amytal and Methedrine Abreaction

She obstinately denied that there had ever been any disharmony between her husband and herself. No guilt or depressive ideas were expressed. She stoutly repudiated the witchcraft confessions she had made: she said she had made them because people were asking her to and because Jesus had said you should meekly submit. She admitted that she saw a *mpese-mpese* standing outside her brother's door one night and was frightened that it had come for her. She protested that she loved everyone in her husband's town and they her. Asked what she thought was the cause of her trouble she said that her mother's sister had sent it to her. Asked by her mother to sing her witch-song she sang a gloomy, moaning, Christian hymn in vernacular and said hymns

were the only songs she knew how to sing. Asked about having drunk
Obosom Nangoro, no conflict or protestations emerged. She said casually
that her husband and a great many other Christians had done the same.

4.10.56. Overnight—and no doubt under duress from relatives—she
thought up another confession concerning the snake in her vagina and
made it before the shrine. Ritual purification was then carried out.
5.10.56. Her mother says she slept well last night after her purification
and ate a good breakfast this morning. She still looks depressed and
anxious.
6.10.56. This morning the relatives reported a completely sleepless
night, though the patient herself perfunctorily says she is quite happy.
The relatives are now anxious only to get the ritual baths over and be
gone, but to-day the patient says—to the relatives' annoyance and
certainly not under duress—that she has another confession to make, viz.,
that she had, in the spirit (i.e., in fantasy), sexual intercourse with two
men other than her husband. She refuses to have further ritual baths till
she has confessed to the *obosom*.
12.10.56. She has anxiously presented herself several times at the shrine
(to the annoyance of her relatives, who want no more confessions from
her). She said that because of her husband's neglect she had resolved to
kill him by witchcraft but failed because he had drunk a protective
medicine. She said it was she who sent him the *babaso* sickness and did
this to make him impotent with other women: that she once collected
a debt of seven shillings on behalf of her family but kept the money:
that she had resolved to kill her mother by witchcraft for grumbling at
having to support her and the children since she left her husband: that
she wanted to kill her mother for making a palaver once when the
mother sent her some palm-oil to sell and the husband sold it and kept
the money himself, and that she had not only the *obayi* thrust upon her
by her aunt but another and worse one which she was born with.
20.10.56. Relatives have succeeded in getting her away without further
confessions. She has resolved never to return to her husband (so says her
mother) but I doubt her resolution.

COMMENTARY

A second attack of anxiety and depression with sensitive ideas of
reference. The first attack was in the puerperium and the second after
miscarriage. People seen on the wall at night and the *mpese-mpese* seen
in the yard were probably misinterpretations not hallucinations. There
is a family history of depression, though the patient's depression has a
strong reactive component. But the making of bad magic against her
husband is an ominous feature and I should not be surprised if this illness
heralded a schizo-affective psychosis.

There is never—in my experience—any conflict in any Christian patient's mind between Christian and heathen *doctrine* and never any guilt about drinking *obosom* medicine, but there is distress when a conscientious Christian woman is married to a good-for-nothing hypocritical catechist of tottering prestige. (See Ewkia A., Case No. 11.)

CASE 20. AFUA G. of Kwahu. F. *c.* 50.

Shrine

Abiri at Awuruwa.

Reason for referral

Self-accusations of witchcraft.

Family History

Mother: Died when patient was a suckling. Non-Christian. Illiterate.

Father: Not mother's cross-cousin. Died many years ago. Non-Christian. Illiterate farmer. He first grew rubber and later cocoa.

Siblings: The patient is the youngest of eight, of whom six died.

Personal History

Childhood: Brought up by her mother's sister in maternal uncle's house.

Schooling: Nil, but she is a Christian. Full communicant.

Work: Cocoa-farmer.

Marriage: Cross-cousin. Patient left him when the last child was an infant because he was keeping many concubines and neglecting her.

Children: Four born; only the fourth survived. Survivor a daughter who has four children, the eldest about ten. The patient was brought to the shrine by this daughter.

Home: She lives in maternal uncle's house with various relatives.

Katamenia: Menopause three years ago.

Previous Illness

She had *babaso* six years ago. She had various native treatments, eventually being cured in hospital.

Previous Personality

Patient says that many people in her house and in the farm don't like her.

Present Illness

Several months ago she had influenza. This abated but left her sleepless and so miserable and "useless" that she could not even sweep the yard. She went to various *abosom*, one of whom told her she was "caught" for witchcraft, after which she went back to her permanent *obosom* and protested that she had drunk for protection from witchcraft but had not been protected so was therefore going to the Christians. She then went to a clinic, was given medicine but felt no better. Then she went to a medicine-man who gave her some *"dufa"* (usually a ball of dried herbal paste). After this she felt worse, dreamt that someone grabbed her by the wrist and then decided that she was certainly a witch and that the *obayi* had been conveyed to her in the *dufa*.

Interview: 17.10.57

She was thin, anxious and frowning. Movements were quite brisk: when first seen she was eating heartily. Unsmiling, irritable, rapid, indignant talk with a slight stammer, but she gives the impression of suspicion and reticent reservations.

COMMENTARY

Post-influenzal reaction in an irritable, aggressive personality of involutional age. Though the patient described herself as miserable and useless, she is not a typical depressive, being more inclined to blame others than herself. The foundation for her irritability may have been laid in infancy (*vide* history).

I place this patient in the "convergent" group because I doubt whether any one of the contributing factors would alone have produced her illness.

§ 4. DEPRESSION ASSOCIATED WITH AGEING

In this group we find people of good personality who have been successful, respected and leant upon by others. Some have imperturbably weathered such adversities as childlessness and the sponging of worthless dependants, and all have survived the involutional age without faltering. But in their declining years, when their friends and relatives become fewer, the changing world more perplexing and their capacity for adaptation and effort less, life takes on a menacing quality and they become, in the words of one of them, "afraid of the world". The balance between demands—emotional and practical—and the ability to rise to them, is overthrown and the patient appears at the shrine in a state which would often perhaps be better described as demoralisation than depression.

CASE 21. AMA M. of Banda district. F. 70+.

Shrine

Kyinaman of Bredi, Ashanti.

Reason for referral

Weeping, agitation, affirmations of guilt.

Family History

Parents: Both died many years ago. Her father was a senior chief.
Siblings: Several brothers and sisters (details unknown).

Personal History

Childhood: No one remembers.
Education and Religion: Illiterate and non-Christian.
Previous illness: Her daughter (herself an old lady) says she has heard relatives say that years ago when she (the daughter) was an infant the patient had a similar illness.
Marriage: She was married three times and widowed each time. Her husbands were all "big men".
Children: Two daughters by her second husband. One daughter died, aged about thirty, leaving two children.
Household: Patient, patient's elder brother (owner of house) and some stranger lodgers. The brother's wife is elsewhere and sends in his meals. Only since the patient fell sick has the daughter brought her meals and looked after her.
Previous Personality: She was an authority on local history and had an impeccable memory. She was much respected and was often called upon to settle family disputes. She was a hard-working farmer till just before her illness.

Present Illness

Onset was two months ago with headache, intolerable burnings in the feet, and she could neither walk nor sleep for pain. She refused food and drink and became restless, with incessant talking and weeping, saying, "People want to kill me because I've done wrong." She also became at times disorientated, saying that her father was coming after her because she had taken his money and the daughter must close the door to keep him out, and must take his money back to him. She said people were coming to take her to Court and judge her: of this she said she was much frightened; and that everything she had ever done in her life was wicked. She was brought to Bredi shrine because three years ago a family elder had a child who died suddenly and fearing witchcraft came to Bredi and drank the medicine there for protection against further sorcery. When the patient fell ill she was taken first to the family *obosom* and to other shrines where all agreed with her that she had done wrong and had been "caught", the most likely catcher being the *obosom* at Bredi.

Informants: Her daughter (old lady) and the patient's sister's four sons. All illiterate, one Christian. Well nourished, well dressed and well disposed.

Interview: 2.11.56

She was a tall, big-boned Banda woman with a big head, big hands and big feet (in contrast to the Akan Ashantis). Her hair was white and she was unkempt. Her skin was very rough, grey and dry. She was dehydrated. There was no paralysis and no oedema. She was strong and vigorous for her age. She was correctly orientated. Her speech was retarded and she was resistive and uncooperative, anxious, groaning and despairing, bowing her head to her knees, covering her face and making other gestures of shame and despair. She walked only when dragged or pushed and would talk only on the subject of her sins. Asked what wrong things she had done, she said she had never done anything right. The only sin she specified was that she once "married" her father. At the shrine she could only mutter "Ma ye boni" (I have done wrong), with which the *obosom* agreed. He ordered purification rites.

Progress

She was taken home the next day and in a few weeks' time I heard that she had died.

COMMENTARY

Possibly this was primary pellagra, due to the patient's neglect of her meals. If the pellagra was secondary, the primary illness may have been "a little stroke".

As well as the delusory ideas of guilt, the general depression appears to have awakened a long-dormant guilt feeling concerning her father. Father–daughter incest is not uncommon and evokes horror.

CASE 22. ABENA N. of Akwapim. F. 60+.

Shrine

(1) Mframa at Mframaso.
(2) Kyinaman at Bredi.

Reason for referral

"Afraid of the world."

Family History

Parents: Not cross-cousins. Non-Christian, illiterate cocoa-farmers. Father had one other wife.

Siblings: Six born. All grew up, but patient is now the only survivor. Of her half-siblings the only survivors are a half-sister and an unpleasant half-brother who has never liked her and never invited her to his "village". He covets her cocoa, some given to her by their father and some by her mother. He took the same attitude to all the other siblings and when they died the patient had to find the money for their funerals. The last time he spoke to the patient—more than a year ago—was to accuse her of killing the half-sister's son by witchcraft. No one in the family has ever been "caught" for witchcraft.

Personal History

Childhood: N.a.d. Father and both wives lived in a cocoa "village" colonising Akim.

Schooling: Nil. Non-Christian.

Work: Cocoa-farmer.

Marriage: Her first husband died young. He was a cocoa-farmer. Her second husband, a cocoa-farmer, cut his foot with a hoe, and developed a "big sore". The leg was amputated and he died. The patient has not married again. Each husband had one other wife but there was never any friction. In both marriages the patient lived in the husband's cocoa-village with his other wife.

Children: Six born, five survive. Four of the survivors are daughters and "their children keep dying". One lost seven in infancy, and witchcraft was feared but nobody was "caught". One lost two of her four. Another had none till the patient supplicated to the *obosom* on her behalf. The other has six living children.

Home: The patient lives in her own "village" in Akim with one daughter and the daughter's husband and children. The cocoa has all died of swollen-shoot disease.

Katamenia: Menopause "many years ago". Uneventful.

Present Illness

Of late the patient's eyesight has become poor, she has lost weight and has been feeling defenceless, apprehensive and incompetent. She sleeps very little but dreams that spirits (*honhom*) come and take her cover-cloth away. Then within a few days of the dream she always loses some property—money is stolen while she is travelling on a lorry, or it fritters away without her knowing on what she has spent it. A few weeks ago when her daughter went travelling and left her in charge of the children she dreamt that a spirit came and said to them, "Your mother has left you to this old woman, and if she should die you would be alone." She woke up frightened and prayed to the *obosom* to help her. Often in her sleep she is beaten all over by spirits and by people and wakes feeling the pain all over her head and body.

First interview: 16.4.57

At the shrine she promised the *obosom* six cows if he would deliver her from her troubles. She seemed a good personality, pleasant, intelligent and self-reliant. She looked deeply anxious, unhappy and apprehensive. She denied tears and said she was able to do her work but not easily. There was no self-reproach expressed. Though friendly she seemed rather reticent. After making her requests at Mframaso she left immediately for Bredi there to repeat the promise of six cows.

18.4.57. Seen in Bredi. Rather more expansive about the unkindness and injustice of her half-brother who started the rumour of her witchcraft. She says she knows she cannot be a witch, for Mframa, under whose protection she has been for some years, would have "caught" her. But lately she has been brooding over her brother's treatment of her. She has also brooded much over the deaths of her daughters' children.

29.4.57. She went home from Bredi after a few days there, but returned three days ago because of a frightening dream and a bad portent. She dreamt that someone who was dead was calling her to come to the place of the dead. One night she heard a cat crying round her house. On three earlier occasions in her life she has heard this and it has always been followed by a death—six years ago by the death of her sister and on two other occasions by the deaths of her daughters' babies. She was reassured by the *obosom* and went home.

COMMENTARY

Anxiety and a sense of insecurity and defencelessness reactive to loneliness, failing powers and lack of sympathy. She is not yet in a depression, but is on the verge. Her case is strikingly similar to that of Yaa T. (Case No. 25).

CASE 23. EKWIA N. of Juaben district, Ashanti. F. *c.* 60.

Shrine

Amfemfi at Asueyi.

Reason for referral

Self-accusations of witchcraft.

Family History

Parents: Not cross-cousins. Father was an illiterate, non-Christian hunter. He died twenty years ago. He had only one wife. Mother was an illiterate cocoa-farmer. She died ten years ago. She set up a shrine of Krakyi Dente in Juaben and was its *obosomfo*.

Siblings: Two brothers, two sisters. All illiterate, non-Christian farmers except one brother who is a literate chief.

Personal History

Childhood: N.a.d. Home was with mother's family.

Schooling: Nil, but she was a Christian till aged about thirty.

Marriage: She married one year after menarche. Her husband had no other wife. Patient divorced him about two years ago because he did nothing for her. She built her own house and he sponged.

Children: One born twenty years ago. Died aged one week.

Work: When aged about thirty she succeeded her mother as senior elder ("owner") of the *obosom* Krakye Dente, but was never an *okomfo*. She gave up the post when she was "caught" for witchcraft by Tigari eighteen months ago. Since then she has made some cocoa-farms.

Katamenia: Menopause nine years ago. Uneventful.

Present Household: Patient owns the house and has with her one of her brother's sons and his wife and child.

Present Illness

Gradual onset eighteen months ago. She became sleepless, with "burnings" all over. She wept a great deal and could do no work. She felt that "something was holding her back all the time" and thought she must be "caught". She went to Tigari, whose medicine she had drunk many years previously, confessed herself a witch and said she had killed her child and taken away her own womb. She resigned from her *obosom* work and took up cocoa-farming. She was improved by confessing but has never felt quite well or happy since. Five months ago she again became sleepless, so she came to Asueyi on her own initiative to seek relief.

First Interview: 21.1.57

Very good personality. Exceptionally intelligent and capable. Very well preserved for her age. No retardation, speech free and fluent, movements brisk. All mental tests done quickly, easily and accurately. Though very pleasant, friendly and smiling in conversation, her face in repose is anxious and perplexed.

10.6.57. Is still staying in the *obosom's* village. Well liked by landlady and fellow-lodgers. Condition unchanged.

10.7.57. She has gone home ostensibly to fetch more money.

COMMENTARY

Involutional depression in a very good personality.

CASE 24. AFUA S. of Kumasi district. F. *c.* 60.

Shrine
Kyinaman, Bredi.

Reason for referral
Someone has made her into a witch.

Family History
    Parents: Cross-cousins. Illiterate, non-Christian cocoa-farmers. Father had only one wife.
    Siblings: Nil.

Personal History
    Childhood: N.a.d. Happy. Lived in a house built by her father.
    Schooling: Nil. Non-Christian.
    Marriage: Not cross-cousin. Her husband, a non-Christian, illiterate cocoa-farmer, died "a long time ago" and the patient did not marry again. The husband took two other wives, senior to the patient, but dismissed them and then took two more. The patient had one fight with a fellow-wife but was on good terms with all the others.
    Children: Nil.
    Work: The patient has her own cocoa-farm but is now able only to supervise the work of labourers. The cocoa-disease has stricken her farm and she had only two bags last year.
    Katamenia: Menopause more than ten years ago.

Present Illness
    For many years the patient had a very close friend. "Whenever I bought anything for myself, say a head-kerchief, I always bought one for her too." One night this friend came and said that she was troubled by lice—invisible to anyone else—walking all over her. She was frightened and asked if she might sleep with the patient. This she did. In the morning after she had risen and gone the patient saw a small bird fly out of the room. She was frightened and called her half-sister, who accused the patient's friend of changing herself into a bird. The friend swore by the *obosom* Kundi that she had not changed herself into any animal and was not a witch. Shortly after that she died, but she never confessed to witchcraft and did not appear to have been "caught" by Kundi. The patient, however, thought that the bird incident meant that her friend gave her an *obayi* on the night she slept with her and she became frightened, sleepless, had palpitations, lost her appetite, grew lean and had pains all over. She went to an *obosom* near her home: he

agreed with her that she had been given an *obayi* but he was not able to take it away. She has been to various clinics and hospitals but has felt no better.

COMMENTARY

Lonely, ageing woman with neither siblings nor children, depressed and daunted by the decline of life's consolations.

CASE 25. YAA T. of Bekwai district, Ashanti. F. ? 70.

Shrine
Mframaso.

Reason for referral
"Big" dreams. Fear of becoming a witch.

Family History
   Parents: Cross-cousins. Illiterate, non-Christian farmers.
   Siblings: Seven born, five died in childhood. A surviving sister is now a thorn in the patient's flesh.

Personal History
   Childhood: N.a.d. Home contained maternal grandmother and her siblings, patient's mother and her siblings. Patient did not move from this home on marriage, has never lived elsewhere and is now the head of it. It is in a forest "village" but there are some neighbours.
   Schooling: Nil. Non-Christian.
   Work: Mother's food-farm and cocoa-farm.
   Marriage: Cross-cousin. Husband had one other wife but there was no friction between the two wives as they lived in different households. Latterly the husband neglected the patient (probably because of her economic independence) so she divorced him about ten years ago.
   Children: Seven born, two survived—a son and daughter, who came with the patient to Mframaso. The daughter is about fifty, has borne eleven children of whom six died in childhood and another recently. This daughter's own youngest daughter has three young children. The daughter is on very good terms with her mother, the patient, and is indignant and concerned for her. She is a thin, frightened, worried-looking woman with a deeply lined face, and of the two I would have taken her for the patient rather than her outwardly composed mother. She says she is sure the mother's sister is a witch and killed the son who recently died as well as the rest of the seven.
   Previous Personality: Hard-working. She was still working till about

a year ago when her eyesight became too poor. Were she not a very good personality the committee of the family elders who decide inheritance and succession would not have awarded to her the cocoa-farm which she inherited from her mother.

Household: The patient's mother's siblings are now all dead but their descendants are still there, together with the patient's sister and her children and daughter's children. The patient's son and daughter are there with the latter's children and daughters' children. The home is unhappy because—according to the patient's son and daughter—the others all covet the patient's cocoa-farm and think she should not have inherited it. They constantly show ill-will, but this is intensified every cocoa-season.

Present Illness

Five years ago the patient drank at Mframa's shrine for protection, but has neglected to come for annual renewal since. This neglect has contributed to her present fears in that she drank not only for herself but on behalf of her children and grandchildren. She feels that the recent death of a grandchild would not have occurred had she not allowed the protection to lapse. She has not yet felt herself to be a witch but has had dreams which she thinks indicate that her sister is a witch and that someone is trying to make her (the patient) into a witch. She dreamt that a hunter whom she knows—an uncouth man, not a relative—brought her the leg of an antelope and told her to eat it. She took it, but found that it was rotten and stinking. Her daughter urged her not to accept it, so she gave it back.

After the funeral of the patient's grandson she dreamt that she saw the severed head of a cow on the ground, but though on the ground it was erect as if alive. (The symbolism may be of a dead fear again rearing its ugly head.) A second cow was alive and chased the dreamer. People shouted at her to run and hide, which she did. The cow charged a wall and pushed its two horns right through, where they broke off and remained sticking. A few days later she dreamt that her sister was about to kill her (the sister's own) grandchild. The dreamer snatched the child away and gave it to its mother. Its grandmother then beat up the dreamer.

First interview: 15.3.57

The patient is very well preserved for her age, except that her eyesight is poor. She is intelligent and seems a very good personality. At the shrine she told her story clearly and related her three dreams. The *obosom* subscribed to her own view that she was not a witch but someone wanted to give her this evil power. At interview she re-told her dreams very spiritedly and graphically. She was in no doubt that the

rejection of the bad antelope meant the rejection of the evil power of
witchcraft. (Both antelopes and meat-eating are features of traditional
witchcraft.) She was quite sure that the dream about her sister's grandchild showed that the sister was a witch. She was anxious and uncertain
about the dream in which the cow broke its horns and asked me what I
thought. I said I thought it an encouraging dream in that something
trying to do her harm had failed and damaged itself. She did not accept
this but said that the old people believed that dreams about dead cows
meant that the dreamer was becoming a witch. Though her daughter
and the *obosomfo* both assure her that it is her sister and not herself who
is the witch, she retains depressive misgivings.

2.4.57. Both the patient and her daughter seemed much happier till the
patient had a message from her son, who had gone home, that all her
money (£500), trinkets and other valuables had been stolen from a box
in her room. (The room was locked but had no ceiling.) She took this
with apparent fortitude but appeared to become physically more feeble.
After the misfortune she dreamt that she and her dead mother were
digging gold. The mother was in a deep hole and found some gold
which she handed up to the dreamer. As the latter was in the act of
taking the gold she fell into the hole.

COMMENTARY

This woman feels defenceless, frightened and depressed by her
menacing circumstances and old age. Her depression takes the common
form of thinking she is becoming a witch. The dream of the dead
mother in the hole seems straightforward. The hole is the grave and
from the grave the mother hands the dreamer gold, i.e., the valuable
inheritance which she did in fact bequeath. This is snatched from the
dreamer—it was in fact stolen. The fall into the grave symbolises the
patient's fear of approaching death.

CASE 26. ABENA W. of Kwahu. F. *c.* 60.

Shrine
  Kyinaman, Bredi.

Reason for referral
  Sleeplessness.

Family History
  Father: He died a long time ago, an illiterate, non-Christian, ground-
nut and yam farmer. He had four wives in all. Patient's mother was the
senior.
  Mother: Still alive. Very old, blind and "broken down".

Siblings: Eight born. Only the patient and one brother survived. The brother is a drunkard, lives in his cocoa-village and seldom comes to town, but whenever he does he quarrels with all his relatives who are afraid of him because they suspect him of possessing powerful *suman*. They say, "Whatever he utters comes true, he must have got some strong powers from somewhere." He boasts that whoever gainsays him will never have either health or prosperity and will die. One sister quarrelled with him and died, whereupon he gloated and has since terrorised the family.

Personal History

Childhood: She lived in her mother's family house. The father was elsewhere.

Schooling: Nil, but she became a Christian after the birth of her third child.

Work: She was a tobacco trader. She is now a market-farmer. No cocoa.

Marriage: She married four times. "Some died: some I left." She married her present husband five years ago. He has no other wives and the marriage is happy.

Children: Five born, one died. The survivors are all by the second husband and the dead one by the first husband. Three sons are all literates, a tailor, a storekeeper and a building contractor. They are all good to the patient. The daughter (seen) is over thirty, craves children and has none.

Home: Mother's house. Husband elsewhere.

Katamenia: Menopause more than ten years ago. Uneventful.

Previous Illness: Two years ago the patient had palpitations and pains all over. She is reticent about concurrent events but is clear that when she came to the *obosom* the illness vanished.

Present Illness

Just over a month ago the patient's brother came to town and while drunk and truculent visited her house, goaded her into an altercation with him, and in the course of it reminded her that anyone who opposed him died. Since then she has had no sleep, has lost her appetite, become thin and been troubled by palpitations. The brother has commented on the loss of weight with fiendish glee. Her daughter says that, though sleepless, she lies quietly and never complains.

Interview

She is tall, thin, dignified and composed, and looks less than her age. She was pleasant and courteous but reticent till reassured by two of the *obosom's* elders. She looked anxious and depressed, had tremulous, fidgeting hands but denied weeping. Asked about her dreams, she said, "How could I dream when I have not once closed my eyes in sleep for a month?"

COMMENTARY

Fear of death in a good personality now dismayed by old age and defencelessness. She is not yet depressed enough to feel guilt. Her assessment of her adversity is fair, but she is a candidate for self-accusations of witchcraft unless the *obosom* restores her confidence.

CASE 27. KODZO N. of Trans-Volta. M. *c.* 75.

Shrine

Mframa, at Mframaso.

Reason for referral

He came on his own initiative, seeking reassurance that his witch-wife had not made him also into a witch.

Family History

No information.

Personal History

Work: Illiterate, non-Christian, cocoa-farmer colonising Akim-Aboakwa district till the cocoa died. He has now planted coffee which yielded for the first time this year—one bag, value 72*s*.

Marriage: He has had four wives, one of whom died many years ago, one left him and two remain.

Elder surviving wife: Aged fifty to sixty? Illiterate Christian communicant. Conscientious, regular church-goer. Sings in choir. Member of "Women's Class". Farmer and trader. Hard worker. Six years ago she started a bread-baking business but has never made it pay. Has always been "*basa-basa* with money". Husband considers her a good woman because she has always "respected" him, never quarrelled, and always soothed him when he was annoyed. "Since I married her I have never fought with her." Everyone liked her. This wife bore three children of whom two survive, aged about twenty and ten. They were troublesome children: they started school but refused to continue. "They don't respect, though their mother is very respectful."

Younger wife: No information except that she gets on peaceably with the elder wife.

Patient's children: Five born, of whom one died many years ago aged ten, and another, an adult with children of her own, about five years ago. No information as to which of the wives bore these.

Household: Patient, two wives and their children, a grown-up niece and her children. All happy till recently except for the naughty children.

Previous Personality: Circumstantial evidence points to an excellent personality. Going abroad into Akim for farming implies enterprise: coffee growing exceptional enterprise. He recently went to Accra for dental treatment, and when his wife was sick he sent her to a clinic and accepted advice to send her to Accra for X-ray. This implies unusual good sense. He is an elder of the Mankrado's stool.

Present Illness

Three years ago the patient's *wife* had a cough. He sent her to a clinic and then for X-ray. The report was favourable: she received some treatment from the local clinic but continued to cough and is still coughing. Nine months ago this wife had some post-menopausal bleeding, the menopause having occurred five years ago. No advice was sought about this. Five months ago she began to develop a mental illness. She complained of sleeplessness, "burnings" all over her scalp and pains in her chest. She refused to sleep on the four-poster with her husband but lay on the floor, waking him at short intervals to complain that she could not sleep. She could do no work or take any interest in anything. Then she said she was a witch, had killed her children and had blocked her own womb so that she bore no more. She also said that people were trying to give her human flesh to eat. Upon this the husband called her two uncles and they took her to the head of her family and asked her who these people were. She mentioned the names of two women who were then sent for. They indignantly denied the charge. The head of the family then referred her to the Mankrado and his elders, before whom she danced wildly and said she had been "caught" by the *obosom* Tigari becuase she was attempting to harm someone under Tigari's protection. She grew steadily worse and began to "shake and dance all the time, and talk *basa-basa*". She was taken to Tigari's shrine and purified, after which she became quiet.

The husband then went to Accra to have some teeth out, but returned to find that "the medicine had caught her again" and that she was not only talking "*basa-basa*" but accusing everyone else of witchcraft. Knowing her to be "*basa-basa*", nobody took this seriously, but later the husband began to think she might have put the evil power into him. No one else in the house felt infected, though she had had ample opportunity to tamper with their food.

The wife's "case" had already cost over £84, but her own kinsmen defrayed it. The husband's expenses only began when he came, accompanied by his niece's son, to Mframaso to consult Mframa not about his wife's established witchcraft but about his own. The niece's son who accompanied him was a quiet, pleasant youth of about nineteen, and said that nobody but the patient himself had any doubt of his innocence.

Interview

He looks ill, thin and worn. At the shrine, while waiting for his turn, he stood in extreme agitation and anxiety looking wretched and depressed and near to tears. His nephew had to tell his story for him as he was incoherent with distress. (The nephew was among those to whom the patient's wife claimed to have given witchcraft, but in contrast to the patient, was quite unmoved.)

The *obosom* said that as the case had already been before the Mankrado of the patient's town he could not touch it without the Mankrado's authority. Upon this the patient appeared quite distraught and was led out by his nephew.

The nephew left him in his lodging and at once set out to see the Mankrado and borrow some more money for the extra travelling. He was gone about ten days, during which time the patient, removed from the proximity of his wife, settled down considerably and was able to give a coherent history of his trouble. Towards the end of the ten days he was no longer afraid that he was a witch but only wished the *obosom* to confirm his innocence. This the *obosom* in fact did, but the patient went home still looking depressed and anxious.

COMMENTARY

Reactive depression and anxiety, verging upon a *folie-à-deux*.

He is a Trans-Volta Ewe and hence belongs to a more depressive breed of males than do the Ashanti. But whatever his innate bias it seems unlikely that a man of his excellent personality would have succumbed to any kind of mental illness had his resistance to adversity not been impaired by old age.

II

REACTION TO FEAR

§ 1. INTRODUCTION

It was said in the preamble concerning the new shrines that the presiding deities promise to kill those of their children who, having transgressed their law, do not promptly come and confess their sin and make amends. It might be expected therefore that the shrines would be the places in which to see people in the grip of fear.

And so they are. At the shrines it is possible to see people gone mad with fear and to see their sanity quickly restored by the removal of the fear. And it is easy for the superficial observer of half a dozen such madmen to denounce "the fetish" for frightening people out of their wits. But a longer and more painstaking acquaintance, not only with the worshippers who thus go mad, but with those who with equal provocation serenely do not, gradually discloses that those who do are usually predisposed. What these various predisposing factors are we shall see later in the case-histories.

Another point to bear in mind is that the fear seen at the shrines can seldom if ever be regarded as "pure" gratuitous fear, such as that which we feel for a few seconds when we see a heavy lorry skidding towards us on an icy road, or see a nearby tree struck by lightning.

The picture of fear, when the fear is of imminent retribution for sin, is a dramatic one and rises swiftly to its zenith. Usually the sinful patient is outwardly normal, though with private misgivings, when he says good-night to his friends and retires to sleep. Then, very often, he has a dream in which he sees the avenging *obosom* coming for him with a club. He wakes in a fright which quickly becomes a panic and soon he is out pacing the yard with half the village up trying to soothe him. Before morning he is in a frenzy, inaccessible and talking *"basa-basa"*. Then, if he is not restrained, he rushes in blind terror away into the bush.

If he is quickly brought in this frantic state to the shrine and grasps that the deity promises forgiveness, he calms down, sleeps off his physical exhaustion and within a few days is well. But if there are several days of delay before he reaches the shrine the picture changes and he arrives, usually much more mad—indistinguishable, in fact, from a classic schizophrenic—inappropriately laughing, smiling, posturing, singing, dancing, replying to hallucinatory voices, standing stock-still and mute, soiling, smearing and so on. But again, in an unbelievably short time, he is restored to normal.

Of the people who are predisposed to the acute transient fear-psychosis the most important are the potential schizophrenics. This fact was established by follow-ups, disclosures of the patients' past histories and character-traits, and by the histories of chronic schizophrenics. The follow-ups often show that the patient recovers swiftly from his fear-psychosis and returns to normal life, only to slip quietly, months later, into a frank incapacitating schizophrenia. Or it may be revealed that, years before, he had a long spell of madness for no apparent reason.

Again, a common transgression precipitating a transient frantic guilt-and-fear psychosis is the making of bad magic against others. This act, quite apart from fear-psychoses or any association with shrines, seems to commend itself especially to incipient schizophrenics and is of ominous prognostic portent. It often ushers in a florid schizophrenia of the psychiatrically commonplace kind, not disturbing to the neighbours but incapacitating to the patient. It seems that the making of bad *suman* is a schizoid type of aggression as distinct from a healthy quarrelsome aggression and hence is highly acceptable to the incipient schizophrenic. Furthermore, it is a frequent feature of universal schizophrenic thought to perceive a mysterious relationship between certain persons and certain things, and the schizophrenic patient may feel impelled to invent new and bizarre bad medicines rather than buy ready-made ones. In phases of insight, at the onset of his illness, he may be guilt-stricken by what he has done, and throw a frenzy of fear.

It is possible that our British mental-hospital psychiatrists see more fear-psychoses of the African kind than they suspect. I can recall one case not so regarded by anyone at the time, but now strongly illuminated in the light of the acute fear-psychosis of Africa. This was the case of a girl of nineteen, a London typist, with a most sinister family history. One parent and (if I remember rightly) three out of six siblings were chronic schizophrenics. She was admitted to a London surgical ward with a supposed appendicitis which was found at operation to be an early, but possibly malignant, ovarian tumour. It was removed, she made a good recovery and was sent home and went back to work. However, through the dropping of a careless remark she had overheard enough of the truth to terrify her. She began brooding, and according to her sister's subsequent story, she came home from work every day weeping and saying she was going to die of cancer. In a few weeks she was admitted to a mental hospital in a violent delirium, incessantly shouting day and night, fighting, biting and needing to be tube-fed for several weeks. At the end of this time she began eating spontaneously and became accessible and manageable; by the time there was a vacancy for her in the insulin ward she was almost well. Her menacing family history obliterated almost every other circumstance of her case from her physicians' vision, but (since "hindsight" is always easy) my own *retrospective* opinion, in the light of African fear-psychoses, is that early reassurance concerning danger of death (had her fear been known) would have aborted the whole psychotic episode, though chronic schizophrenia without external provocation may well have been her ultimate destiny.

Another type of patient prone to the fear-psychosis is the depressive whose guilt has no foundation in fact. Such fear-ridden depressives are not unknown in our own hospitals. I have already referred to one who thought she was going to be hanged for her purely imaginary sin: she cowered in terror at the hallucinatory sounds of the approaching executioner's footsteps, but she was well in ten days when her depression was treated.

As might be expected, a circumstance which often precipitates a fear-psychosis is febrile or toxic illness. The patient feels unwell and restless, remembers some small offence committed in a heedless moment and disregarded, thinks the deity has laid a hand on him, becomes frightened and then frenzied. In one case a thimbleful of liquor, well within the drinker's capacity, sharpened rather than blunted the edge of anxiety and quickly whipped him frantic with fear.

We shall also examine a group of patients who, though having as much occasion for apprehension as any others, nevertheless fall short of a fear-psychosis and develop only a very severe anxiety.

§ 2. FEAR-PSYCHOSIS WITHOUT DISCOVERABLE PREDISPOSITION

Out of all the cases of fear-psychosis, I can find only one without a predisposing factor in the shape of febrile illness, potential schizophrenia and so on. The patient was an undoubtedly good personality, though he showed, by African standards, a reckless lack of self-restraint.

CASE 28. KWESI P. of Tainso district, Ashanti. M. *c.* 40.

Shrine

Oboo at Offuman.

Reason for referral

"Caught" by the *obosom* for blasphemy.

Family History

No information.

Personal History

No information except that he is an ordinary non-Christian, illiterate farmer.

Previous Personality

Hard-working, generous, warm-hearted, and reliable.

Present Illness

Six days ago the patient's niece died. The circumstances were these: The niece was pregnant, and about the seventh month began to feel ill and became very lean. When delivery was due she became "mad" and talked "*basa-basa*". She was taken to the *obosom*, who said she was "caught" for some sin, probably that of trying to bewitch her relatives who had all put themselves under the *obosom* protection. She was unable to talk so could make no confession. She quickly died (seemingly in an eclamptic fit) with the child undelivered. (To die with an undelivered child is an "abominable" death, quite apart from witchcraft.) The customary post-mortem Caesarian operation was performed and the two bodies buried in the "disgraceful" cemetery without any rites.

When the uncle, Kwesi P., heard the news of these happenings he was overcome with grief and fury, and seizing a stick, he beat the ground with it, crying out against the *obosom* who had killed his niece. When his rage had spent itself he began to have misgivings concerning his own impious outburst. Would the *obosom* kill him? He began to feel "caught". He had "burnings" in his belly, pains in his ribs "like an *obosom's* knife" and dreamt that he was being chased by the *obosom*. Later in the night he could not sleep at all, woke his house-mates in great fear and agitation, told them he had done wrong, was being killed and must be taken to the *obosom's* shrine. By the time they reached Offuman—about thirty miles—he was (according to the literate chief and other good witnesses) raving mad, talking gibberish and unable to see, hear, eat or drink. He was taken at once to the shrine where others told what he had done. He was able to assent when the *obosom* asked if it was true. Having thus confessed and been promised forgiveness after an appropriate sacrifice, he immediately calmed down.

Interview: 10.7.56

I did not see him till several days after his appearance at the shrine. He was then rational and composed but looked fatigued. He corroborated the other witnesses' testimony, described the onset of the illness but said he could not remember the journey or the arrival in Offuman. He gave a rueful little laugh, said he had had his lesson and would never again revile an *obosom*.

26.9.56. A few weeks ago I went to his home-town to look him up and to see whether his normal personality appeared in any way unstable. He was not at home but to-day he spontaneously appeared at Mframaso (about twenty-five miles' journey) to return my call and bring me a present of a fowl. He seemed a very good personality—intelligent, pleasant, cheerful and certainly exceptionally friendly and courteous.

COMMENTARY

Acute psychotic reaction to fear in pure culture, exhibited by a good personality.

3. FEAR-PSYCHOSIS IN POTENTIAL SCHIZOPHRENICS

In this group of nine cases, one patient had his fear-psychosis and recovered from it a year or so before I met him, but I witnessed his subsequent quiet collapse into unprovoked and unmistakable schizo-phrenia. Another had recovered from his wild psychosis a few days before I met him, but I watched him, over a period of months, settle down into an almost mute schizophrenic. Another, whom I saw at the height of a transient fear-psychosis from which she recovered within a week, had, years before, spent months as a certified hospital patient. Another, whom I saw in a wild fear-psychosis which she had developed on account of very trivial guilt, made a dramatic recovery from the frenzy but settled down with a body of quite irrelevant delusions and hallucinations. Another whom I saw make an apparently perfect re-covery from a tumultuous transient fear-psychosis later relapsed into ordinary madness. Three others whom I saw recover dramatically from transient psychoses I judged on accumulation of evidence backed by personal impression to be potential schizophrenics. The last case which I have included in this group is that of a youth whose antisocial activities, though not indubitably schizophrenic, certainly place him outside the pale of normality.

CASE 29. KWABENA B. of Kwahu. M. *c.* 27.

Shrine

Mframa at Mframaso.

Reason for referral

Recurrence of mental illness.

Family History

Parents: Cross-cousins. Both illiterate farmers, both Christian communicants. His father died about twenty years ago. His mother married a second time. The relatives have always practised cross-cousin marriage.

Siblings: Four born, one died. All Christian communicants. Patient and one brother have been to school. The literate brother is a foreman in the Department of Agriculture: the other is a tailor.

Personal History

Childhood: N.a.d. disclosed.

Schooling: Standard VI. (Top class is Standard VII.)

Work: Blacksmith. (*Vide infra.*)

Marriage: He married a Kwahu woman about four years ago. The wife left him during his first mental illness and he has not married again.

Children: Three young children who are with their mother.

Previous Illness: About five years ago the patient came to *abisa* at Mframaso complaining that though he had learned the blacksmith's trade he had no money to buy tools to start work on his own. He promised a cow if the *obosom* would prosper him and enable him to buy the tools. In a few months he returned with the cow. He then married and went to Takoradi to work.

About three years ago while working in Takoradi he succumbed to the temptation to buy a bad *suman* to kill a moneyed relative and share in her money. He also performed a sorcery (under the tutelage of a bad medicine-man) to become rich by unearned windfalls at the expense of people who simultaneously became poor by unmerited ill-luck. Within a day or two of making these medicines (one of which involved eating magical kola-nuts) he became raving mad. As he had been to Mframaso it was thought likely that Mframa had "caught" him for some violation of *obosom* law, and he was brought by his mother, her brother and her husband. During the two days when he was waiting in Mframaso to go before the shrine he was uncontrollably mad, attacking people, tearing off every stitch of clothing and dashing away into the bush in terror. On one occasion, the search-parties failed to find him and invoked the aid of the police, but by the time the latter were mobilised—the following day—he had been found. He was brought before the *obosom* bound with trap-wire. The *obosom* said he was "caught" for wrong-doing. He was able to confess, was purified and in a few days had completely recovered. After this he asked if he might stay in Mframaso and work. Consent was given, he built himself a smithy and settled down as a blacksmith. He lodged in the house of the young hornblower, who gave me this history corroborated by various other good witnesses and later by his mother.

Previous Personality: When I first came to Mframaso he was an exceptionally hard-working and highly-skilled blacksmith. I saw several remarkable examples of his work—an excellent gun of which he had made every part except the tubing of the barrel, a jack to enable timber-sawyers to raise heavy logs, and some ingenious iron fetters which I saw in use on the hands and feet of disturbed and violent patients. His more hum-drum work was the making and mending of hoes and cutlasses. He took no interest in anything but his work, and to this he was closely devoted. His smithy was within earshot of my quarters and I often heard him hammering till very late at night and again very early in the morning.

In appearance he was unlike other Africans, having stooping shoulders, a forward-poking head, a pointed nose, a wide, thin mouth turning up at the corners and a perpetual empty smile without warmth or merriment. He was solitary, uninterested in women, and though his smithy was nearly always full of sociable loafers watching his work he took little notice of them and never answered their cracks. I occasionally gave him a lift if I overtook him on the road carrying headloads of palm-nut charcoal for his work, but he never revealed that he could speak English. Most English-speaking Africans visiting Mframaso made a point of calling on me to air their accomplishment. Only once did I see him in the *obosom's* yard before his second illness. He came to *abisa* one evening asking the *obosom* to help him recover some money he had lent his late wife to set up in trade. This was a normal request.

Present Illness

After about three years of good health and hard work—I had then been living about six months in Mframaso—there was a Fofie festival to which came the female relative against whom the patient had made the bad medicine. She came only to thank the *obosom* for the birth of a child, but her presence seemed to revive the blacksmith's unease of mind. He began to leave his work in the middle of a job to walk restlessly from one end of the village to the other. He left hoes and cutlasses in the fire till they were ruined and then protested that there was nothing wrong with them. Then he started taking his tools into the bush and hiding them. His landlord used to rescue them secretly. People said that he sometimes talked "*basa-basa*", but I never heard this. They also said that he made some *suman*.

Then he appeared one evening before the shrine, placing himself in the dock reserved for witches and other sinners. While awaiting his turn he chewed his nails, picked his nose, buttoned and unbottoned his shirt and smiled his empty, foolish smile. He told the *obosom* that the kola-nut he had eaten as a part of his bad medicine three years ago was still inside him and was "troubling" him again. The *obosom* said that if he could not vomit it out the *obrafohene* would give him medicine to destroy its evil power. He left the yard apparently satisfied, but later told his house-mates he had made up his mind to go back to Nzima to buy more bad medicine to make money by causing other people's deaths. The next day he broke up the hearth in his smithy, saying that the man who supplied the mud-bricks for supporting the hearth wanted them back. His landlord then sent a message to his relatives to come and look after him. They came and took him away to Kwahu.

COMMENTARY

When I first heard the history of his first illness and knew him only as a hard-working blacksmith I regarded that illness as a fear reaction in pure culture. However, I later realised that he was an example of two principles which gradually came to light in other case-histories: (1) the potential schizophrenic is especially vulnerable to the acute guilt-and-fear psychosis; and (2) the making of bad magics against others is a schizoid type of aggression (as distinct from a healthy quarrelsome type of aggression) and frequently ushers in a classic schizophrenia.

CASE 30. AKOSUA K. of Kwahu district. F. *c.* 30.

Shrine
   Amfemfi at Asuoyi.

Reason for referral
   Mental disturbance.

Family History
   Parents: Cross-cousins. The mother is alive and well, an illiterate, Christian farmer. The father left the mother years ago. The patient does not remember him. The stepfather is satisfactory.
   Siblings: Four survived and are grown-up. Some died.

Personal History

Childhood: N.a.d. disclosed.

Schooling: Nil. She was baptised a Roman Catholic but is not a communicant.

Marriage: Unsatisfactory. The husband does not fulfil his economic obligations and treats her badly.

Children: Three born, two alive, the younger being about two months old.

Previous Illnesses: Two years ago she had an illness said to have been exactly like the present one. She had been to a Kramu medicine-man and had a bad medicine made against her husband because he was ill-treating her. She herself had not drunk at the Asuoyi shrine at the time, but her mother's brother had drunk on behalf of all his potestas, so she was "caught", became mentally disturbed, and confessed at the shrine what she had done.

Previous Personality: Always very shy and quiet, but respected. The Mankrado of her town made a contribution to her expenses because of her good character.

Present Illness

The onset was sudden, three days ago. She was perfectly well on the previous day. She had no fever, headache or other physical discomfort.

She was brought immediately to the shrine by two male relatives—unpleasant, truculent people, unwilling to give any information. They left immediately after *abisa* at the shrine, and the *obosomfo*—who knew her from the last illness—later told me her history.

Interview: 5.9.56

She was seen at the shrine, sitting between two restraining male relatives, awaiting her turn for *abisa*. She was quite inaccessible and sat mostly mute, staring with dilated pupils and looking terrified, as if about to bolt at any moment. She drummed with her feet and sang at intervals, "Haba, haba. . . . Hoo, hoo. . . . Krafi, krafi", meaningless words of her own coining, and uttered nothing sensible. The relatives made *abisa* on her behalf as she was unable. The *obosom* asked what they wanted him to do. They said, "Save her." He asked whether she had made any relevant statements. They said, "No." He said she was "caught" again because she was again planning evil against her husband, for his continued shortcomings. The relatives left, putting her in charge of the *obosomfo*, who gave her a room in his own compound. 6.9.56. The next day she was in ceaseless activity, mainly vocal. They said she had shouted and raved throughout the night and taken no food or drink since the previous day. She stood giggling and grimacing behind a parapet which fenced off a small verandah, and leaned over shouting and spitting at the people in the yard below. She drummed with her fingers on her head and chest, whistled, sang, shouted, pointed at everyone in turn, dribbled and manipulated her breasts. Her shoutings were mainly the same meaningless words of the previous day, but were interspersed with sentences, many of a guilt-flavoured kind. "If you do wrong, God will pay you out. . . . I won't do it, I won't do it. . . . If you don't keep quiet, speak the truth. . . . When you do evil it will torment you. . . . No one is punished without a cause. Mad, mad, talk, talk. . . . Something is there, something is there and I have come near to it. . . . There are some things God forbids. . . ."

Physically, she was in good general condition, very well covered, in striking contrast to the Ashanti.

10.9.56. (Floods and bad roads prevented my going to see her again till to-day.)

A very different picture. She was lying asleep, but got up when asked. Drowsy. (The *obosomfo* afterwards admitted, on questioning, that he was keeping her under the influence of hypnotics. He said these were herbal, prepared by himself, but would not divulge the name of the herb. Though this secretiveness is normal among the Ashanti, it may well be that he possessed an illicit supply of European sedatives, probably bought from a hospital dispenser, or smuggled across the French frontier from the French Ivory Coast.) Slow, and heavy, but correctly orientated. Answered questions slowly but sensibly.

The *obosomfo* said she had quietened down gradually, and that she had confessed to adultery with several men.

28.9.56. Still very slow, silent and oppressed. Not agitated. She replies to questions only after a long interval, but correctly and to the point, without depressive commentary. Unless stimulated she seems only half-conscious.

12.10.56. Still slow, bewildered-looking, standing about looking confused. She does not smile in greeting and only slowly raises her head. She answers questions slowly or not at all. She herself describes some confusion or maybe thought-blocking. "When I am going somewhere I stand still and don't know what to do." They say she does a small amount of work and gives no trouble. She is breast-feeding her child. She looks in very good general physical condition.

23.10.56. Everyone said she was much better and had gone to the stream to wash clothes. Her mother and ten-year-old son have joined her. The latter is an exceptionally intelligent child.

8.11.56. Greatly improved. She was pounding *fufu* for another patient —he sitting and turning the lump—and was calling him to order for chatter and inattention to the work.

3.12.56. She seems to have made a good recovery. She now presents as a shy, quiet but attractive woman of above-average intelligence. To-day she was smiling quietly but appropriately, talking spontaneously, and taking a normal interest in everything going on, though less exuberant, than her fellows. I had brought some snapshots and she came forward to join the group who were trying to identify the various photographed figures.

10.12.56. She was gone to a farm three or four miles away to help with the work. Everyone says she is quite well and working very hard.

10.1.57. I have seen her several times since the last note. No change. She seems very well and hard-working. It may be she postpones her departure because of reluctance to face again the marital situation and the irksomeness of bringing it to a head. She looks distressed when asked about going home.

COMMENTARY

Acute transient guilt-and-fear psychosis in an unhappy, shy woman who has had one previous similar episode. The making of bad magics is an ominous feature and I should not be surprised if she eventually developed schizophrenia.

CASE 31. ABENA K. of Kwaso district, Ashanti. F. *c.* 30.

Shrine
Mframa at Mframaso.

Reason for referral
Self-accusations of witchcraft.

Family History
Parents: Illiterate, non-Christian cocoa-farmers. The father is dead. The mother came with the patient. She is a serene and sensible old lady.

Siblings: Mother had eleven children, of whom seven survived and are grown-up. Several are literates. One is an ex-teacher who now manages a book-shop in a town. One is a lorry-driver. These two brought the patient. All are Christians.

Personal History
Childhood: N.a.d. disclosed.

School: She attended for a short time (Standard I) and was clever, but her uncle soon tired of paying the fees.

Work: She is a trader; her husband says she is very successful.

Religion: Christian.

Marriage: Happy. The husband is an illiterate cocoa-farmer and came with her to the shrine.

Children: Seven born. One died aged four. The eldest is eight. The youngest is eighteen months. Two miscarriages: one recently. Patient is still suckling the youngest child.

Previous Personality: She is always busy, happy, kindly, popular and, the husband says, "clever". He also says, "She has never quarrelled with anyone since I married her, not even with me". She is interested in everything and gained a Mass Education certificate recently, i.e., learnt to read vernacular. She is learning sewing. She is a full Church member.

Previous Mental Illness: Twelve years ago she had an illness similar to the present illness except that she attacked people with a cutlass and was very dangerous, and presumably fell into the hands of the police, for she was sent to Accra Mental Hospital where she stayed for more than six months. The onset was when the first child was a few months old. The husband and the brother contradict one another as to whether witchcraft figured in this illness.

Household: Cocoa-"village" near Kwaso. Contains the late father's five brothers, the patient's five sisters (all married except the patient's youngest sister who is at school) and the patient's and her sisters' children.

Present Illness

The onset was sudden one week ago, three days after a miscarriage in which the patient lost a good deal of blood. She began to talk "*basa-basa*" and also said she was "caught" by Mframa because she had tried to damage by witchcraft her mother—who had drunk at Mframa's shrine on behalf of herself and all her children.

Interview: 15.3.56

She arrived in Mframaso with two days to wait before the next session at the shrine. She spent the two days in ceaseless excited activity and talk. She crawled about in the street, scraping up sand, shouting, singing, squirting milk from her breasts at bystanders, talking about Mass Education, the C.P.P. and a variety of jumbled topics, smiling, laughing, grimacing, but always recurring to the theme, "I am wicked. I have done wrong." She seemed to know whither she had come and why, and was to some extent accessible, though too distractable and excited to keep to any point for more than a few moments. When asked what wrong things she had done, she would begin to recount them, but always rambled off into other topics.

17.3.56. The *obosom's* clerk took down from her relatives a list of the "confessions" she had made at home and read them to the *obosom* before the shrine. They were all of the stereotyped kind except that she had by her witchcraft spoilt her recent pregnancy. At her first appearance there she seemed fully to appreciate the situation, and was co-operative, assenting to everything the clerk read out, though she made various irrelevant interruptions. At one point she said, "I'm very wicked and deserve to die. You ought to kill me instead of going on with this." Asked whether she had anything to confess concerning her mother and her husband, she said she had but as she was too incoherent to confess it, the hearing was adjourned.

As soon as the first hearing was over she was strikingly quieter and more composed.

18.3.56. The next day, looking very tired, she walked quietly up to my door with her child and said she would sit with me because all the talking in her lodgings was making her mad. I gave her a seat and went on with my writing. However, she was fidgety, smiling inappropriately, and rather interfering. Then she suddenly said she was going immediately to pack her things to return to her town at once.

20.3.56. At her second appearance at the shrine the clerk read the further confessions she had recounted to him in the interval. These were atypical in that she gave reasons for what she said she had done. She had taken away, she said, her mother's luck because her mother gave her too small a share of the money from the sale of a family cocoa-farm. Concerning her husband, she said she had changed him into a snake in the bush and in that form had beaten him with a stick because he did not take her advice.

In reply to a question from the *obosom* concerning her witch-associates, she said, "I don't know, because the *obayi* has now gone from me." And so it seemed, for after this second session she was almost well and slept peacefully. The following day she went quietly down to the stream and washed her clothes and, except that she sometimes went off at a tangent in conversation, she talked normally.

21.3.56. To-day her brother brought the cow for her to sacrifice. She appeared now more overtly depressed, and was languid and listless. She sat tearfully, saying that she had done wrong and eaten human flesh, but added that now she had a cow to sacrifice she would be cleansed of her sins. She had a herpes simplex: Hb. 55–60% and E.S.R. 98 mm. first hour and two symmetrical patches of follicular keratitis on the back of her neck.

29.3.56. After offering her cow and being purified she stayed a week for daily ritual baths. One day during that week she brought her child to me. I thought it had pemphigus and suggested taking her with it to the hospital out-patient department. She was keen to co-operate and while at hospital a gynaecological examination was carried out. She was found to have a sub-involuted uterus, a patulous cervix and leucorrhea.

She promised to go to a local clinic as soon as she reached home. As she was an intelligent, sensible woman, she probably did so.

30.12.56. I have heard of her several times from other Kwaso people visiting Mframaso. She always sends greetings and gifts of fruit and eggs and everyone says she is well and active.

COMMENTARY

Brief depressive illness after miscarriage, blood-loss and probably infection. Secondary acute fear-psychosis.

This is the only case I have met at any shrine where the patient had ever had mental-hospital treatment. The question arises, whether the present illness would have cleared up so quickly in a mental hospital. I think probably not. Where depression gives rise to delusions of witch-craft-guilt a secondary fear of retribution is added. The picture of pure fear is a psychotic picture. The fear is readily filtered off at the shrine and the psychotic element dramatically disappears.

CASE 32. AFUA D. of Akim district. F. *c.* 26.

Shrine

Dimankoma at Akrofrom.

Reason for referral

Self-accusations of witchcraft. Making bad *suman*.

Family History

Parents: Not cross-cousins. Both died when the patient was very small. Illiterate, non-Christian cocoa-farmers, as are all her other relatives.

Siblings: The patient has two older brothers.

Family Illnesses: Several daughters of the mother's sisters have been "caught" by *obosom* Tigari but soon recovered after cleansing and ritual.

Personal History

Childhood: She was cared for by her mother's sister till she was old enough to go to her father's brother's house. The father's sister was there and her son whom the patient subsequently married.

Schooling: Nil.

Marriage: Cross-cousin, ten years ago. Ex-soldier. He has a driving licence but does not drive. A successful cocoa-farmer. He is illiterate, non-Christian, as is the patient. He looks less than his years, he is cocky and not very kindly. He has two other wives, one he married six years ago, the other, one year ago. He lavishes gifts and attention on the new one, provides reasonably for the second but neglects his bare obligations to the patient, who says she never really wanted to marry him.

Children: Three born, all alive, aged seven, five and two.
Work: Food-farming; she wanted to be a petty trader in draperies, but the husband would not find the capital for her to start.

Present Illness

The onset was sudden, five days ago. No fever or other physical indisposition. The house-mates heard her crying out in the night. She said she had felt something hit her in the face and knew that it was the *obosom* Dimankoma who had "caught" her for making two bad magics against her husband (who had drunk at Dimankoma's shrine). She produced one *suman* which she said was only to make her husband give her money, but said the other was lost. Then she said she was also a witch and had killed people, then her talk became and remained "*basa-basa*".

Interview: 2.1.57

She looks physically very well. Not agitated or depressed: the picture is schizophrenic. She sits quietly unconcerned, occasionally looking hallucinated and puzzled. She declines to look at food and has to be led and urged from place to place. She is silent unless addressed, when she starts talking incoherently, but introduces into her talk the topic of her husband's neglect and her jealousy of the other wives.

"I hit my husband with a child's sandals, and thought the sandals were a black snake. All this is because I am jealous of his other two wives, but I am worried because the sandals were a snake. I went to the Apostolic Church and danced and clapped but they sent me away." (She has never been to such a church.) "My husband has made a binding medicine (*kyeredua*) against me because he doesn't give me clothes and is worried about the sandals that were a snake. I have an *obayi* but I am not ashamed of it: I am pleased with it. Some people say I have committed adultery but it isn't true. Ekwia has drunk every medicine there is: she said neither of us had a child's shoe but it was night and I haven't committed adultery. . . ."

She has moments of accessibility. Asked whether she felt sad or happy, she said, "Sad. I feel as if I had left my child, though know it is here with me." She replied correctly when asked the name of her town and the one to which she had just come, but was disorientated for time and was quite unable to pay any attention to simple verbal tests.

At the shrine she could give no account of herself, but appreciated the situation enough to produce one of the *suman* (which consisted of a pellet of dried leaf-paste stuck in shea-butter in a small glass jar). The *obosom* said she would be forgiven even though she could not confess, but she must bring a sheep, £22 and a bottle of rum (which the relatives then produced).

Progress: 4.1.56

Mute. Preoccupied. But they say she is eating.

8.1.56. Ritual purification was carried out on the evening of 4.1.56. When seen to-day she was astonishingly better, though preoccupied at times. She does not appear depressed. Superficially she is socially adequate—smiles appropriately, returns greetings, looks after her child. Could not take in simple questions about money. When told that to-day was Tuesday she could supply that to-morrow would be Wednesday but could not name yesterday. She is reluctant to speak, but when she does speech flows freely. After two narrations of the adapted cowboy story she said: "A farmer went to Kumasi with his dog and came home." After the first narration of the boy-bicycle-antelope story she said, "A boy went to Techiman hospital and died." She can tell the name of her own town but not where she is now. Her movements are few but brisk. When I left the house she remained sitting, staring, but later jumped up and hurried after me to "put me on the road" (a common courtesy).

10.1.56. Unbelievably improved. Mental tests all very well done, indicating very good intelligence.

COMMENTARY

I had no doubt when I first saw this patient that she was schizophrenic, and still think that she may be, though the acute attack cleared dramatically. Any non-Christian woman of normal "drive" in her marital situation would have got out of it without ado, and a normal woman who wanted to engage in retail trading would start off somehow, husband or no husband. The use of bad *suman* is an ominous prognostic feature. Again, it is the schizoid personalities who tend passively to accept cross-cousin marriage. Her description of her feelings, "I feel as if I had left my child though I know it is here with me," tallies with the feeling of desolation often described by our own psychotics at the onset of illness. One of these said, "I felt as though I hadn't a friend in the world."

CASE 33. KODZO B. of Ahafo district, Ashanti. M. *c.* 17.

Shrine

Mframa.

Reason for referral

"Caught" by madness for using bad *suman*.

Family History

Parents: Not cross-cousins. Father died eight years ago. Non-Christian, illiterate cocoa-farmer. Mother alive and well. Non-Christian, illiterate cocoa-farmer.

Siblings: Patient is second of five sons and three daughters. Elder brother, aged twenty, brought the patient. This brother has his own cocoa-village. All are unmarried, younger ones are children. None has been to school.

Personal History

Childhood: N.a.d. Parents lived together in husband's cocoa-village. At the age of fourteen the patient left home to live in his maternal uncle's cocoa-farm.

Present Illness (*from brother*)

About a year ago the patient bought a *suman* from a Kramu medicine-man. This *suman* was of a versatile kind, able to kill enemies and able to attract women to its owner. The patient thought he might someday put it to the former use, but did not, but he did seduce two girls, including a young pre-menarche virgin. About four months ago the patient came with his uncle to Mframa's shrine to ask for prosperity. On returning home he became frightened because Mframa's law prohibits *suman*, so he gave the *suman* to his elder brother who was not under Mframa's wing. This brother promised to destroy it, but left it in his room, whence it was stolen by another younger brother who used it to "tie up" an eminent man and seduce his wife.

About ten days ago the patient was taken with fever and pains in his head and belly. He thought Mframa had "caught" him and had frightening dreams in which an *obosom* rushed at him brandishing a weapon. He told his house-mates that he had caused his own sickness and rapidly became more terrified till he was "like a madman"—shouting, talking "*basa-basa*", and rushing away to bush. He was taken to a local *obosomfo* who said that only Mframa could release him, but he poured a libation to his own *obosom*, imploring it to arrange with Mframa not to kill the patient till he had had time to reach Mframaso and make full confession. Upon this the patient became quiet and set out with his elder brother for Mframaso. Both brothers appeared at the shrine and surrendered the *suman*, which was a small horse-hair switch with a length of twine attached—the latter for the ritual binding of a victim's spirit. The *obosom* said that the elder brother, as an accomplice, was also culpable and should be fined one sheep. The patient was fined a sheep and a cow.

Interview: 5.6.57

At the shrine the patient gave a laconic account of his wrong-doing. The elder brother acknowledged complicity when questioned. Interviewed later the patient appeared depressed, languid and completely unsmiling but did mental tests fairly well. Both brothers were well-developed, presentable youths.

17.6.57. The elder brother has gone home to fetch money for the cow and sheep. Patient is still miserable and apathetic.

23.6.57. Purification ritual completed but patient has not cheered up. He wanders vaguely about the town and moons around his landlord's house. He comes to see me when invited but sits abstractedly and doesn't talk. To-day he went to the *obosom* and said he had more to confess. He had used his bad *suman* to kill two people and was also a member of the witch company that had killed a member of his family. He himself ate the victim's foot.

30.6.57. Is not much brighter, although he says he has slept better since his last confession.

15.7.57. Deteriorating. When asked concerning the period before he ever drank Mframa and before he bought the *suman*, he said he had not felt like work for some months because something was spoiling his thoughts and making them *basa*. The poverty and vagueness of his responses make it impossible to get any clear information out of him.

20.7.57. His mother has come. She was not present when the trouble started, but says he has always been a silent, solitary person.

11.8.57. Went to the *obosom* to-day and said he was no better. Could give no details. When seen later he gave only empty replies.

6.9.57. He is still here with his mother. He is decidedly worse, sits around sluggishly, does not smile and seldom responds to greetings.

8.10.57. Getting more inert, unresponsive and silent.

COMMENTARY

This is an example of the common association between the secret use of bad *suman* and incipient schizophrenia. It also illustrates the finding that the potential schizophrenic is especially vulnerable to the acute fear-and-guilt psychosis.

CASE 34. ABENA B. of Berekum district, Ashanti. F. *c.* 30.

Shrine

Kyinaman at Bredi.

Reason for referral

Mental disturbance with self-accusations of witchcraft.

Family History

Parents: Illiterate, non-Christian cocoa-farmers. Not cross-cousins. Both died shortly after the patient reached puberty.

Siblings: Two brothers, one sister. All are illiterate. A brother is a petty trader but closes his store in the cocoa-season and becomes a cocoa-labourer on the *busa* system for an absentee farmer.

Personal History

Childhood: N.a.d. disclosed.

Schooling: Nil. Non-Christian but she often goes to church with a Christian uncle.

Marriage: Twice married. It was not disclosed why the first marriage ended. (Probably infertility.) The second marriage was two years ago. There is no other wife. Like the patient's brother, the husband is a part-time petty trader and a part-time *busa* cocoa-farmer.

Children: One son, aged about twelve, by first marriage. No other pregnancies.

Work: She helps her husband in both the store and the farm.

Previous Personality: Industrious and clever. Friendly and popular— "likes laughing and talking". Kindly. "She is always the first person to bring a stranger a drink." Relatives say that although she is fond of children she has never, until this illness, displayed any discontent at having only one herself, but has always been cheery and apparently happy.

Home: Patient lives with her maternal uncles, aunts, brother and aunt's children.

History of Present Illness:

About three weeks ago the patient's uncle came to Bredi and drank at the shrine for the prosperity and protection of himself and all his relatives. About a week after that the patient suddenly complained of pain in her head and chest. There was no cough, and no fever. She said she had committed many sins, had made up her mind to kill her brother, had a bad mind against her uncle and had spoilt her own womb. The *obosom*, she said, had now "caught" her to kill her.

She rapidly became *"basa-basa"*, mad, wild and dangerous to herself and others. She smashed things, attacked people and ran away to the bush—her relatives thought to commit suicide. Though talking mainly *"basa-basa"* she picked on people's physical defects, crooked legs, missing teeth, ugly noses and waddling gaits—and worked these into uninhibited wounding insults. The relatives said she never slept, but ate and drank.

First Interview: 20.6.57

When first seen she was manacled with her arms round the slender trunk of a shade-tree so that she could either stand, move round the tree or sit on a stool. She was clad only in *pietu* drawers. She was of boyish habitus (very unusual among African women), with long, slender limbs, slim hips and only rudimentary breasts.

She was shouting and yelling in delirium, interspersed with piercing shrieks. The content of her speech on this occasion was despairing but not self-reproachful; she was more inclined to blame others. She was almost entirely preoccupied with her infertility. When I approached she shouted out: "Oh European, how can I manage to bring forth? . . . Jesus, Jesus. . . . God, God. . . . The child is in my belly but it won't come out. . . . I have brought forth three, but people have thrown them away. . . . If they take these manacles off I shall conceive. . . . Oh Mother, Oh Mother, release me and I will bring forth immediately, and if I die in so doing I shan't mind. . . . I have finished with this world. It is better to die. . . . European doctor, do an operation and take the child out of me. Our Father which art in Heaven. . .", continuing the whole Lord's Prayer in Ashanti.

She was not wholly inaccessible and answered questions correctly, but in the next breath slipped back into her preoccupation with childbirth.

When asked her name and the name of her son she replied correctly, but when asked the name of her town said "Womfie near Berekum. When I was there I was barren but in this place I have conceived."

Q. "What is the name of this place?"
A. "I don't know, but I came here to bring forth. I have brought forth three here to-day."
Q. "Will you sit down and talk to me?"
A. "If I sit down it will spoil the child in my belly."
Q. "Have you done anything wrong?"
A. "No, no. It is my sisters who don't want me to conceive."
Q. "Do they dislike you because you have done wrong?"
A. "No, no. It is the people who prevent me from bringing forth."

Physically she was in good condition and not dehydrated, though very thin. She was co-operative towards me, showed me her tongue when asked and quietly let me percuss her chest.

23.6.57. Striking improvement. They said she became quiet immediately after going to the shrine. She is no longer in manacles, and is said to be working industriously, helping people with their farms, fetching water, cooking, etc. When seen she was sitting quietly, sharing a meal. She remembered me and jumped up, embracing me in effusive welcome. She was most exuberant, talkative, smiling and cheerful, but her mirth was not infectious and the affect not really warm. Her conversation was mostly perfectly rational and very pleasant, but still a little "*basa-basa*" here and there; e.g., she said she hoped I was looking after all her children now she was away from home.

When asked to do some mental tests she gave them close attention and did them excellently, revealing an exceptionally good intelligence. She was friendly towards everyone. She insisted on coming a part of the way home with me and carrying my oddments.

26.6.57. She has relapsed. I found her again in manacles, though not bound to a tree. She was quite accessible, quiet, friendly and able to converse pleasantly. She remembered my two earlier visits and all other recent events with no confusion. The affect was shallow: she was only casually resentful of the manacles, otherwise inappropriately cheerful and broadly smiling. She was quite rational on all topics except children, of which she said she had borne seven who all died.

The relatives said they had fettered her again because she had wandered away and got lost. Search-parties had been organised and she was found in a village about four miles away. I asked her why she went away. She replied that *mmoetia* (bush dwarfs or fairies in whom everyone firmly believes) came and offered her some money and told her to follow them. Asked whether she had ever seen them before, she said often lately. At first she was frightened, but when she found they were friendly she liked them. Asked what they were like, she said they were happy, they danced and sang and were all sizes from one foot to two and a half feet (indicating with her hand). They were a mixed company of men, women and children and wore funny little white hats.

The relatives were planning to take her home immediately because of her proneness to wander away and the trouble and expense of organising search-parties among strangers.

COMMENTARY

The chain of mental events appears to have been: slight normal guilt-feelings (bad mind against uncle remembered only when her uncle went to a shrine) → exaggerated guilt feelings → fear of retribution → precipitation of psychosis by fear → removal of fear leaving marked residuum of psychosis unrelated to the initial guilt. This is another example of the potential psychotic being more prone to disturbance by fear.

CASE 35. ADWOWA F. of Agogo district, Ashanti. F. *c*. 28.

Shrine

Mframa at Mframaso.

Reason for referral

Self-accusations of witchcraft.

Family History

Parents: Not cross-cousins. Illiterate, non-Christian cocoa-farmers. Father is dead. Mother has not remarried. Mother is very intelligent and capable and is reputed to be much sought after as a courtesan by chiefs and wealthy men.

Siblings: Ten born, eight alive. All grown-up and well. The youngest and only male is the young *okomfo* of a new *obosom*. For the past eighteen months he has been in training at Mframaso and his *obosom* was captured from the sky by a Mframaso expedition to his town a few months ago.

Personal History

Childhood: N.a.d.

Schooling: Nil. Non-Christian.

Marriage: Cross-cousin. Husband is a cocoa-farmer and sandal-maker. A meek, well-disposed little man, much attached to the patient. There is no other wife.

Children: Four born, all alive. Youngest suckling.

Present Illness

Four months ago at the time when the new *obosom* of the patient's *okomfo* brother was captured, the patient, together with various other spectators, became from time to time "possessed" and danced *akom*. I saw her on several of these occasions. She was not strenuously or conspicuously affected. She made no noise, danced with the minimum of movement, her baby on her back, and had the unmistakable, expressionless mask-like face of the dissociated *okomfo*. Between these possession fits, each of which lasted about an hour, she was quite normal except that she went to the shrine and complained that lactation was failing. The *obosom* said that this was due to *akom* dancing.

The patient returned home with her mother and brother. The new *obosom* was left in the Mframaso tabernacle pending the raising, by the patient's family, of the large sum of money still due to be paid to the Mframaso expedition which captured the new *obosom* and a further sum necessary to build and furnish a tabernacle in Agogo.

With the help of the patient's capable mother the patient's child was successfully put on bottle-feeding. The patient continued to be possessed from time to time in the traditional manner on appropriate occasions, and was quite normal between these.

Meanwhile the family was in much financial anxiety, trying to borrow money. The patient's husband contributed generously and also pledged his unharvested cocoa-crop. The patient no doubt felt some resentment towards her brother and his *obosom* because of the money poured out for them to the privation of everyone else.

It was then noticed that when the patient was possessed she frequently did not talk sense. For instance, she would pluck a bunch of leaves and give it to a male spectator, saying, "I see you are a barren woman. Take these herbs and you will conceive." Between possession fits she was quite normal.

A fortnight ago she stopped being possessed and cried a good deal, saying that she was a witch and had wanted to spoil the power of her brother's *obosom*. Her coven, she said, had given her medicine for this purpose and the *obosom* had now turned and "caught" her. She then grew worse, talked "*basa-basa*" and became mad. She tore off her clothes, slit them up with her teeth, fought, scratched and bit. She reviled everyone, said her mother was a witch and her husband a monkey. Towards her husband her greatest savagery was directed. Several times she ran wildly away to the bush. She also ate faeces and smeared her head and face.

She was then brought to Mframaso, but at the shrine was too wild to say anything. The *obosom*, however, said she would be pardoned if she brought two cows, one for himself and one for her brother's new *obosom*, both of whom she had offended.

All witnesses affirmed that at the onset of the illnesses she had had no influenza or other fever, and was physically well.

Interview: 20.10.57

The patient had already been taken to the shrine but was still in a state of furious catatonic excitement. She was stark naked, having torn off even her waist-beads. She was fighting, kicking, spitting, biting, and shouting, "I shall die and you will eat me and eat my children. . . . You are all fools and witches and prostitutes. . . ." It took half a dozen strong men to put her into knickers and bind her wrists and ankles. Her husband was sitting aside weeping.

22.10.57. No longer aggressive and she has been released from her bonds. She was dancing—though it was not a dancing occasion—up and down the street, posturing, grimacing and singing, with a typically schizophrenic, broad empty smile with laughing and giggling. This continued for almost two days and was quite different from a possession dance in which the dancer has always an expressionless mask-like face, and is possessed only for an hour or two.

25.10.47. She is clothed and quite rational, but is languid and apathetic.

27.10.57. The improvement has been maintained. She is quite well and smiling and will go home tomorrow. Now that all has ended well the family have become pleased that the new *obosom* has given this public demonstration of its power, for this will attract new clients.

4.11.57. She did not go home but was left behind by her family to finish a course of ritual baths. She is quite well, travels to Wenchi market, works quite hard and tends her child. A small degree of lactation has returned.

22.12.57. She went home quite well a few days after the last note. News has come that she has now relapsed and is very mad indeed.
20.2.58. Latest news is that she is still mad.

COMMENTARY

The sequence of mental events appears to have been: resentment towards the new *obosom* with appropriate guilt feelings → fear of the *obosom's* disapproval → transient schizophreniform fear-psychosis, clearing up with removal of fear → interval of good mental health followed by unprovoked onset of chronic schizophrenia.

This appears to be another example of the common finding that the potential schizophrenic is especially prone to the acute transient guilt-and-fear psychosis.

In regard to the *akom* dancing (fits of dissociated personality) I do not think there is any direct connection between this and the schizophrenia. In a population where the schizophrenia rate is very high, and where large numbers of ordinary people have the aptitude for occasional dissociation, it is inevitable that a few people should fall into both classes. The schizophrenia rate among *akomfo* is probably the same as that among the general population.

CASE 36. KWABENA T. of Bekwai district, Ashanti. M. *c.* 20.

Preface

I did not see this patient as he stayed in the *obosom's* town just under a week and was gone when I next went. However, I saw the people in whose house he stayed and various other good witnesses, while his behaviour was still fresh in their minds. As his case clearly falls into a familiar group I think it worth recording at second-hand.

Shrine

Kotokro, at Nkyiraa.

Reason for referral

"Madness", caused by using bad *suman* against others.

Family and Personal History

No information.

Present Illness

The patient went to a medicine-man named Badu and bought a medicine to bury in his farm to draw the goodness out of his neighbours' crops into his own. He asked the same practitioner for a medicine to enable him to see any evil thing that threatened him and was given a potion to drink made of a goat's tongue. He drank it, felt ill and came home vomiting. He thought he was "caught", became frightened and confessed to having bought three other *suman*, one to make him strong and vigorous, and two to make other people mad. These two latter, one of which contained human blood, were directed against a man who had threatened to make the patient mad.

The patient complained of a severe headache, became much agitated, talked "*basa-basa*" and then became raving mad. He shouted continuously, assaulted everyone including his mother, smashed up the house and ran away to the bush. When pursued he stoned his pursuers. He was captured, brought back and bound. He was then brought, bound hand and foot, to Nkyiraa, together with such *suman* as his family found on searching his room. At the shrine he was told that he would be pardoned for using bad *suman*, whereupon he became quieter but not quite sane for several days and not before he had made other confessions. He had stolen three loads of cocoa, he had resolved to kill his uncle for borrowing and not repaying £5 and had vowed he would kill a girl-friend who had cheated him out of £3. Asked whether he had practised witchcraft he said he had two *obayi*, one in his blanket and one in his cover-cloth, and with them he had caused a pregnant woman-relative to miscarry. He had resolved to kill his mother and two other women. The witchcraft confessions, unlike the others, were not spontaneous.

COMMENTARY

Fear reaction engendered by guilt in a youth much addicted to secret antisocial sorcery. This kind of behaviour often characterises the potential schizophrenic—who also seems more vulnerable to acute transient fear-reactions. I should not be surprised to see this patient again.

CASE 37. EKWIA T. of Nkyiraa, Ashanti. F. c. 20.

Shrine
  Kotokro, Nkyiraa.

Reason for referral
  Self-accusations of witchcraft.

Family History
  Parents: Not cross-cousins. Illiterate, non-Christian, cocoa-farmers. The mother died when the patient was suckling.
  Siblings: Three. All well. Farmers.

Personal History

Childhood: Brought up in Nkyiraa by her mother's sister in the maternal grandfather's house where she still lives. The father lives eight miles away.

Schooling: Nil. Non-Christian.

Marriage: She is married to her cross-cousin who is an illiterate, non-Christian carpenter about her own age. A confident, debonair type, he treats the patient in an offhand, facetious, rather bullying, contemptuous fashion. She appears to be the butt of both him and his workmates and resents their derision. The fact that she was sleeping with her mother and not with her husband when first taken ill suggests that he consorts with other women. It was not officially acknowledged that he was about to take an additional wife, but carpenters make good money and he may well be about to do so. Relatives all admit that the patient and her husband often quarrel.

Children: First child died aged one week, about a year ago. Patient is now in the second half of her second pregnancy.

Household: The patient lives in her grandfather's house with his sons, daughters, nephews, nieces and the women's children and grandchildren, all illiterate and non-Christian. The grandfather is both a cocoa-farmer and a weaver, wealthy, intelligent and respected. He still farms, though he can no longer see to do the fine weaving. The husband lives elsewhere with other relatives.

Previous Personality: Everyone agrees that she was shy, retiring and "didn't like talking".

Present Illness

Sudden onset six days ago. No prodromal fever, headache or malaise. She was sleeping with her "mother" in her grandfather's house when she suddenly woke her companion and said she was "caught" for having a bad mind against her husband and his brother, planning to kill him by witchcraft and for killing her child. She then talked "*basa-basa*" and stretched out her limbs and became rigid, mute and resistive. From then till the day of going to the shrine attacks of stiffness and almost mute "*basa-basa*" agitation occurred about three times daily. Between them she was normal except for being miserable, languid and monosyllabic. Sleep was normal and undisturbed.

First Interview: 11.2.57

First seen at the shrine, where she was mute, stiff, resistive yet clearly agitated. Though unable to speak, she assented to her relatives' statements of the confessions made at home. These were that she was a witch, had killed her own infant, had planned to abort by witchcraft her present pregnancy in the seventh month and had planned to spoil her husband's work and that of a bricklayer colleague. Her *obayi* abode in her waist-beads and handbag. (These objects were surrendered at the shrine for detoxication.)

She was ceremonially purified and was then pushed and pulled to her husband's room where I interviewed her. She was lying down, almost but not quite mute, retarded, yet agitated and resistive. Her limbs were stiff and she slowly moved them into awkward positions. Her eyes were wide and frightened with dilated pupils. She was not inaccessible but was too anxious to pay any attention. When firmly pressed she sat up and with difficulty and wringing her hands answered correctly and in a whisper a few questions such as, "What is your name?" The only thing she said spontaneously while I was there was, "I must have my bath in the *obosom's* medicine", a calabash-full of which lotion had in fact been brought.

I was able to stay only a few hours and during that time her "caught" state did not change, though the relatives said it came and went and they were expecting a remission at any moment.

13.2.57. She was lying quietly relaxed, not stiff or apprehensive. Depressed and retarded, speaking slowly in a whisper. When asked questions on money-arithmetic, etc., she answered correctly but reluctantly. My impression was of good intelligence. She was in her husband's house in his room, which is unusual with a mother and maternal grandfather near. The husband may have insisted on keeping her under his eye as it was against him that she had had "a bad mind". He and his young colleagues were hanging around making goading cracks.

17.2.57. She is now in her grandfather's house. Acute attacks have ceased. She sits apart looking miserable. She is reluctant to speak but her withdrawal now seems wilful. Her eyes are aware and a little resentful. When asked questions, she said she could not answer them because she was sick. Later on the same day she went again to the shrine, saying that she had additional confessions to make. She said she had often wanted to divorce her husband because she disliked him, but had also determined to cause him, by witchcraft, to fall off a high roof.

24.2.57. Grandfather said she was quite well and had gone to the farm.

21.4.57. Since the last note I have seen her several times in her grandfather's house, always sulky and monosyllabic, on one occasion sitting alone speaking to no one, having just had a quarrel with one of the other women in the house. To-day (I had not been to Nkyiraa for a fortnight) they said she delivered a (?) premature child a fortnight ago but it died after one week. Surprisingly, she seemed more serene and less depressed than I have ever seen her, and evinced no inclination to blame herself. So far as I could gather there was no suspicion of witchcraft concerning the child. The patient had been purified by the *obosom* and the child's

death was "*osani*" (natural). Her general bearing, attitude to others and theirs to her give me now little doubt that she is a schizophrene.
12.5.57. She has gone to the Northern Territories with her husband, who has a carpentry contract there.

COMMENTARY

Reactive depression with guilt and consequent fear-reaction during pregnancy in an unhappily married young woman of schizoid personality. An example of a schizoid personality drifting into marriage with her cross-cousin, who despises her. This differs from the usual run of witchcraft cases in that her first guilt-feelings grew out of a genuine ill-will towards her alleged victim.

§ 4. FEAR-PSYCHOSIS WITH HYSTERICAL FEATURES

There are only two patients to place in this group. Though they were both hysterical personalities, they were undoubtedly impelled into their behaviour by fear rather than the common hysterical motives.

CASE 38. ABENA M. of Offuman. F. *c.* 14.

Shrine
Kumaninitwie, Offuman.

Reason for referral
"Caught" by the *obosom*.

Family and Personal History
No information except that the patient is a relative of the youth who is the *obosomfo* of a recently established new *obosom*, Kumaninitwie.

Present Illness
One evening the patient and some women were eating their supper when the women made some disparaging remarks about the new boy-*obosomfo*. The girl then said, "If his *obosom* has any power, let it show what it can do." They all then went to bed, the girl sharing a room with several younger children. About midnight the children ran out saying that Abena was dying and had been talking "*basa-basa*". The parents found her naked, "mad", stiff and staring, unable to recognise anyone, see, hear or speak. An uncle "smoked" her with medicated smoke without effect. They then hired a lorry and rushed her in the night to Amoma, a village with a Kramu medicine-man. He told them that she had insulted an *obosom* and was "caught". They then carried her to the

228

new shrine where the *obosom* said he had indeed caught her and was about to kill her. They implored his forgiveness, which he granted in return for a sacrificial sheep. The patient became immediately well.

Interview: 14.10.56

I did not see the patient till several days after the episode. Her uncle (an ex-soldier) was the informant. He was a good witness, but suddenly became suspicious when I began to ask family history, said he was busy and made off without taking me to visit the home.

The girl was a loutish, loud, loose-mouthed, unintelligent type and seemed to have thrown off her illness without any embarrassment.

COMMENTARY

Fear reaction in a hysterical personality.

CASE 39. ADWOWA M. of Wenchi district. F. *c.* 25.

Shrine

Mframaso.

Reason for referral

Disturbed behaviour with self-accusation of witchcraft.

Family History

Parents: Marriage not cross-cousin. Father native of Wenchi. Illiterate non-Christian, petty store-keeper. When he died, patient's mother married a literate stranger (Trans-Volta Ewe) working in Wenchi.

Siblings: The patient is the elder of two daughters of mother's first marriage. There were no children by second marriage.

Personal History

Childhood home: The house in Wenchi town belonged to the mother's uncle and contained the mother's sister and many other maternal relatives. There was no change of household on the mother's second marriage.

Schooling: Nil. Non-Christian.

Work: Food farmer.

Marriage. Not cross-cousin. Husband is an illiterate non-Christian, a native of a small country-town near Wenchi, but lives mostly in his farming "village" some miles away. The marriage was satisfactory till the husband was given a cross-cousin as second wife. Quarrels between the two wives are frequent: the patient is always the aggressor.

Children: The first pregnancy miscarried. Two subsequent children are aged three and one-and-a-half—the younger still suckling.

Household: The husband's cocoa-"village" contains patient's husband and elder brother, the latter's wife and three children, patient and her two children, and patient's new co-wife who as yet has no children. There are no neighbours. The contrast with the Wenchi urban household must be considerable.

Present Illness

The onset was sudden, about six weeks ago at night. The husband was sleeping with the other wife and heard the patient shouting, "Thieves, Thieves!" He came and found the patient pointing to the ceiling, saying, "See there, a thief in a small loin-cloth holding a small stick!" The next morning the patient became "mad", ran away to the bush, was chased and brought back talking "*basa-basa*". She said there were insects inside her head and that she had pains in her chest. She was not breathless or ill, but her eyes were bloodshot. Then she complained of stomach-ache and vomited. Every night she was disturbed and frightened, and said she saw lights and was a witch. She also said she saw the *obosom* Mframa who had come to "catch" her. She said she saw two dogs which did not, however, chase her but came and slept by her side (dogs are Mframa's taboo and are not allowed in Mframaso). In the daytime she was restless, walked about and several times again ran to bush, always allowing herself to be caught and brought back. Vomiting continued till the day she came to Mframaso, when it stopped abruptly.

First Interview: 25.2.57

At the shrine she was unabashed and talked fluently without signs of depression, smiling persuasively as she begged the *obosom* not to kill her. Onlookers commented that she did not look "caught". She confessed that she had cursed her husband to the deity of a stream because he left off sleeping with her, and that because he gave her only a meagre share of his last catch of bush-meat she had maliciously "sat upon" his iron trap (i.e., had ceremonially polluted it by contact with her perineal cloth) so that it would catch no more meat. These were concrete and deliberate deeds, not fantasies.

Asked if she were guilty of witchcraft, said, "Yes" perfunctorily and without the conviction of the depressive true witch. Her *obayi*, she said, came from the sky, she had killed five people, had often washed her child with witch-medicine, had cooked the faeces of her sister's child and set it before her husband, though he didn't eat it, and that her witch coven had planned to spoil the power of an old *obosom* at Wenchi and kill its priest. At interview later she was not in the least depressed and seemed in excellent health and good spirits. She said she had felt ill mostly at night (presumably when her husband was with the other wife), and did not remember the bush-running incidents. When she came to Mframaso, she said, her "head was turning" and her chest painful, but she felt better the moment she entered the *obosom's* yard. At mental tests she was unusually quick and her general knowledge well above that of an average illiterate.

27.11.57. Now says she sleeps well and has quite recovered. Looks very well.

6.12.57. Went home quite well.

COMMENTARY

This is an aggressive, not a depressive type of woman who became afraid of the effects of her acts of aggression. The running to bush was possibly an hysterical dissociation. The vomiting and pains were almost certainly hysterical demonstrations. The witnesses, however, are certain that she became "*basa-basa*" and hallucinated.

§ 5. FEAR-PSYCHOSIS PRECIPITATED BY FEBRILE OR TOXIC ILLNESS

Though febrile illnesses such as pneumonia and malaria are common and hundreds of people succumbed to influenza during 1957, the fear-psychosis is never simple delirium. Guilt is the operative factor, and reassurance at the shrine promptly quells the disturbance though the fever remains unabated.

The first of the following group of nine cases is that of a youth whose febrile fear-psychosis was aborted by confession at the shrine within an hour of its onset. The others (all save one) ran longer and more severe courses. The last case must be regarded as toxic, though the toxin was only a little alcohol.

CASE 40. KOFI P. of Kumasi family, living in Mframaso. M. *c.* 25.

Shrine

Mframa, Mframaso.

Reason for referral

"Caught" by the obosom for theft.

Family History

Parents: Not cross-cousins. Both are alive, well and cheerful, though the father is almost blind. They came from Kumasi district to grow cocoa in north-west Ashanti and there became friends of the Mframa priest who was their neighbour, also growing cocoa, before he became a priest. When he set up the Mframa shrine they came at his invitation to make a household to receive pilgrim-lodgers. The father is one of the *obosom's* elders.

Siblings: Three brothers, four sisters.

Personal History

Childhood: N.a.d.

Schooling: Nil. Non-Christian.

Work: He is assistant *obrafohene* to the *obosom* and does most of the work of the shrine, including ritual bathing and any auxiliary herbal treatment prescribed by the *obosom*. Because he has a clear ringing shout he is the gong-gong beater or town-crier who makes public announcements.

Marriage: Very happy. He has one wife only: intelligent, gentle, sunny-tempered.

Children: Four. No deaths.

Household: Patient, wife and children, and always some pilgrim-lodgers.

Previous Personality: An exceedingly pleasant, brisk and merry fellow. He is the only one of the *sinkwafo* who carries out his duties conscientiously and cheerfully and is popular with the patients.

Present Illness

Sudden onset. His wife sent for me about five o'clock in the evening saying that Kofi had just come back from his farm talking *"basa-basa"* and was dying. I found him a few minutes later sitting on his sleeping-mat, which was spread in the middle of the courtyard, wolfing a bowl of food and seeming to be eating quite automatically without any attention to the action. He was completely inaccessible, staring with protruding eyes, looking both hallucinated and terrified. Suddenly he dropped the bowl and flung himself flat, howling in terror, "They are coming, they are coming!" His wife said he had been hot and cold and shivering in the morning but had done his shrine duties and in the afternoon had gone to his farm. He returned gibbering with fright and saying that people were after him with clubs and cutlasses. His temperature was 102°, he was sweating and his heart was pounding. I went to fetch him some quinine and returned in a few minutes to find that he had been taken to the *obosom's* evening session. When I reached the shrine a minute or two later he was standing answering the *obosom's* questions and giving a clear-headed account of himself. He said that two days previously when sweeping the *obosom's* yard, he had picked up a small gold trinket and instead of handing it in had kept it. For this the *obosom* had sent people to kill him. He said he was returning from his farm when he saw a red man holding a basin of "*to*" (a food made of yam and sheep's blood) and a black man who tried to make him eat the food and die. He refused to accept it, struggled with the man and was knocked down.

The *obosom* said he would be forgiven of his sin and immediately purified. The *obrafohene* took one of the *obosom's nkotoba* clubs and stroked his body with it and then gave him a long sharp sword and told him to dance a sword-dance to the drums, which he vigorously did. He was then dismissed. I followed him home. His terror had dramatically vanished, he was perfectly restored and composed, and though shivering with fever was without any suggestion of "light-headedness". The next day, after some quinine, he was practically well and had had no more mental disturbance.

COMMENTARY

This man had had malaria many times—I myself had often given him quinine for it—but he had never before, in either his parents' or his wife's experience, been "*basa-basa*". The malaise of the malaria had probably made him feel that the *obosom* had stricken him bodily, and the fever, though not primarily involved, had whipped up his anxiety and fear of retribution for sin. The fortuitous opportunity, within an hour of onset, of prompt confession and purification, probably aborted an attack of that acute excitement so often seen as a schizophreniform fear-reaction.

CASE 41. KWASI B. of Techiman district, Ashanti. M. *c.* 35.

Shrine

Dimankoma, Akrofrom.

Reason for referral

Self-accusations of witchcraft.

Family History

Parents: Illiterate, non-Christian cocoa-farmers. The father is dead; the mother is alive and well, a pleasant, good personality.

Siblings: The patient is one of ten. One died, and the rest are all grown-up. The youngest has seven children.

Personal History

In early childhood the patient was with his parents, all being in the same compound. At the age of about six he was adopted by his maternal uncle and lived with him in his "village" six miles away. He lived with that uncle till the uncle's death, when he succeeded to the house and farm in the "village".

Marriage: He left his wife one and a half years ago because she was a witch "caught" by the *obosom*. (See Yaa A., Case No. 18.) He has not succeeded in getting another wife.

Children: Nil, though the wife was pregnant twice.

Work: Farmer, chiefly of food-stuffs, but he has a few young cocoa-trees.

Home: He lives entirely alone, doing his own cooking. In the "village" he sees only the people who go to buy food-stuffs.

Previous Personality: He is one of the *obosom's* drummers at Akrofrom. He walks six miles each way, twice weekly, to drum. He is strong and hard-working, but an unprepossessing, socially awkward personality, and knows this.

Present Illness

The onset was sudden, about two weeks ago, with severe febrile illness and delirium for which he was taken to Techiman Hospital where a diagnosis of a meningococcal type of meningitis was made. He recovered rapidly with heavy doses of antibiotics but insisted on leaving, in a semi-confused state, before full recovery.*

He came out of hospital to his mother's house in her home-town and a few days later said he had been "caught" by the *obosom* (whose medicine he drank six years ago) for buying bad *suman* and for being a witch.

A messenger was sent to his village to bring the *suman* from the place where he had hidden it and it was brought to the *obosom*. Three *suman* were brought. Two he said he had bought from an Angwula man to protect himself from harm, but it was only after his illness that he realised they had turned him into an *obayifo*, for which sin the *obosom* had "caught" him and made him ill. One of these two *suman* consisted of a string of beads and various small oddments in a round pot, the other of a small calabash containing stones and cola-nuts. The third *suman* was a cigarette-tin containing some scented ointment in which was stuck a penicillin-bottle containing powdered leaf, and what looked like a small phallic object. The function of this third *suman* was to make him attractive to women so that they would come and sleep with him, adulterously if necessary.

Interview: 25.8.56

He has an unusual and very odd face, the longest and narrowest I have ever seen anywhere, pointed at both vertex and chin, giving it a

---

* I am indebted to the Medical Officer of the Roman Catholic Hospital, Techiman, to whom I wrote, for this information.

spindle shape. He is languid after his illness; very gloomy, apathetic and unhappy. Asked whether he was lonely in his "village", he said it was right to succeed his uncle there, so how could he dislike it? He seemed probably the type of butt whose advances women merely ridicule.

2.9.56. Not seen. They said he had recovered and had gone back to his "village".

14.9.56. They said he would not return to Akrofrom till after the cocoa-harvest.

30.1.57. He is still in his "village". When I enquire after him they say he is well, but always laugh at the mention of his name as if he were a general butt.

COMMENTARY

Post-infective depression with guilt-feelings in a schizoid and brooding personality.

CASE 42. FRANCIS KWAME B. of Wenchi district, Ashanti. M. *c.* 25.

Shrine
   Mframa at Mframaso.

Reason for referral
   "Madness."

Family History
   Parents: Not cross-cousins. Illiterate, non-Christian cocoa-farmers. The mother was widowed and married again while her children were small. The second husband had another wife beside the patient's mother. This wife has seven children.
   Siblings: Three born, two survived. Ama J. (Case No. 65) is the other survivor.

Personal History
   Childhood: N.a.d. disclosed.
   Schooling: Nil, but he is a Christian.
   Work: He served two years' apprenticeship to a goldsmith. For the past three years he has been working for himself and shares a workshop with four other goldsmiths each of whom has his own bench and tools.
   Marriage: He is happily married to a young woman who farms and trades. There are two children.
   Home: (Seen.) This is the stepfather's house and contains the patient's wife and children and the step-father's wife and children and some

grandchildren. The step-father is a resentful asthmatic, seen in considerable respiratory distress, and anxious to know who sent him his misfortune. The patient's mother and sister were absent at their "village".

Present Illness

The onset was one month ago. Shortly before that a man had come from the Northern Territories selling medicines to bring prosperity. The patient bought one to prosper his trade. It included a potion to drink and a *suman* to put under his pillow. One night he looked at the *suman* and thought it was shining in the dark. Then he thought it was turning him into an *obayifo* and making him "get up at night" (i.e., fly away to witch assemblies). After a few nights of anxiety and sleeplessness he heard the voice of the family *obosom* say that it had seen him "get up" and that he must throw the *suman* into the latrine. (This is the recognised method of destroying the power of any *suman*, good or bad.) This he did, but the part of the medicine that he had drunk continued to disturb his belly. He did not tell his family about the medicine, only about trouble in his belly, so they sent him to hospital where he was admitted with a diagnosis of malaria and delirium. The doctor was not told the content of his ravings, which was that he was "caught" for making a bad medicine. Whenever the doctor was off duty, his fear and raving increased and the charge-nurse, with the help of a watchman, bound his hands to the bedstead. (The charge-nurse* confirmed this in a private interview after the doctor had left the country.) His family considered that the bad medicine had made him mad, so they took him from hospital. He became quite sleepless, violent and more mad, so they took him to the *obosom*.

At the shrine, though much agitated, he was able to assent to the statement made by his family to the *obosom*, that the bad *suman* had made him into an *obayifo* and that the power of the potion he had drunk remained in his belly. The *obosom* said this was true, but added that, though an *obayifo*, he had never killed anyone. The patient said he had made a young relative sick with a view to killing him. The *obosom* consented to remove the evil and restore the patient.

First Interview

Immediately after this reassurance the patient became calmer. At interview, shortly after, he had by no means settled down. He was tremulous with a fumbling handshake, and had a wide-eyed restive stare showing a margin of sclerotic beneath the iris. He was smiling and over-talkative, could give no clear account of himself and eluded the point of questions. He was taken to his own town immediately after interview.

* The charge-nurse, a fully-trained, competent S.R.N., subscribed to the view that bad magic was the cause of the illness.

Progress

During the next few weeks he came twice to the shrine, but arrived only in time for evening *abisa* and left immediately afterwards, so that I had no chance of talking to him till I sought out his home. I went first to the goldsmiths' workshop. The other goldsmiths said he had not been to work since his illness. They told me where he lived and I found him.

He looked physically well, but though it was mid-morning he was sitting around doing nothing and had a smiling shallow affect. Asked what work he had done since his illness he said he had done some farm-work and made ear-rings and other trinkets. (The former may have been true but the latter was not.) It seemed to me touch-and-go that the *suman* heralded (as often happens) the onset of a schizophrenic attack.

He remained off work for about five months but went to the farm and gradually improved. He has now gone back to the goldsmiths' shop and is doing some intricate work requiring great skill and close attention, but though he is always cheerful I think his affect is shallow. He regards himself as having been mad, for on one of my visits to his home he said, "There is another man like me not far from here. I will take you to see him if you like." He took me to see a florid schizophrenic, shackled to a log.

COMMENTARY

As in other similar cases, it is likely that the fever only whipped up the fear into an acute psychosis; he must have had countless attacks of malaria—though without guilt—in his life before.

CASE 43. YAW P. of Nkoranza district, Ashanti. M. *c.* 20.

Shrine

Kokoro, at Nkyiraa.

Reason for referral

Self-accusations of witchcraft.

Family History

No information. Father and maternal uncle brought him to the shrine. They were well-disposed, sensible people. Illiterate farmers.

Present Illness

Onset was sudden, about a week ago, with a cough, pain in the ribs, sleeplessness and *"basa-basa"* (i.e., delirious) talk. He said the *obosom* had "caught" him.

Interview

At the shrine he said his *abayi's* names were Atufaa and Gyene. He said he had decided to kill his father because the latter wanted him to learn carpentry and refused to buy him any new clothes. He said he had decided to kill his sister because she refused to marry a man whom he liked, and his uncle "because he is always against me without reason".

Later I saw him in his lodgings in the town. He had lobar pneumonia.

Progress

As the purification ritual at Nkyiraa is completed on the day of confession the patient was permitted, on the day after, to accept additional remedies. I sent a messenger with sulpha-drugs and instructions, and when I went to Nkyiraa a week later the patient had made a good recovery and gone home.

Commentary

This case differs from the general run of febrile fear-psychoses in that the patient accused himself of witchcraft. The witchcraft "confessions", however, are not typical of those of a classically depressed witch, in that the patient expressed genuine and comprehensible resentments and gave good reasons for them, whereas the common witch feels primary guilt, no animosity and can give no reason except her own wickedness for her self-declared misdeeds.

CASE 44. AKOSUA F. of Kumasi district. F. *c.* 30.

Shrine

Kyinaman at Bredi.

Reason for referral

"Caught" for using bad medicines.

Family History

Parents: Not cross-cousins. Illiterate, non-Christian cocoa-farmers. The father is dead. The mother (seen) is a pleasant, sensible woman.

Siblings: Five born, two died. Non-Christian, illiterate cocoa-farmers

Personal History

Childhood: N.a.d. No schooling, non-Christian.

Work: Gathers wrapping-leaves in the bush and sells them in the market.

Marriage: Her husband is literate. He is an agricultural officer. He has no other wife as yet, but the patient is apprehensive.

Children: Six born, three died. The eldest is about twelve and the youngest eighteen months.

Home: Her husband lives in Kumasi, where he works. The patient lives in a cocoa-village with her mother and mother's kinsfolk.

Present Illness

Onset two weeks ago. The whole household had influenza, but the patient was worse than the others, with pains in her head and all over her, fever and vomiting. She said she was "caught" by the *obosom* for wrong-doing. She became quite sleepless, walked about all night talking *"basa-basa"* and took no food for six days. She wept and cried, laughed inappropriately, was violent and attacked people and tried to rush away to the bush. At one period she echoed in a loud chant everything other people said. She was brought to the shrine where she at once became quiet, though not able on that day to give an account of herself. She took some food and that night she slept quietly and deeply and awoke quite composed and sensible.

Interview: 31.10.57

Seen the day after arrival. She was asleep but woke while her mother was giving her history. She seemed physically well, was clear-headed, not depressed but rather over-talkative. She said she remembered nothing of her illness, that her eyes "were darkened" and she did not know how she got to Bredi. She said that three or four months ago she went to a Kramu medicine-man and had him make a medicine to prevent her husband from taking another wife. She also bought a binding medicine and "tied up" her brother because he didn't respect her and failed to keep a promise to her. (He is a palm-wine tapper and lives in the same house with her.) Recently she missed some money, so she cursed the thief to God. When she fell ill and was worse than the other influenza patients, she knew that she was "caught" and that the *obosom* was about to kill her for her sin.

5.11.57. More miserable, anxious and talkative. She says she is a witch. She has sent a messenger to fetch another *suman* which she bought and now thinks contains as *obayi*. She says she has eaten four people. No hallucinations, thought-disorder or other schizophrenic stigmata. She says she thinks she will get better.

13.11.57. Much better, cheerful and sensible, though physically under par, pale and thin.

COMMENTARY

Transient psychotic reaction to fear, with echolalia, in an aggressive personality. Precipitation by febrile illness.

CASE 45. AKOSUA D. of Kwahu district. F. 25–30.

Shrine
Mframa at Mframaso.

Reason for referral
Adultery and self-accusations of witchcraft.

Family History
Parents are both dead. Illiterate, non-Christian farmers. The patient feels that her *obayi* was given to her by her mother, but disclosed no concrete facts about her.

Personal History
Childhood: Lived with her mother and her relatives; her father was elsewhere. She stayed in this compound with her siblings and their children till marriage. Patient is one of a pair of twins.

Schooling: Nil. Non-Christian.

Work: She has a sewing-machine and sells the garments she makes. She is industrious and makes money.

Marriage: Husband has a beer-shop in a town other than the patient's home-town, which she left to marry him.

Children: Two born. Elder died, aged five, about two and a half years ago. Younger is about six months.

Previous Illness: About three years ago she had a mental illness similar to the present one. She had drunk of Mframa's medicine and broke one of Mframa's taboos—a trivial one about eating onions—and "the medicine caught her". She became "*basa-basa*" and shouting. She was brought to Mframaso and recovered within a week. No witchcraft was invoked on that occasion.

Present Illness
About six days ago the patient confessed to her husband that she had committed adultery with four other men and said the *obosom* had "caught" her and given her pains all over. She became more and more agitated and then said she was a witch and had killed her first child. The adultery was confirmed as a fact and the husband brought her to Mframa to thank the *obosom* (with an offering of a sheep) for having "caught" her.

They arrived in the evening (24.5.56). No one in her lodgings had any sleep that night because she went round rousing, shaking and slapping people to tell them she was a witch and had killed her own child, and that if her husband left her it was no blame to him.

In the morning she was hoarse after the night's shouting. She was inaccessible, manneristic, posturing, grimacing, laughing, interfering, and said nothing about witchcraft. She would not eat the food offered to her but went round snatching from other people's dishes. During her poking round the house she found a pot of white clay and smeared herself all over with it. (This is a symbol of innocence.) Physically she was well nourished and looked healthy.

Later at the shrine, whither her husband took her, her manner was different. She appeared to appreciate her situation and looked anxious and frightened. Her husband raised only the matter of adultery and thanked the *obosom* for "catching his enemy", but the patient when questioned admitted the adultery and brought up also the matter of witchcraft. She was incoherent but relevant and kept repeating that she had done wrong and was "caught" for it, was a witch and had killed her child and many other people. The *obosom* said she must go and make a full confession to his clerk, who would write it down and read it out at the shrine.

To the clerk she was accessible enough to make the usual stereotyped confessions—a snake in her belly, feasting on human blood with her witch-companions, etc.; she could be heard whimpering.

In the afternoon she had become less disturbed and was sitting feeding her child, but babbling about witches. When I appeared she asked me if I too was a witch and whether I was friendly with *mmoetia* dwarfs. She laughed and chattered, but the laughter was not warm or contagious.

In the evening she was brought again to the shrine, with her cow, for ritual purification, and there exhibited a picture which none would have hesitated to designate schizophrenic—grimacing, posturing, smiling inappropriately, and walking round interfering, quite inaccessible. Yet when her relative was pleading on her behalf she too knelt in supplication, and as soon as the drumming started for her ritual purification dance, she danced whole-heartedly, snatching off her shawl, flinging it about and careering wildly round the yard. When the drumming stopped she went meekly to the *obrafohene's* pot, knelt appropriately and bowed her head to receive the broken egg. She laughed all the time her head was being shaved.

19.5.56. She is still rather trying to her house-mates but is able to do cooking and normal jobs.

6.6.56. She made a final appearance at the shrine after daily ritual baths for a week. She is now composed, perfectly behaved and shyly rendered her thanks for her deliverance.

Later, interviewed in her own lodgings, she was perfectly normal. When asked how much she remembered of the episode, she said, "It seems to me as if I have been dreaming." Asked whether she ever heard voices reproaching or frightening her, she said No, but all her dreams had been frightening—e.g., she dreamt that four people lifted her up by her four limbs over a big fire to throw her in.

She went home quite well.

COMMENTARY

Acute transient guilt and fear-psychosis in a woman who had had a previous episode on more trivial provocation.

I include this case among the febrile illnesses on the rather slender evidence of "pains all over". The history of the patient's earlier illness, however, makes it equally likely that she is predisposed to psychotic excitement by virtue of being a potential schizophrenic.

CASE 46. AFUA P. of Asamankese district, Akim. F. *c.* 35.

Shrine
Mframa.

Reason for referral
"Caught" by *obosom* for cursing husband.

Family History
   Father: Farmer. Non-Christian. Illiterate.
   Mother: Marriage not cross-cousin. Still al'v and well. Good personality. (Came with patient.)
   Siblings: Six born. Patient only survivor.

Personal History
   Childhood: N.a.d. Household same as now.
   Schooling: Nil. Non-Christian.
   Worker: Farmer and trader.
   Marriage. Husband non-Christian, illiterate lorry-driver. Not cross-cousin. No other wife. He does not own the lorry. He is always borrowing money from the patient and seldom repays. Recently there was a quarrel because the husband refused to repay £5 which he had persuaded her to borrow for him from her mother's brother's son. Patient then cursed him to God with consequent feelings of guilt.
   Home: Patient lives in her mother's brother's house, together with mother, mother's brothers and sisters, and the latter's children, some of whom go to school.
   Children. Seven born, two died. Eldest survivor fourteen, youngest one month.

Present Illness

When the last child was born a month ago, patient had a retained placenta and, in danger of death, was taken by her mother's people to hospital where it was successfully removed. She was in hospital a fortnight, during which time she talked "*basa-basa*" and also told the African nurse that the *obosom* had, by this illness, "caught" her for cursing her husband. The nurse did not tell the doctor, who, presumably, observed only delirium. When the patient came out of hospital she was restless and sleepless and confessed to having cursed her husband, whereupon she was brought to Mframaso.

First Interview: 6.1.57

At the shrine she made a brisk and fluent confession. Asked if she was also a witch, she said perfunctorily, "Yes", and was told to go away and get some scholar to take down her witchcraft confessions. A schoolboy relative did this. A very long list of items, all of the stereotyped kind, was read at the next session, after which she was cleansed. At private interview she looked thin and pale but composed and not in the least depressed. She seemed a good personality and told her story with straightforward matter-of-factness. She said she had been extremely frightened when she nearly died, knowing that she had indeed done wrong. Concerning the witchcraft, she said casually that she had not known she was a witch till she went to the shrine. She appeared happily absorbed in her child, her serenity completely restored.

14.1.57. After a course of ritual bathing she went home quite well.

COMMENTARY

Presumably this was a combination of a fear-psychosis and a toxic psychosis (from toxic absorption from retained placenta) in the puerperium. Mental distress was enhanced by well-founded guilt related to unhappy marriage. It is almost certain that she was given sedatives which considerably modified the extreme frenzy which is apt to seize guilty people when they believe that the hand of death has gripped them. I therefore include this case among the fear-psychoses precipitated by toxic illness.

CASE 47. YAO. N. of Akrofrom. M. *c.* 20.

Shrine

Dimankoma.

Reason for referral

"Caught" by *obosom* with madness.

Family History

Parents: Not cross-cousins. Non-Christian, illiterate cocoa-farmers, both alive and well.

Siblings: Seven born, all alive and well. All illiterate.

Personal History

Childhood: N.a.d. No schooling, non-Christian.

Work: Cocoa-farmer. Is clearing to make a new farm of his own.

Marriage: One wife. Not cross-cousin. One child.

Home: Lives in maternal uncle's house. Uncle is one of the *obosom's* elders.

Present Illness

Five days ago the patient, together with others of the household, had influenza. During the illness he became restless and excited, could not sleep, wept, and said he was "caught" for offending the *obosom*. He became worse, talked "*basa-basa*", was wild and unmanageable, shouted, snatched things away from people and then ran shouting to the bush. He was brought back and taken to the shrine where he was told that he would be pardoned. He immediately became quiet and later confessed that he had broken the rule which forbids all servants of the *obosom* to engage in sexual intercourse on the night before entering the tabernacle.

First Interview

Patient was sleeping when I arrived and had been almost continuously asleep since his confession. He woke and talked to me, was composed and clear-headed and seemed a good and pleasant personality. He said he did not remember running to the bush but dreamt that all the towns-people were chasing him because he had done wrong.

COMMENTARY

Brief fear-psychosis precipitated by febrile illness which the patient felt to be punitive.

CASE 48. EKWIA G. of Techiman district. F. *c.* 25.

Shrine

Gomli at Agosa near Bonkwai.

Reason for referral

"Madness", after confessing to the ownership of a bad *suman*.

Family History

Parents: Cross-cousins. Non-Christian, illiterate, cocoa and ground-nut farmers. Father died about twenty years ago. Mother married again and lives with second husband in his village.

Siblings: Two born. Only patient survived.

Personal History

Childhood: N.a.d. "Village" life always.

Schooling: Nil. Non-Christian.

Marriage: Husband is a cocoa-farmer. Marriage is very happy. He had another wife whom he left when he married the patient.

Children: Only one born, a daughter now aged about eight.

Home: Patient lives with her mother and mother's people in their village, the husband in his own village near by.

Present Illness

Sudden onset. Malaise and giddiness when preparing evening meal. Later in the night she woke with palpitation and pain in ribs. She became rapidly worse, shouted what she had bought a bad *suman* and was "caught". She then talked "*basa-basa*" and reviled the household, bawling that they were fools and had monkeys' faces. She attacked them with a knife, ran away to the bush, was pursued and put under restraint. After a few days her stepfather went to the shrine at Bredi and made an *abisa* on her behalf. He was told to go and fetch her, but came back to say that she was too wild to be brought. The Bredi *obosom* then said it was the *obosom* Gomli who had "caught" her, and that she must make amends to him.

I had difficulty in finding her home, which was more than thirty miles away and involved several hours of walking in the forest. When I at last reached her she was convalescent, the illness having suddenly lifted after a week of "madness". Patient remembered nothing of the "mad" episode, but when told that she had shouted about owning bad medicines she confessed to having bought a money-making medicine of the kind that brings the owner unearned windfalls while simultaneously bringing others unearned losses. She also said she had bought a magical finger-ring from a pedlar and later felt that it had conveyed to her the power of witchcraft, although she denied that she had ever killed anyone.

Interview: 20.11.57

Patient was convalescent and quite rational, sitting combing her hair. She had been to the *obosom* Gomli—in her own village—and made her confessions, since when she had slept and eaten well. She said she felt rather weak and tired, but otherwise looked in surprisingly good condition. She appeared to be a somewhat over-active, over-talkative type and was combing her hair with unduly savage tugs.

COMMENTARY

Presumably this was a lobar pneumonia which resolved suddenly by crisis. The patient had well-founded guilt-feelings which she successfully ignored till physical illness and fever brought the fear of imminent death, with consequent guilt-and-fear psychosis.

CASE 49. KWAKU F. of Techiman district, Ashanti. M. *c.* 21.

Shrine
Boame at Bonkwai.

Reason for referral
"Madness."

Family History
Parents: Not cross-cousins. Non-Christian, illiterate cocoa-farmers. Alive and well.
Siblings: Patient is one of eight: all alive.

Personal History
Childhood: N.a.d.
School: Nil. Non-Christian.
Work: Cocoa-farmer.
Marriage: Unmarried.

Present Illness
Four days ago the patient was feverish, with headache, malaise and pains in his joints (influenza?). He rapidly became anxious, restless and then excited, saying the *obosom* had "caught" him. He quickly grew worse, became "mad", talked "*basa-basa*", shouted abuse, attacked people with a cutlass and fled in fear to the bush. He was captured and brought back, and taken to the *obosom*, who said he would be pardoned. He at once became quiet and able to confess his sin. He said that at the beginning of the cocoa-season he worked out a scheme for stealing some of his father's cocoa and intended to put it into practice, but the *obosom* caught hold of him.

First Interview
Seen the day after his confession—a healthy-looking, well-favoured youth. He had completely thrown off his attack of fever and was sitting in the yard making a basket deftly and swiftly. He was mentally quite well, though resentful and aggressive in manner. He said it was quite true that he had plotted to steal cocoa and had been "caught" for it, but he had never had anything to do with witchcraft or made any bad medicines and if anyone suspected him of that they were wrong.

COMMENTARY
Brief fear-psychosis, based on legitimate guilt-feelings and prompted by mild febrile illness.

CASE 50. KWESI K. of Offuman district. M. 40.

Shrine

Nkrewi at Offuman.

Reason for referral

"Caught" by the *obosom* for wrong-doing.

Family History

Parents: Not cross-cousins. Non-Christian, illiterate cocoa-farmers. Mother still alive, over seventy, pleasant and intelligent.

Siblings: Eight born, five died.

Personal History

Childhood: N.a.d. No schooling, non-Christian.

Marriage: Has three wives, the last two are his cross-cousins. There are ten children.

Work: Cocoa-farmer. He has also been the *okyeame* of the *obosom* since its establishment eight years ago.

Present Illness

Onset sudden, yesterday. Patient was at the funeral of someone who had been "killed by the *obosom*". This is forbidden to the *obosom's* servants. After a short while at the funeral, during which time, all witnesses confirm, he had drunk only a small amount of palm wine, well within his capacity, he came home to his mother, looking much frightened, and told her that he had seen the ghost of the man killed by the *obosom*. He then fell down and lay stiff, mute and inaccessible for about an hour. Then he became agitated, excited and "wild", though still mute, and would have rushed to the bush had not strong men restrained him. He was carried to the *obosom*, who told him that his offence would be pardoned. He immediately became calm, recovered his power of speech and told the *obosom* that he had further offended by working on his farm on the *obosom's* sabbatical day. He then walked home fully restored. The whole incident lasted less than two hours.

First Interview: 29.11.57

Quite well and rational. Pleasant, lively man.

COMMENTARY

Fear-psychosis, aborted by prompt action of friends. Everyone asserts, "if he hadn't gone to the *obosom* immediately he would have died or become mad".

Compare Cases Nos. 40 and 47, also *obosom* servants who transgressed regulations.

Although this patient was not, by all accounts, anywhere near drunk, he had taken drink, presumably enough to impair his judgment in assessing his offence.

§ 6. FEAR-PSYCHOSIS NOT ASSOCIATED WITH SUPERNATURAL SANCTIONS

I have grouped the following three cases together because they demonstrate—if such a demonstration be needed—that "superstitious fear" is not necessarily more devastating than mundane fear and that literates may be given new fears for old without much change in their reaction to them. The basic predisposition—the "psychiatric risk"—is probably the crucial factor throughout.

These three patients were all literates, and though it is certain that none of them lacked the usual rural credulity concerning supernatural matters the latter were not involved on the occasion of the fear.

Two of the patients were teachers and were not seen at shrines. Both, when seen, were on the verge of fear-psychosis of the familiar kind, both had ominous histories, and in both the illness was aborted by the use of sedative drugs and the removal of the fear. One of these teachers had been found out in peculations and thought that Nemesis had overtaken his career: the other had been brooding on half-baked ideas concerning venereal disease and thought himself to be going mad and his unborn child destined for the same fate. The third patient I did not see till he had had three acute psychotic attacks, all apparently precipitated by fear of death on a hospital operating-table.

CASE 51. SAMUEL R. S. Native of Akwapim, stationed in Ashanti. M. *c.* 45.

Reason for referral

  "*Basa-basa*" talk and behaviour.

Family History

  Parents: Both dead. Not cross-cousins. Father an ordained pastor, mother a baker.

  Siblings: Three brothers and two sisters, all literate and all wage-earning clerks. One brother has two children, students in Europe.

Personal History

  Childhood: The family moved about from place to place and the children from school to school as the father was transferred from church to church. The father was very strict and beat the children hard and often.

Schooling: After Standard VII, the patient spent four years in a teacher-training college, finishing in 1928.

Work: Since he started work he has taught in eight different middle schools. He has been in money-trouble before. He is now head teacher of a middle-school in Ashanti.

Marriage: He did not marry till he had been working twelve years. His wife was a capable seamstress and baker and was able to earn her own living. There were frequent quarrels and fights, mostly because the patient failed to fulfil his financial obligations. After the last fight she left him, taking the only child, aged six.

Previous Personality: Has never been able to look after money, is always in financial trouble and has been to various Kramu medicine-men and *abosom* seeking prosperity. He is regarded as a very odd personality. His neighbours are reticent, but say, without any malice, that his strange doings would fill many books.

Present Illness

A few days ago the teachers who worked under him complained to the school manager that the patient had not paid them their salaries, which were due. He was also found to have failed to hand over the fees he had collected from the school-children. The manager told him that he must pay up or lose his post.

Three days later his landlord went to the manager complaining that the patient was "*basa-basa*" and had been walking about day and night without eating or drinking for three days.

On Examination

A large fat man, walking slowly round the yard and in and out of his room. His eyes were popping, his pupils dilated and he stared around apprehensively. He was almost mute and only intermittently accessible. Now and then he broke into a wide inappropriate smile. He could say nothing coherent and stopped every sentence after a few words. When approached he backed away in startled terror. He would not allow himself to be touched. As he could not co-operate in any way it was necessary to obtain the help of a posse of teachers and give him a sedative injection. When this had begun to take effect he was driven to hospital, where he had sleep and nourishment. He was kept under sedatives for two days, during which the School Manager told him that he would be transferred to another school where he would not have to handle money and his debt would be deducted by instalments from his salary. Saved from the prospect of dismissal with disgrace he accepted reassurance and made a good recovery.

COMMENTARY

COMMENTARY

Extreme anxiety verging on a fear-psychosis, the latter aborted by hospital treatment.

CASE 52. YAW B. of Sunyani district, Ashanti. M. 26.

Shrine

Nil. I made his acquaintance by chance when he was on sick-leave complaining of fever and nightmares.

Family History

Parents: Not cross-cousins. Illiterate, non-Christians. Father was a farmer and hunter, with his heart in the hunting. Hardworking, kindly and respected. He died aged sixty-five when his wife was in her early twenties. Mother was the daughter of an *obosomfo*, cheerful, generous, but with fits of anger.

Siblings: The patient is the fifth of six and the only literate. The patient says the eldest brother, a farmer, though hardworking and generous, is a pronounced recluse and seldom at home, preferring to live in a forest hut entirely alone. At intervals he drinks too much palm-wine and then talks round the clock, without ceasing, and eats nothing. I myself saw this brother on two different occasions. On the second occasion he was sitting mute and hardly accessible, and was obviously schizophrenic. Neighbours also said he was often mad but "not harmful".

Personal History

Childhood: When the patient was eight months old the father died and the mother and her children were inherited by a kinsman of the father's. There was strife between these two, the husband resenting the wife's attachment to her children. He wanted her to abandon them to the care of her sister and accompany him to the Northern Territories. This she reluctantly did when the patient was aged two. His earliest recollections are of quarrels between his mother and his stepfather. He also remembers the harshness of the aunt, who fed him inadequately and, when an antelope was killed, never let him share in the meat.

The mother had one child by her second husband. She divorced the husband for neglect when this child was eighteen months old. She returned to her own family and was reunited to the patient when he was seven years old. He did not remember her and could not believe she was his mother. He and his younger half-brother became much attached to one another and the attachment continues. As a child the patient often dreamt of cows chasing him and of people pursuing him with sticks.

Schooling: When the patient was ten his maternal uncle, who was a minor chief, selected him from among all his young relatives as the most suitable to become the family scholar. Later the uncle was de-stooled, became poor and the patient completed his schooling under great deprivation, working at weeding for a few pence in his spare time, late for school nearly every day through water-carrying and other household chores for his landlord's wife, and having only one meal a day, and that not till evening. He nevertheless did well at school, was recommended by the school for secondary education, passed the entrance examination, but found it financially impossible to proceed further.

Work: On leaving school he was a pupil-teacher for two years and was then awarded a scholarship to a mission training college for teachers, where he became fully certificated. He was then appointed to the mission school in which he was working when I first met him.

Marriage: Marriage with an illiterate young woman from his own town is not very happy: the patient has little desire for sexual intercourse and the wife is dissatisfied. The wife has one insane sibling and several insane kinsmen in the older generation. The patient sometimes worries lest her children should become insane.

Children: One child about two.

Home: One room in urban town. There is no garden, though the patient and his wife both like gardening.

Present Illness

A week ago he was admitted to hospital with malaria, nightmares and shouting at night. After the malaria cleared, the nightmares continued.

First Interview: 6.6.56

Very pleasant, good, discerning personality. Fine-skinned, delicately modelled limbs and features. Face in repose is deeply anxious.

When asked point-blank and matter-of-factly whether anyone hated and wished to harm him, he said, Yes—two people. One was his elder brother, who had always jealously hated him because he was a literate and tidily dressed. "He stands quietly watching me and then starts talking quietly and murmuring, but he doesn't show his feelings and is always very kind." Patient had often been afraid that this brother might kill him by sorcery.

The other enemy was the African head-teacher under whom he worked. This senior had unnecessarily put the patient to work which was outside both his qualifications and his contract. The patient appealed to a higher authority, who upheld his plea. Thereafter the chagrined head-teacher made the patient's life a misery with petty fault-finding and, in the patient's opinion, was not only out to ruin his career but was likely to kill him by supernatural means.

The patient said his main fear was of death, which he thought near. Many of his dreams, which were clear, well-constructed allegories, not mere jumbled nightmares, involved funerals and mourning, and many possibly symbolised the funeral of his hopes and ambitions rather than the funeral of himself. In one dream the coffin was carried by "a literate at one end and an illiterate at the other"—presumably the head-teacher and the brother. One dream of a "Mohammedan coffin" probably referred to fear of bad medicines, which are usually purchased from Kramu (Moslem) medicine-men.

He said his mother wanted to put him under the protection of her *obosom*, but he thought the associated lotions and potions "unhygienic" and that he might catch diseases from them. He then revealed a good deal of hypochondriasis engendered by school and training-college hygiene-lessons and by newspaper advertisements.

As there seemed to be no doubt that he had damaged the dignity of his head-teacher and was paying for it, it was suggested that he might apply for a transfer to another town. He declared himself much relieved by relating his troubles which he said he had hitherto kept completely secret.

Progress

5.7.57. I did not see the patient again for more than a year, but I did go to see his mother and his family. They all closely resembled him, being of an "overbred" type with delicately built limbs and features. The mother was comely and charming.

One day in July, 1957, the patient suddenly appeared at my door having made a considerable journey. He was looking so distraught that I did not at first recognise him. Even before taking a seat he blurted out, "Can't you help me? I think I am going mad." And indeed he seemed to be on the verge of one of those acute fear-reactions so often met. However, he was able to give a clear-headed account of himself. He said his new environment was all he could wish. His new head-teacher liked him and they were, in fact, close friends. He had a garden and was growing tomatoes. His brother, who had hated him, often sent him gifts of farm produce and appeared to "love" him. "He may hate me spiritually, but he shows me a kind face." Further, he had, at the instigation of his mother, taken her *obosom's* protective baths. He could not therefore account for the recurrence of nightmares more terrifying than ever. He had been off work for several days, his head-teacher being kind and sympathetic. "He wants me to get better."

His dreams had lately become disorganised nightmares in which he was chased, beaten or stabbed by a man with a knife. He always woke shouting, panting, sweating and exhausted. Asked whether he had ever done anything which occasioned him shame and fear, he revealed that years ago he had seduced a girl, been fined £10 by her relatives because she was already betrothed and had lately seen her again in his present town: this made him think that everyone knew about the incident and was talking about it. Asked whether he had had similar feelings on other occasions he said that a friend had once tried, unsuccessfully, to smuggle him into a "ball dance" without paying, and he was beaten up by the gate-keepers, after which he always thought, when he saw people talking, that they were talking of his incident and plotting to beat him again.

He further said that his wife was pregnant and was due for confinement at any moment. He himself had once had "G.C.", and though both he and his wife had had hospital treatment when the infection was discovered in his wife at the antenatal clinic before the birth of the first child, he had read in a hygiene book that some effects of venereal disease could never be cured, might lead to madness and could be disastrously transmitted to children. This was his most tormenting fear.

He was given explanation and reassurance and assured that he was not going mad but was probably projecting anxiety which had lain mostly dormant since the fear-ridden insecurity of the early separation from his mother. He accepted this with evident relief. He was given sedatives and also anti-malarials as he had described some feverishness.

He appeared again two week-ends later. His wife had delivered a healthy child, his nightmares had ceased and he had returned to work. He had had only one dream, and that of pleasant affect seeming to symbolise his current situation. He dreamt that he was a passenger in a lorry, rushing out of control towards a building. Just before it crashed he had jumped clear, which salvation left him feeling thankful and happy. He had also dreamt that he had been swept away while crossing a stream, but had caught at a liana and managed to pull himself to safety.

But he revealed for the first time that ever since his first illness he had had visual and occasionally auditory hallucinations. They never occurred when he was actively occupied, but only when he relaxed in a chair or on his bed. The visual ones he called "moving pictures". They moved slowly and silently across his field of vision from right to left. They looked either "fearful" or ridiculous, but always passed by without molesting him. There were such things as a man upside down, a man slowly changing into a dog, moving trees, lizards, antelopes, animals without heads, ferocious-looking wild beasts, and household articles such as cups and chairs. On one occasion as he sat relaxed in a chair a "man" suddenly appeared right in front of him with an open mouth out of which no sound came. After a few seconds the man disappeared Sometimes he heard "rough" voices shouting, "Hoh! Hoh!", or ordering him about saying, "Come on, now!", but they never gave definite orders and never reviled him. Since he stopped worrying about insanity and syphilitic children the hallucinations had "died down", except for a few to which he no longer paid any attention. He betrayed no thought-disorder, flattened or inappropriate affect, indolence or diminished ambition. He was keen to go on a teachers' refresher-course. He has remained well and working for three months.

December 1957. He writes that his wife "troubles" him and they are considering divorce.

COMMENTARY

The ideas of reference, the hallucinations, the hypochondriasis, the disinclination for sexual intercourse and the family history all taken together add up to a potential schizophrene. Had events in July, 1957, aggravated rather than allayed the fear-component—so often the explosive ingredient in fulminating psychoses—I feel little doubt that this would have precipitated an acute attack.

It is noticeable that most of this patient's fears were the result of his literacy: the illiterate brother's supposed envy, the clash with the head-teacher and the garbled ideas about venereal disease.

It is usually held that when schizophrenia attacks two or more siblings it attacks them in a similar manner. The difference between this patient and his "mad" brother may be due to the different way of life of the literate. The illiterate is seen withdrawing peacefully without a struggle; the literate has insight, puts up a fight, and suffers intensely.

CASE 53. CHARLES N. of Akwapim. M. 15.

Medicine-man

Private practitioner from Akropong, now practising in Suhum. Patient was resident in practitioner's house for treatment.

Reason for referral

Episodes of violence and wandering, with total amnesia for the episodes.

Family History

Father: Akwapim family, literate Christian, Government officer. For the last six months he has been stationed in a distant town, wife and younger children with him. Annual home-coming to Akwapim.

Mother: Illiterate Christian from husband's town.

Siblings: Patient is eldest of seven.

Personal History

Childhood: N.a.d.

School: Demonstration school attached to one of the best teacher-training colleges in the country. Is now due to enter Standard VII. Good scholar. Ambitious to go to England on scholarships and have a brilliant career. Already speaks excellent English.

Home: When father was transferred to a distant station he left patient with his grandmother to remain at his good school. Household also contains mother's brothers and sisters and the latter's children.

Previous Illnesses: About three years ago the patient had attacks of abdominal pain and someone told him he would very likely have to have an operation. The idea terrified him because an aunt had died in hospital during an obstetrical operation. The attacks of pain continued and nearly a year later he went to Dr. A. of Koforidua, who gave him medical treatment but did not tell him the diagnosis. (I contacted Dr. A., who told me that he had diagnosed worms and malaria.) Both of these are apt to recur unless treatment is repeated, and patient did not report again.

Previous Personality: Well behaved at school. Was head-master's private waiting-boy. Swept his room and served his meals.

Present Illness (from patient)

Onset about twenty months ago. Four attacks in all, each beginning with abdominal pain and fear, sometimes of several days' duration.

First attack: Patient remembers nothing except that he regained "consciousness" and found himself walking alone in Accra (some thirty miles from his home), having presumably travelled on a passenger-lorry. He was lucky enough to find a threepenny piece on the pavement and with this he bought some bread, ate it, and then feeling very sleepy he found a quiet place and slept—he does not know for how long. When he woke his head was quite clear and he realised that he was in Accra, in which town he had once lived when his father worked there. He also found that he was in Scout's uniform, so he went to the Scouts' headquarters, had another long sleep there, after which someone lent him his fare home.

Second attack: He was sweeping the headmaster's room and was aware of stomach-ache and was afraid. He remembers no more till he became "conscious" two days later. He immediately realised that he had been interrupted in sweeping so he went back and finished. Then he slept for some hours, and on waking was told that he had spent two days in mad violence, had taken a stick and smashed all the pots in his grandmother's house and had attacked the occupants.

Third attack: Remembers abdominal pain and fright and then nothing more till he came to himself in the police-station in Accra, four days later. This time he had not been violent but had gone by lorry to Accra and had gone to the house of a man whom he knew and had asked for somewhere to sleep. The man thought his behaviour strange and took him to the police-station.

Fourth attack: Remembers several days of abdominal pain and that he
went into the examination-room to sit his terminal examination feeling
very unwell and frightened. He does not remember writing anything,
but he did, in fact, write a worthless paper and failed. He "woke up" to
find himself cut and bruised, having had several days of madness and
violence.

About a fortnight ago his mother brought him to the medicine-man
in Suhum and left him there.

The medicine-man told me that he had divined that someone had
maliciously made a bad medicine (*adutu*) against the patient and had
concealed it so that the patient unwittingly walked over it. A "poisoned"
needle had then entered the patient without his knowledge. To prove
this the medicine-man gave the patient a purge, examined the stool and
then produced an ordinary sewing-needle which he said the patient had
expelled. He then undertook to remove by prolonged treatment the
poison the needle had left.

First Interview: 31.12.55

Looks less than fifteen. Well-nourished. Nothing physical found except E.S.R. 70 mm. first half-hour; 105 second half-hour. Malaria could
account for this. Mentally he looked intensely unhappy but denied that
anyone had any ill-will against him. His account of his illness was clear
and straightforward and expressed in excellent English.

1.1.56. *Amytal and methedrine abreaction.* Wept copiously in the
deepest distress. Said that whenever the stomach pain comes on he thinks
he will die because of what was said about the operation. He remembers
an aunt who went to hospital in labour, had an operation and died, and
he becomes terrified of approaching death.

Asked again whether anyone had any ill-will against him, he said
passionately that the women in his grandmother's house were witches
and had sent the illness. Even before that they hated him and he thought
they were "devils", determined to prevent him from succeeding in life.
There was also a boy who had always hated him because he was a good
scholar.

He said he never wanted to go back to his Akwapim town because
everyone there thought him a madman. His parents were also afraid of
him. He wept bitterly about his interrupted education and said he had
loved his lessons and furthermore had always been "a *good* boy".

Asked about his dreams he described one in which the "bad boy" and
the "bad women" who hated him were trying to shoot him with a gun
and the gun burst. He also dreamt that he was in an aeroplane with the
other boys. The aeroplane flew across the sea and then he noticed that
there was no one but himself in the plane and no "driver". He was
terrified, but called out three times the name of a good and friendly

medicine-man in Akwapim (not the one who was treating him in Suhum) and instantly was in his own house. Another dream was of a policeman chasing him and some other boys for swimming in a river. The other boys ran away and the policeman turned into a tall, threatening boy. He further dreamt that at the gate of the medicine-man's house in Suhum he saw a tall woman who wanted to catch him. He said he was satisfied that now he had come to Suhum for treatment his enemies could do him no more harm, but he expressed bitterness and depression at his interrupted education.

Progress

His mother came to visit him a few days later. She was convinced that family witchcraft was the cause of the trouble and wanted him to stay under the protection of the medicine-man in Suhum. She arranged that he should go to school in Suhum.

I left for Ashanti a few days later and arranged for Dr. B. to keep an eye on him through his dispensary assistant, a kindly young woman who lived in Suhum.

I had news of him from time to time. He was disappointed in the standard of education in his new school compared with that of Akwapim. The medicine-man exploited him, making him spend his week-ends walking miles into the bush to collect herbs, so that, lacking time to wash his school uniform, he became dirty and unkempt. He was made to do chores for the medicine-man's wife, had not enough to eat and became justly resentful and discouraged. After about a year his father visited him and was dissatisfied with his surroundings and removed him to a new school in Akwapim.

He had one attack of malaria in Suhum and was off school and laid up for a week, but he developed no mental symptoms. Twenty-one months after he was first seen he still remained free.

COMMENTARY

The four attacks were all triggered off by the same pain and associated fear of death. The two fugue-like episodes of travelling to Accra may have had the motive of escape. The two episodes of violence seem to have resembled the schizophreniform catatonic excitements frequently seen in Ashanti as reactions to fear. It may well be that malaria was a factor in helping to whip up the fear (*vide* Case No. 40), but the fact that the patient, after accepting reassurance, had a fairly severe attack of malaria without any mental manifestations supports the probability that the fear and not the malaria was the operative factor.

It should be noted that there was no guilt associated with this fear. No *obosom* can be incriminated, but there was much preoccupation with human malice.

The possibility remains that the patient is a potential schizophrenic, and, as such, especially prone to brief episodes of fear psychosis. Again, the four attacks may have been epileptic equivalents, but their non-recurrence suggests otherwise.

§ 7. ANXIETY STATES REACTIVE TO FEAR

People disturbed by fear of imminent retribution for sin do not invariably rush into psychotic frenzy. The following group of eight cases show patients whose states all fall short of psychosis and present a considerable variety of forms.

CASE 54. YAA F. of Wenchi district, Ashanti. F. 30.

Shrine
Mframa.

Reason for Referral
"Caught" by *obosom* for making bad medicine.

Family History
Parents: Cross-cousins. Non-Christian, illiterate farmers. Mother died two years ago. Father alive and well, good personality.
Siblings: Seven born, six survived. Farmers.

Personal History
Childhood: N.a.d. disclosed.
Schooling: Nil. Non-Christian, illiterate.
Marriage: Cross-cousin. Twelve years ago. Husband non-Christian, illiterate farmer, about patient's own age. Marriage satisfactory till about a year ago when husband took a second and younger wife and neglected obligations to the patient.
Children: Seven born, two died, one of these shortly after birth about one week ago.
Household: Father's house occupied by father, patient and her children and some road-labourer lodgers. Mother's sister has moved in since patient became ill.

Present Illness
A week ago the patient was delivered of a full-term child, normal delivery. The child was apparently normal but died on the same day. The following day the patient was seized with pains in her body, head and limbs. She felt that she had killed the child and was "caught" for

wrong-doing. She had "no sleep" through fear and agitation, but had enough to dream that a great crowd of men, women and children were present and that she seized one of the children. The next morning she told her father that she was frightened because she was "caught" by Mframa. Her agitation and sleeplessness continued and she was brought to the shrine.

First Interview: 1.3.57

She came into the yard bending over a stout staff and grimacing with pain. She was agitated and frightened but not overtly depressed. She gave a voluble and fairly coherent account of herself. She said she was "caught" for wrong-doing. When her husband took a second wife he neglected her and gave her no food-money, so she cursed both him and the new wife to the deity of the local river. She also went to a Kramu medicine-man in Wenchi and bought several bad medicines, including one which she put into the new wife's oven to bring about her death and another which consisted of a piece of hyaena-skin which she burnt where her husband would inhale the fumes and thereby take a dislike to the new wife.

Her agitation was much allayed by her confession, but the *obosom* told her to go home and reflect, search her heart for any residual sins and return next session. She left the yard much more composed.

2.3.57. Seen in her own home. She appeared in good health, no more than her circumstances would warrant, spoke freely and without any self-reproach. Took the healthy attitude that though she had done wrong she had been provoked. She seemed more of an aggressive than a depressive type.

7.3.57. Came to the shrine again and said she had no more to confess. The *obosom* ordered her to bring a cow and she went home to arrange about this. I saw her after the shrine session: she said she was quite well and seemed so.

18.3.57. Relatives came to Mframaso to report that the patient died two days ago of a sudden uterine haemorrhage. "She hadn't confessed all, so the *obosom* killed her."

COMMENTARY

Fear and agitation, not inappropriate to circumstances, in an aggressive personality.

CASE 55. KWAKU D. of Akwapim. M. *c.* 30.

Shrine

Mframa at Mframaso.

Reason for referral

Physical illness believed by himself to be due to transgression of Mframa's injunctions.

Family History

Parents: Non-Christian, illiterate farmers. The mother is alive but the father is dead. They were not cross-cousins.

Siblings: One sister, three brothers: all illiterate, non-Christian farmers.

Personal History

Childhood: N.a.d. disclosed.

Schooling: Nil. Non-Christian.

Work: Cocoa-farming near Asamankese, Akim.

Marriage: One wife, roughly his own age. They are on good terms.

Children: Three. Two are at school. The youngest is about a year old. The wife was pregnant when first seen.

Household: In both the home-town and the cocoa-village he is in the household of the witch Ama K. and her two satellite witches. (Case No. 71.) His wife lives with her own family except in the "village".

Present Illness

Ten years ago the patient had "*babaso*" (gonorrhea). He was treated by a native medicine-man and recovered, or so he thought. A year ago the illness returned. He went to a doctor who has a European medical qualification and was given one injection (which cost him five shillings) and was told to come again. Though convinced that European injections could cure "*babaso*" as such, he felt—as is usual—that this was useless till the sender of the illness had been put out of action. As the household contained three avowed witches he fled in terror to Mframaso to obtain immunity from witchcraft, without waiting to finish his course of injections. He partook of Mframa's protective medicine, was given some potions to take home to cure his "*babaso*", and was forbidden to engage in sexual intercourse till he had recovered. He disobeyed the injunction, the "*babaso*" became worse, he thought, and he felt himself "caught" by Mframa and in danger of death. He hurried back to Mframaso, confessed his offence and was fined a cow, a sheep, a fowl, a bottle of rum and some eggs.

Interview: 2.3.56

The patient had been three weeks in Mframaso when I arrived. So far as I could discover from the shrine officials, he was not floridly in the grip of fear when he arrived but placed himself quietly in the transgressor's dock and confessed.

He was thin, looked ill, dispirited and languid but had no mental symptoms beyond apathy. His wife and his youngest child were with him, the wife being pregnant. They appeared almost destitute after their travelling expenses and shrine fees and were glad to earn a few shillings doing some jobs for me.

Progress

He stayed several months, apparently afraid to go home, taking ritual baths but not much to eat, and continuing thin and listless. He went home only when his wife approached the end of her term of pregnancy. He returned three months later that his wife might give thanks for her new child. The patient had had a course of injections and looked better.

COMMENTARY

I did not consider this case of much interest till I met Ama K. and the other relatives on whom she has her tentacles.

The patient seems to have begun with a somewhat paranoid anxiety concerning his physical illness, but it was not till he himself had been guilty of disobedience to *obosom* commands that he felt his life in imminent danger. He felt that his sin had nullified the *obosom's* protection, laying him open to attack by witches.

CASE 56. YAA M. of Akwatia district, Akim. F. *c.* 35.

Shrine

Mframa at Mframaso.

Reason for referral

She came alone, pregnant and near full term, asking to stay in Mframaso for safety during her confinement.

Family History (probably incomplete)

Mother: Alive and well.

Father: Policeman. He died about five years ago. The patient's mother left him when the patient was about four.

Siblings: The mother bore three daughters of whom one died.

Personal History

Childhood: The patient says she was happy. She lived with her mother and her mother's brother. The latter has since died. When the patient was ten her father took her to live with him. (This implies some unusual circumstances.)

Schooling: She only reached Class II. She enjoyed lessons but left because the teacher was harsh.

Search for Security

Religion: She was a communicant but stopped communion when she married a man who already had one wife. She still goes to church regularly and is a singing-band member.

Marriage: First husband worked in the mines. He had two additional wives. The patient appears to have left him because he denied her sexual intercourse. Her present husband is an ex-soldier who owns two stores in a big town and is prosperous. He has two other wives, one with more children than the patient, the other with fewer. The patient is reticent about her marriages, especially the first, the unhappiness of which appears to have contributed to her first illness.

Children: The patient has three children, the eldest at school, the youngest about eighteen months. She is now pregnant.

Previous Illnesses: (1) Her first illness occurred in 1952 and many good witnesses in Mframaso still remember it. She came alone, complaining that she was a witch and impressed everyone, firstly, by the fact that "nobody would have guessed that she was a witch if she hadn't said so" —i.e., she was outwardly calm and normal, neither agitated, depressed nor *"basa-basa"*, and secondly, because her witchcraft confessions included the assertion that she often changed herself into a man. The latter act is not orthodox witchcraft, and for some reason seemed to the informants infinitely shocking.

The records of witchcraft cases kept by the *obosom's* clerk are only for legal "coverage" and consist usually of the statement that the confession was made without threat, followed by a list of the persons the witch says she has killed or harmed. In this woman's case, however, the confessions were so unusual that the clerk took them down in detail and was able to look them up for me.

He emphasised that all the things the patient confessed to have done were done "in the spirit", i.e., were fantasies. I found them to be of two kinds and have so rearranged them here, though they were produced mixed haphazard.

A. Stereotyped delusions of guilt, and claims to have brought about misfortunes which had, in fact, occurred.
B. Original fantasies. Some of these appeared to reflect something of the patient's unhappy sex-life.

A. *Stereotyped Delusions*

Her *abayi's* names were Ahum, Akura and Onanka (tornado, mouse and python respectively). They abode in her vagina.

She took away her first husband's prosperity and made him impotent.

She attended witches' assemblies with her relatives.

She planned to kill her son, but instead of this caused a bicycle to knock him down.

262

She made her own son impotent and spoilt his scholastic success.

She caused the financial ruin of her husband's brother and of a woman relative.

She prevented her own half-brother from confessing when he was "caught" by Tigari for witchcraft. He could, therefore, not be cured. (I have no information concerning this half-brother.)

She killed her uncle and another relative.

She caused another relative to be unsuccessful as a goldsmith and to come to poverty.

She tried to make her sister barren but did not succeed.

She spoilt the local diamond industry.

She is the queen-mother of her group of witches.

She cursed her ex-husband for refusing her sexual intercourse and taking another girl.

She helped to kill Kofi X after making him impotent.

She killed a woman's child and made the woman into a prostitute.

She caused her husband to get dysentery, hoping to kill him, but he recovered.

She killed Abena X and her husband and their children.

She influenced the town chief's stool so that the holder must always be de-stooled and must also be a drunkard.

B. *Original Fantasies*

When married to her first husband she often pulled off his penis and used it herself. She did the same with her second husband.

She had an iron bedstead which she used for prostitution.

She put wire-netting round her mother's house and imprisoned people in it.

She took sheet-iron off her mother's house and used it as human skin.

She used one of her mother's cooking-pots as a container for the human flesh which her witch-colleagues shared.

She influenced a bottle in her mother's house in such a way that when it was corked anybody bitten by a snake died immediately and when it was uncorked any woman in labour had an easy delivery. The bottle contained human flesh and also contained the honour and respectability of the patient's husband.

A key belonging to her mother she often took with her when she flew to steal away the luck or money of any victim.

She took her mother's beads with her when she travelled to witches' meetings.

She used a box of trinkets and oddments belonging to her mother to work evil deeds.

She turned her mother's and her husband's clothing into human skin.

She changed a table into a human trunk to be eaten at witches' assemblies.

She took her husband's writing materials to assemblies to bring him financial failure.

She sold her son for 2s. 6d. but redeemed him later.

She used her mother's sewing-machine for making human skin into witches' dresses.

Because her husband denied her sexual intercourse she obtained satisfaction with a broom and a candle.

Any sexual partner who failed to satisfy her was sprinkled with water from the snake in her vagina and acquired *babaso* (gonorrhea) and was reduced to poverty.

Instead of putting animal blood on the sacrificial stone in her mother's yard she put human blood and menstrual blood.

(2) The second time the patient appeared at the shrine was in June, 1956, when I first saw her. I had not then heard her earlier history and should not have singled her out for special notice had she not come, shyly and pleasantly, to my quarters to greet me. I asked her why she had come to the shrine, and she said because she was pregnant and had had a disturbing dream. She dreamt that a barren woman—a lodger in her house—was taking the foetus out of her womb. She took this to indicate that the woman was plotting, out of jealousy, to send her a supernaturally provoked miscarriage. After the dream she was frightened, so she took an egg to the bush, prayed to Mframa, gave him the egg and then came to Mframaso to commend herself anew to his care.

She was a tall, well-nourished, comely woman, gentle, serene, pleasant and soft-voiced. She seemed of above-average intelligence, quietly competent, industrious and self-reliant, remarkable only for her quiet, pleasing personality, and her distinguished but reposeful appearance.

She went home after a few days.

Present Illness

Early in September, 1956, the patient arrived again in Mframaso, and made *abisa* at the shrine. She seemed in very good health, mentally and physically and simply asked for permission to stay in Mframaso for her confinement, which was near.

She came again to greet me, shyly and courteously as before. She seemed in no anxiety, but I thought it strange that she had come completely alone, except for a two-year-old child, with no female relative to help her in her confinement. I thought this implied some estrangement between herself and her mother and sister but she was calmly reticent on this point. It was not till I commented in the village on her loneliness that I heard her witchcraft history.

She called on me again several times, still very composed and gentle. By that time I realised that she was being apprehensively cold-shouldered by the other women, but I still could not detect any overt anxiety in her demeanour. When I asked her whether she had ever been in Mframaso because of illness, she said, Yes—pains in her head and limbs.

About ten days after her arrival I was knocked up about midnight by the senior wife of the senior elder of the village, together with a party of other women who had brought the patient. I found her lying on the ground writhing and crying out that she had pains in her belly and was dying. The other women, with faces of grim displeasure, asked me whether she was in labour or not—the alternative, of course, being that the *obosom* had "caught" her for renewed witchcraft. I thought she was not in labour, but being apprehensive for her said that she probably was and that I would see her again in the morning. Before daybreak they were all back again, the patient even more agitated and moaning and saying that the pain was now not only in her belly but in her head, her chest and her limbs. The women were obviously anxious to wash their hands of her and were relieved when she accepted my offer to take her into hospital for a more expert opinion. It was there confirmed that she was not in labour, but the nursing Nuns grasped the situation and said they would admit her and give her sedation till her delivery. This probably averted an acute fear-psychosis.

Three days later, however, she discharged herself and came back to Mframaso. She looked anxious and apprehensive, her hands trembled and her neighbours looked at her askance. She was, however, well controlled, and reticent about her reasons for leaving hospital, saying that she felt quite well. I gave her sedatives daily, but after another three days she appeared at the shrine in the morning groaning with pain, this time complaining of her knee. The knee was in bandages, she was walking bent double and clinging to a stout stick, grimacing, wincing and contorting her face. The morning session at the shrine was over before her turn came. After it I gave her another heavy sedative and she lay down quietly till the evening session when she made her *abisa* in much distress.

She told the *obosom* that she was again "caught" for her wickedness. She said that neither her husband nor her mother would have anything to do with her and that the worry of bearing a child without help was so great that she had guiltily planned to have no more children but to procure a criminal abortion if she ever became pregnant again. The *obosom* said that this was indeed wicked and she must bring a sheep for atonement. He reduced the penalty to a fowl and she paid it immediately.

Her agitation continued and I wanted to take her back to hospital. She said she could not go till she had asked the *obosom's* permission on the next day of *abisa*. However, before that day arrived she went into labour and quickly delivered the child without any fuss. Immediately after, she was beaming with pleasure, and about ten days later, after ceremonially thanking the *obosom* for her child, she went home appearing very happy.

11.8.57. She paid a brief visit to the shrine to render thanks because her son had won a scholarship to learn electrician's work in Europe. She also gave thanks because her husband had promised her £100 as trading capital and she asked the *obosom* to make him keep his promise. She and the child both looked well.

COMMENTARY

Acute anxiety, reactive to stress, in a woman of good personality who had a transient psychosis four years earlier.

The dream in which a barren woman attempts to take away the patient's foetus frightened the patient and was interpreted at the shrine as a warning that the barren woman was jealously thinking of making a bad magic to cause miscarriage. However, the patient's last confession at the shrine indicates that it was a wish-fulfilment dream, charged, because of the guiltiness of the wish, with an unpleasant affect, and that it was the dreamer who was jealous of the other woman's barrenness.

Many of the fantasies of the first illness seem to be of the type which one has met in English patients at the onset of schizophrenic illness when the patient has full insight and clear consciousness. One such English patient was tormented by sexual fantasies of an absurd kind—such as carpets and tables having intercourse with other pieces of furniture—but was outwardly so composed that she came to hospital only after a suicidal attempt. She had only subjective symptoms and was discharged from hospital after a few weeks.

CASE 57. KWAME S. of Trans-Volta. M. *c.* 20.

Shrine

Mframa at Mframaso.

Reason for referral

"Caught" by the *obosom* for theft.

Family and Personal History

No information except that all are illiterate, non-Christian cocoa-farmers, except the patient, who is a lorry-driver's mate. His mother and a brother brought the patient.

History of Present Illness

About a year ago a traveller on the patient's lorry left a bag containing £18 in the lorry while he went to make a market-purchase. The patient stole the money. The traveller suspected either the driver or the patient, but they both swore by God (who is but little feared because He does not punish sin in this life) that they were innocent. The complainant replied that he himself had drunk at Tigari's shrine, but as Tigari was a slow worker he was resolved to travel forthwith to Mframaso, put himself under the care of Mframa, and ask Mframa to kill the thief of his money. This he did. The patient began to have dreams in which he saw a threatening figure standing over him and holding out hands to receive money.

During the next six months he became steadily worse, but according to his mother his illness was almost wholly physical. He had pains in his head, neck, "waist", and jaws, and said he could not open his jaws. He had no sleep at night, but, according to his mother, he never talked "*basa-basa*" but became bewildered, confused and incapable of knowing what to do next. He used to ask her, "Shall I eat? Shall I wash? Shall I go to the latrine? What must I do?" When he was unable either to stand or to eat, his brother sought out the complainant and offered to restore the money, but the complainant replied that the matter was already in the hands of Tigari and Mframa and restitution could be made only through them.

The patient went first to Tigari, carried by four people who had also to hold him on his feet before the shrine. Having confessed, he regained the power to eat and to stand. He was then brought to Mframa.

First Interview

When first seen he was lying on his mat with his face to the wall. He was then worried and languid but not otherwise ill. He gave a halting but clear-headed account of himself tallying with that of his mother and the plaintiff. He was able to walk to the shrine where he confessed. He was ordered to restore the £18, offer a sacrificial animal to the *obosom* and also pay the plaintiff's costs. These included a further £18 which the plaintiff had promised the *obosom* if the stolen money should be restored.

Progress

He recovered very rapidly and went home after a week, apparently quite well.

COMMENTARY

Anxiety with physical prostration, reactive to guilt and fear. This case differs from many in that the patient did not become wildly disturbed.

The plaintiff was a smooth-spoken ingratiating literate. He came to call on me, told me he was a Christian and gave me some tracts. He was the secretary of a society called The Society of the Secret Power of Jesus, whose aim was to find out the wonder-working secret magics by means of which Jesus wrought miracles which, if known, would have great market-value.

CASE 58. ABENA P. of Nkyiraa, Ashanti. F. *c.* 23.

Shrine

Kotokro at Nkyiraa.

Reason for referral

"Caught" by the obosom.

Family History

No information.

Personal History

Scanty information. Born and bred in Nkyiraa. Married to a man in Wenchi and lived with him there. Two children, the youngest a suckling. Marriage unhappy. Husband failed to support her: constant recriminations and quarrelling. She therefore left her husband and came back to her mother's house in Nkyiraa with her children. There she consorted with another man before completing the formalities of separation from her husband, the new relationship being therefore adulterous.

Present Illness

Shortly after her adultery she was going one day to her farm when she was seized with pains in her belly. She fell down and lay groaning and crying that the *obosom* had laid hold of her for her sins. She was carried home where she complained of terrifying dreams in which she was chased by something, she knew not what. She was taken immediately to the shrine where she made a confession and was instantly cured.

She said she had been resentful towards her husband because she had helped him to make a farm and he had given her no share in its profits. She therefore cursed him to a river, promising the river a lizard if it would kill him for her. Asked by the *obosom* if she was also guilty of witchcraft said perfunctorily, yes, and that she had resolved to kill her three brothers and her young daughter "for witches' meat".

First Interview

Not depressed. No irrational self-reproach. Resentful and aggressive.

Progress

Uneventful.

COMMENTARY

Concrete aggressive act followed by rational guilt and consequent fear-reaction taking the form of somatic symptoms. Nothing resembling a fear-psychosis was described. The witchcraft confession was perfunctory, not spontaneous.

CASE 59. AMA S. of Nkoranza district. F. *c.* 40.

Shrine

Ate at Bonte.

Reason for referral

"Caught" by the *obosom* for wrong-doing.

Family History

Parents: Cross-cousins. The mother is alive but the father is dead. Illiterate cocoa-farmers, both Christians.

Siblings: Five born. All alive. The sisters are married with children. The brother is a cocoa-farmer.

Personal History

Childhood: N.a.d.

Schooling: Nil, but she is a Christian, a communicant.

Marriage: The husband is an illiterate Christian communicant and Church leader. He was a cocoa-farmer till the cocoa-trees died, when he removed to a "village" some fifteen miles from Wenchi to work as a palm-wine tapper, taking his wife with him. They are not cross-cousins. He drinks a good deal of palm-wine and at interview was much elated. During the war the husband worked for a time in Kumasi as an army labourer. His wife was with him. Before his marriage the husband had *babaso* and gave it to the patient. Both were "cured" with native medicine.

Children: One daughter only, born after the earthquake in 1939. (Gonococcal one-child sterility?) This daughter is married and has two children.

Work: The patient markets her husband's palm-wine, taking four 4-gallon tins by passenger-lorry to Wenchi. She is a hard worker.

Habits: Diet consists mainly of koko-yam and palm-wine. Some relatives thought the koko-yam must be the cause of her illness. She chews much tobacco. She has long been under the protection of two *obosom*.

Present Illness (from the husband and daughter)

The onset was eight months ago. The patient came back from market one day, having eaten nothing, but having drunk considerable palm-wine, and started "walking like a spider" and fell over in various directions. Then she lay down and became quite stiff and mute. The next morning she had recovered, but had further attacks of stiffness and muteness and between them complained of palpitations. Witnesses were quite clear that the attacks were not epileptic fits. The episodes of muteness became longer, sometimes lasting one to three weeks. The husband sent the patient home to her family where she went to the *obosom*. The *obosom* asked her whether she was a witch and she assented. She was fined a sheep and cleansed and recovered briefly but soon relapsed. Her appetite failed and she became very lean. She went to various other *abosom* and medicine-men, one of whose treatment included three bottles of stovarsol tablets (obtained from an undisclosed source). She became steadily worse.

Interview: 14.11.57

Exceedingly wasted. She is unable to walk. She whimpers with each breath. Hb. 50%. Signs of avitaminosis and gastritis (alcoholic ?).

Anxious and much agitated. She speaks in an almost inaudible moaning whine and says she is going to die because she has done so much wrong but does not specify what. She consented to enter hospital.

21.11.57. Hospital find no blood or intestinal parasites. No cough. Sputum negative. Macrocytic anaemia. Treated with food, vitamins, iron and campolon. Her physical condition is improving but she is still anxious and whimpering. She says she is going to die.

10.12.57. *Amytal and methedrine abreaction.* She said she had done a great many bad things for which she was dying. She was resentful against her husband because he took concubines and spent on them money which she had earned. He also seduced a chief's wife and was fined £100 which money the patient had to provide out of her savings. She therefore cursed him to streams, to trees and big rocks, calling upon them respectively to drown him, fall on him and crush him. She also cursed him to God. Then she went to a Kramu medicine-man and bought *suman* to destroy the attachment between him and his concubines. She also put in his food a bad medicine made by washing her pudendal cloth in water. She furthermore herself committed adultery with another man. She denied that she was a witch.

Having unburdened herself of this guilt her outlook towards the future changed and instead of anticipating only death she began to plan laying out a new farm.

12.12.57. She is whimpering again but her Hb. is going up.

20.12.57. Discharged herself from hospital. She went first to the house of the local catechist, who was very kind to her, and then went home, still whimpering. He said that she told him the nurses were unkind to her and that they said she deserved to die for being a witch.

COMMENTARY

This appears to be a combination of hysteria, alcoholism and malnutrition, the two former reactive to valid guilt feelings in an aggressive personality expressing no irrational self-approach. The attitude of the nurses is not unusual: Christians do not disbelieve in witchcraft.

ACKNOWLEDGMENT

I am indebted to Wenchi Methodist Hospital for co-operation in this case. The Mission generously supported both the patient and her attendant daughter while she was in hospital.

CASE 60. EKWIA P. of Mampong district, Ashanti. F. *c.* 28.

Shrine

Mframa at Mframaso.

Reason for referral

"Caught" by the *obosom* for cursing her husband.

Family History

Parents: Not cross-cousins. Father illiterate, non-Christian cocoa-farmer, still alive, but mother left him five years ago because he "did her wrong". He was a satisfactory father when the patient was a child. The mother is an exceptionally intelligent, capable illiterate and brought the patient to the shrine. Because the patient has been unable, since she fell sick, to suckle her child, the patient's mother has successfully bottle-fed it—a feat denoting great enterprise and adaptability in an illiterate elderly woman. The mother is a non-Christian, but says she is going to join a Church.

Siblings: The patient is the only child except for one half-brother by the mother's first marriage. This brother went to school and is now a clerk in Government service.

Personal History

Childhood: N.a.d. disclosed.
Schooling: Nil, but was baptised in childhood. Not a communicant.
Work: Petty trader.
Marriage: Husband is sometimes a lorry-driver, sometimes a watch-repairer, and sometimes farms his mother's cocoa in her village. The patient does not accompany him there. The patient and her husband often quarrel: he is truculent but fulfils his financial obligations. Recently, the patient went to her husband's house to sleep but found another woman (not another wife) with him. Patient made a scene and he beat her.

Children: Five born. Two died. Youngest about seven months.

Household: Patient lives with her mother and a number of her mother's siblings and their children.

Previous Personality: The patient has always been indulged by and dependent upon her capable mother, from whom she has never been separated. The mother looks after the patient's children. The patient is peevish and irritable at home, quarrels with all the other house people, but is charming and taking with strangers.

Present Illness

The onset was about a month ago immediately after the quarrel with her husband. She complained of pains in the back of her neck, hung her head and could not lift it. (The metaphorical expression used by people who have been publicly humiliated is "Mintumi ma mi ti so"—"I can't lift up my head.") She went to two different clinics and received courses of treatment, was always better for the rest of the day of a hospital visit, but just as bad on the next day. Then she confessed to having cursed her husband and said Mframa had "caught" her.

First Interview: 11.9.56

At the shrine she stood in the sinner's dock, wept conspicuously and said she had done evil and been "caught" with an affliction of the neck. She was duly fined and cleansed.

In her lodgings she was sulky, peevish and irritable, lying all day on her mat, waited upon by her mother and complaining that she was not getting better. Physically, she seemed extremely well.

19.9.56. She appeared in the dock again, trembling and terrified. She said she was not getting better and knew why, viz., that she had committed adultery with four different men before the quarrel with her husband.

20.9.56. Her confession yesterday transformed her. She says she is now quite well and looks it. She also says the milk has come back into her breasts. She has resumed suckling her child.

25.9.56. Appeared again in the dock, again miserable and with more to confess. There was a big crowd of suppliants and she did not get a turn.

28.9.56. Her husband has arrived and they appeared at the shrine together. She produced the names of more men with whom she had committed adultery and was fined another sheep. She and her husband engaged in a loud altercation before the shrine, and the *obosom*, annoyed, promptly "went to sleep" and closed the session.

3.10.56. The husband has gone off in a huff. The patient is apparently resigned. To-day she brought her sheep and rum. The mother has taken all this very casually. She probably knew of her daughter's promiscuity and seems content with the outcome.

1.2.57. Returned to tell the *obosom* that her husband had divorced her. She looks well, plump, smiling and coquettish. To me she complained —wreathed in smiles—of all sorts of aches and pains all over.

COMMENTARY

Conversion hysteria and guilty anxiety in an immature, irresponsible personality.

CASE 61. GEORGES DUBOIS of Mampong district, Ashanti. M. 30.

Shrine
Kyinaman, Bredi.

Reason for referral
"Caught" by *obosom* for transgression.

Family History
Father: Frenchman. Trader. The patient's mother consorted with him when she went to the French Ivory Coast to visit a relative trading there.

Mother: Illiterate Fante, trading in Kumasi. She is one of the two sisters who brought the patient Adzwowa A. (Case No. 96) to Bredi about fourteen months ago.

Personal History
Childhood: The home in Kumasi contained the patient's mother and mother's sister Ama G. who died in Bredi. The patient maintains that this aunt loved him and brought him up, whereas his mother has never cared for him and he has always hated her.

Schooling: Anglican school. Reached Primary Form II, second in the class. He could go no higher because of lack of money. He regards himself as an Anglican Christian. His schooling was paid for by his aunt, Adwowa A.

Work: He has been a cocoa-buyer for a big firm for ten years. He also has his own farm.

Marriage: One wife. Illiterate. A happy marriage. His mother never approved of this marriage as the wife is an Ashanti. (I saw the wife; she was intelligent and pleasant.)

Children: Three. Eldest at school.

Home: Patient, wife and children.

Present Illness
Shortly after the death of the aunt (Adwowa A., Case No. 96), fourteen months ago, the patient's mother was in trading difficulties from

which she would formerly have been rescued by the aunt. She applied to the patient for money. He retorted that she had never done anything for him and had always hated him. There was a violent quarrel in which he said he hated her and wished her dead. He cursed her to God.

Some weeks later his mother appeared again and upbraided him for neglecting her. There was another quarrel in which he vowed he would never see her again. He furthermore resolved that he would murder her with either a gun or a cutlass. While brooding on this intended murder he remembered that he had drunk at the *obosom's* shrine, as also had his mother, and that the *obosom* punished evil intentions towards others. He grew frightened, trembling and ill with asthma and palpitations. He had never had asthma before.

For six weeks before coming to the shrine he had been off work and his employers had paid for him to attend various doctors and a hospital, but none had succeeded in relieving the asthma for more than a few hours. His dreams became terrifying: he dreamt that fierce people carried him away into a thick forest and made him stand up while they rubbed poisons all over him to make him die. He became convinced that he was dying and "couldn't think about anything else except going to die". He had no sleep at all for three weeks and admits that he was mentally quite "*basa-basa*".

His wife brought him to Bredi.

First Interview

I saw the patient two days after he had confessed at the shrine and been freed from the fear of death. The asthma had disappeared immediately after confession and had not returned. He had had two nights' sleep and said that except for slight palpitation he was feeling quite well. He looked fidgety, anxious and tremulous and was wringing his fingers nervously. He had still to face his mother, with whom the *obosom* had ordered him to make peace.

Progress

Two days later he said the palpitations had stopped. He seemed quite composed. On my next visit to the shrine, after another two days, he had gone home, by all accounts quite well.

COMMENTARY

Asthma and mental disorientation, reactive to fear and guilt.

III

ANXIETY UNRELATED TO GUILT

It has already been pointed out, in the account of the troubles and desires unfolded every day at routine *abisa*, that a host of aches and pains, palpitations, feelings of weakness, restlessness and so forth, are deemed by the priest, rightly no doubt, to be due to the patient's faulty relations with other people. In fact, minor "anxiety states" take as heavy a toll of serenity, efficiency and happiness as in our own society, but do not, as a rule, incapacitate the patient. He struggles on, conscious of poor sleep, pains all over and so on, though he may take a day off to come to the shrine and say, "I have never been happy in my life", or, "I dream that I am stuck in the mud."

At the other end of the scale of anxiety is the dramatic spectacle of the man who has committed a cardinal offence against the deity and is in a mad frenzy of fear.

In between these two extremes are a number of anxious persons not conscious of wrong-doing, who are either in or upon the verge of incapacitation. Some articulately attribute their state of mind to a plausible cause: some have no explanation.

Since these anxious patients include some who come complaining only of vivid dreams, this is a convenient point for making a few general observations about the dreams of rural Africans in this part of Africa.*

1. There is often little or no difference between the manifest content of a dream and the latent content. For instance, a teacher who lived in fear of death through the combined machinations of a literate colleague and an illiterate kinsman dreamt that he saw himself being brought to his grave in a coffin carried by a literate at one end and an illiterate at the other.

2. The dreams which people call "big dreams"—clear, vivid dreams with a haunting affect—usually enunciate, as did the dream just quoted,

* It must be remembered that Africa is a large continent containing many different races and people, some no doubt with other methods of thinking and dreaming.

275

the dreamer's current manifest situation. That situation must, of course, be heavily charged with emotion. Seldom does any deeper layer of consciousness appear to be tapped, at any rate in the dreams that people bring to shrines. One patient described to me a "big" dream of happier affect than most. He was staying at the shrine of a prosperous priest who was famous locally for possessing grand iron bedsteads even in his "village". The patient, after telling the priest his troubles, dreamt that he was in a room containing a grand iron bedstead, and also in the room to his surprise he found his father (who had in fact been long dead). That was the whole dream. There we have, no doubt, the priest in his rôle of psychiatric father-figure.

3. People in identical anxiety-charged situations tend to have identical stereotyped dreams. For instance, a person who has transgressed his *obosom's* law and anticipates punishment, dreams that he is fleeing from a shaggy-haired *obosomfo* brandishing an *obosom's* wooden club and that he is overtaken, hit on the head and falls down. Again, people who have taken radical measures to avert impending disaster dream that they jump out of a runaway lorry and are thereby saved when the lorry crashes. People afraid that they are becoming witches dream that other witches are calling, "Get up and let's go!"* (to the witches' revels), or that they are refusing to eat human flesh or other proffered meat.

4. Most dreams sum up a situation in simple parabolic metaphor. Concrete objects are not used to disguise other equally concrete objects but to represent, in allegorical symbolism, such abstracts as danger, death, fear, ambition, treachery, witchcraft, etc., which must be provided with concrete images before they can act on the dream stage. Not only has the simple parable proved a highly acceptable aid to understanding ("And without a parable spake he not unto them") and a common mode of dreaming at night, but it is perhaps the easiest mode of talking by day. It is easier to say, "I have missed the bus", and to dream of missing a bus, than to say, "I am in difficulty because I failed to make prompt use of a transient opportunity." The shapes and other physical properties of the objects in this allegorical dreaming are irrelevant. If a cocoa-farmer dreams of a snake in the grass it usually means exactly what we mean when we *speak* of a snake in the grass—treachery: the dreamer suspects a smooth-spoken neighbour of stealing his cocoa. If he dreams of a house it is probably as a symbol of security—"as safe as houses". Over and over again we find the rural African, when overwhelmed by a sense of impending disaster, dreaming out exactly the

* The words never vary: "*Sore! Mayenko!*"

same metaphors which rushed to the lips of the psalmist who cried, "Save me, oh God, for the waters are come in even unto my soul. I stick fast in the deep mire where no ground is. . . . Let not the flood drown me, neither let the deep swallow me up. And let not the pit shut her mouth on me."

5. There are certain dream symbols traditionally associated with certain topics. For instance, people worrying about witchcraft expect to dream of mushrooms, and do. I doubt if such symbols were ever instinctively chosen: their association with their topics was probably once quite obvious but is now lost in the mists of antiquity. The association between dream-mushrooms and sorcery is widespread in Africa and elsewhere: it probably stems from the use, now forgotten in Africa, of hallucinogenic mushrooms by soothsayers. Mr. Robert Graves tells me that the Delphic sibyls—in relatively recent times—inhaled the fumes of such mushrooms, and he thinks the "emerods" on the Mosaic ark were also representations of these mushrooms. Modern West Africans are inclined, however, to invent their own highly characteristic explanation of the association between dream-mushrooms and witchcraft. "When there is witchcraft, you never know who is a witch. It is the same with mushrooms: you have to be careful because the bad ones often look just like the good ones."

CASE 62. WILLIAM KODZO M. of Cape Coast district (Fante). M. 40+.

Shrine
   Mframa at Mframaso.

Reason for referral
   Impotence.

Family History
   Father: Dead. Non-Christian illiterate of Moree.
   Mother: Not cross-cousin. Patient's father was a widower when she married him.
   Siblings: Patient is the third. Two brothers, two sisters. One brother is a carpenter, one a fisherman. Patient is the only literate and the others are envious of his literacy—or so he thinks.

Personal History
   Childhood: Traditional type of home, with father in separate house from mother and children: the latter lived with maternal grandmother, her children and grandchildren.

School: Mission school. Reached Standard V. Became Church member. Maternal uncle paid for schooling and the patient lived with him during school years. Schooling was intermittent because uncle was erratic in paying fees. After leaving school and beginning to earn he took a Bennett College Correspondence Course.

Work: (1) Apprentice carpenter. Later, wage-earning carpenter.

(2) Builder's foreman, European firm. Reason for leaving not disclosed.

(3) Builder's foreman to another firm. Reason for leaving not disclosed.

(4) Building contractor on his own, but the business failed six years ago.

(5) Jobless and "helpless" for two years. Lived on relatives.

(6) Obtained a loan and bought a portable cinema with which he travels round on public passenger-lorries and gives evening shows. The work does not pay and he does not know whether this is due to bad medicine by envious people or to witches in his family. He came to Mframaso for protection three months ago, but the work has not improved much.

Marriage: Married ten times. "This is a big trouble."

(1) First marriage shortly after leaving school. Three children by this marriage. After four or five years the wife died.

(2) Patient divorced the second wife for promiscuous infidelity ("going here and there").

(3) The wife died pregnant.

(4) One child. Patient says he divorced this wife because she was dirty.

(5) Divorced for "going here and there". After being divorced "this woman put a medicine on me to make other woman go away, because she thought that if I couldn't get another woman I would go back to her".

(6) (7) (8) (9). These all divorced the patient. He believes this was because of the medicine put on him by the fifth wife, though various medicine-men have told him that witches among his kin are responsible.

(10) Married six months ago. The wife is a young schoolgirl who was pregnant by a schoolboy at the time when the patient made his betrothal commitments with her parents. The pregnancy was then disclosed and the marriage postponed till the child was five months old. This wife has never felt any regard for the patient and once ran away, but was brought back by her father.

Present Illness

Recently the patient left his wife for three weeks to travel with his cinema. On his return she wanted to divorce him for desertion. Her father reconciled them, but the patient then found that he was impotent.

278

"She is a young girl and she wants to go to a young man, but she has no excuse to leave me so she has made a bad medicine to take away my power." The patient had never been impotent before.

Interview: 12.7.57

This patient made his *abisa* in the evening at dusk, and I saw him only once later, on the same evening by the feeble light of a lantern. African faces require strong illumination to be adequately seen at night, so I could not judge whether he was ill-favoured or what was his facial expression. In build he was big, slightly obese and slow-moving. Unlike other Africans, he spoke in slow, deliberate measures without either animation or indignation. He gave a clear, straightforward account of himself without heat. My impression was that he belonged to the "simple-minded, good-hearted" type that often develops schizophrenia simplex. He declined a small "dash" for cigarettes, saying that he did not smoke. I have known only one other informant who declined a similar "dash".

COMMENTARY

Anxiety with impotence in a simple-minded, elderly, unsuccessful man, always attracted by flighty young women and always repeating his rôle of dupe and cuckold. Probably a well-preserved schizophrene. Under traditional "tribal" conditions he would no doubt have "got by" without difficulty, but cannot organise his own affairs successfully.

I have not placed this patient among the paranoid anxieties because I think it likely that his anxiety is secondary to repeated failures in work and marriage and the necessity of explaining them away.

CASE 63. KWABENA A. of Konongo district, Ashanti. M. *c.* 50.

Shrine

Mframa at Mframaso.

Reason for referral

Sleeplessness.

Family History

See Yaa N., sister (Case No. 4).

Personal History

Non-Christian, illiterate cocoa-farmer. He has had several wives and sixteen children, eight of whom survive. The dead ones would now be adult had they lived. The survivors are still children.

Household

The patient, his elder sister and a younger sister. The latter has thirteen children and some grandchildren, most of whom are in the house. The elder sister was "caught" by Tigari five years ago, and proclaimed herself a witch, and from being a hard-working asset became a burden, miserable, restless and unable to work. She and the patient are always irritable with one another. He taunts her with being a witch.

Present Illness

The onset was eighteen months ago. A few days previously the depressed sister went to a local medicine-man to seek relief from her illness. The patient came to know of this and became uneasy lest she should be making bad medicine against him. A day or two later the iron bedstead on which the patient was sleeping with his wife collapsed in the middle of the night and shot him on to the floor. This convinced him that evil was being wrought against him and a few days later he became unable to sleep. His sister was the focus of his fears. He says he has had no sleep for eighteen months except under hypnotics bought (illicitly) from a dispenser. He has spent £10 on these. He showed me a bottle labelled Soneryl.

Interview: 13.5.56

A sharp-nosed, sour, anxious, restless, suspicious man: quite sure that his sickness is someone else's fault. His physical condition looks satisfactory, though he is thin. He shows no signs of psychosis or intellectual impairment. He came to ask me for hypnotics but divulged nothing of significance concerning himself. Most of what I learnt was told at the shrine or by his sister. He denies that he has any worries. Asked what he thinks about when he is lying awake, says he lies wondering why he cannot sleep.

He organised the expedition to Mframaso and brought his sister and a group of relatives. He says he still works on his farms, but not so hard as he would if he could sleep.

1.6.56. He stayed for a few weeks after his sister had left, presumably to be under the *obosom's* wing till she had caused the medicine-man to nullify the bad magic. He then became disgruntled with the *sinkwafo's* treatment and went away to another neighbouring shrine.

20.11.56. He reappeared at Mframaso but stayed only long enough to attend *abisa* and thank the *obosom*. He said he was in too great a hurry to talk to me, but he looked happier.

COMMENTARY

Anxiety due to fear of sorcery and death in an aggressive, suspicious man at the involutional age. The fact that the first indication—as it seemed to him—of an attempt on his life occurred in his sleep probably provoked an unconscious fear of going to sleep.

Though he is an unattractive personality and afraid of his sister, I should not call him unduly paranoid.

CASE 64. AMA G. of Kwahu. F. *c.* 50.

Shrine

Amfemfi at Asueyi.

Reason for referral

Dreams indicative of enticement by witches.

Family History

Parents: Cross-cousins. Illiterate, non-Christian cocoa-farmers. Both still living.

Siblings: One sister alive. One brother dead. The sister has only one child and the patient believes her envious of her children. She lives far away in Koforidua, trading.

Other Relatives: Patient thinks that her mother and all her mother's family envy her, although she seldom sees them.

Personal History

Childhood: N.a.d. Parents and children in father's "village".

Schooling: Nil. Non-Christian.

Marriage: Husband a cocoa-farmer, formerly a blacksmith. A big, sensible, friendly man. Patient is his only wife.

Children: Seven born, all living. Some are literate. Eldest took a commercial course and is a counter-clerk in a big Accra store. Daughters married and have children.

Present Illness

About a week ago the patient dreamt that she heard someone calling, "Ama! Get up and let's go!" She was terrified and thought witches wanted her to go off with them and be a witch. She felt sure there were witches among her mother's family although no one had ever been "caught". The next night she dreamt that she was walking and someone whom she did not see put a heavy load on her head. She woke her husband in a panic and told him witches had put something heavy on her head. Later, during the night, she wanted to go out to the latrine, but her fright was such that her husband had to go with her. On the way there she said the load was still on her head. She says she has felt it there ever since. She has hardly slept at all since the first bad dream.

First Interview

A small, ill-favoured, skinny woman. Very fidgety and anxious. Her face was deeply lined as with long, habitual worrying. Outstanding feature—voluble indignation. She insists that people have always disliked and envied her. No self-reproach. No hallucinations.

Progress

She was seen only once, and then in the presence of an audience. She went home the day after putting herself under the protection of the *obosom*. She reported good sleep on the night after this ceremony.

COMMENTARY

Involutional misgivings in an irritable, anxious and paranoid personality.

CASE 65. AMA J. of Wenchi district, Ashanti. F. *c.* 28.

Shrine

Mframa at Mframaso.

Reason for referral

Suspicions by relatives of witchcraft. Sleeplessness, troubled dreams, blindness, fear of impending disaster.

Family History

Whole sibling of Francis Kwame B. (Case No. 42).

Personal History

Schooling: Nil, but she is a Christian.

Work: She makes and sells bread and fried cakes. She was successful till her illness.

Marriage: Husband is a non-Christian petty trader. There are no other wives. The patient went back to her mother at the onset of her illness.

Children: One only, now about seven years.

Previous Personality: She is said to have been hardworking and on bad terms with no one.

Present Illness

The onset was about six months ago. She had back-ache, headache, belly-ache, and pains all over. When she ate, she felt the food turn into a lump in her belly. She said she knew she was going to die. She was sent to hospital, where she stayed twelve days and then discharged herself. (Diagnosis from hospital: Chronic G.C., trichomonas and lavae of strongyloides.) On leaving hospital, she went to a Kramu medicine-man, but thought he maliciously gave her something to make her worse.

She had frightening dreams: (1) that she was tied with a rope, (2) that she was lost in a strange town, (3) that her *kra* was bowed down, and (4) that she could not see her way. She then became sleepless and felt that the house was going to fall on her. She also, at times, became unable to see.

Shortly after this one of her male relatives, one of the chief's elders, was with him in a car which skidded into a ditch. No one was hurt, but the patient's relative considered that some witch must have caused the accident and it was thought significant that the patient appeared to have been "caught". A half-sibling, who was a drunkard, openly accused her, in his cups, of being the cause of his addiction. So she was brought to the *obosom*.

Interview

At the shrine, when addressed by the *obosom*, she annoyed him by uttering only squeaky moans and whimpers and the hearing of her case was adjourned.

At interview in the interval, she presented as a diminutive, thin woman, resentful rather than depressive. She said that everyone thought she was a witch, whereas she was not, that the Kramu had deliberately made her worse and that her family were to blame for her condition for sending her to hospital instead of to the shrine when she first fell ill.

After several appearances at the shrine, still unable to talk, she at last appeared accompanied by the uncle who had been in the car and the relative who complained of being a drunkard. The *obosom* told each of them that some witch in the family was responsible. Thereupon the patient, when next asked if she was a witch, said, "Yes", and was told to go and make a full confession to the clerk.

Her "confession" contained no fantasies. She mentioned all the deaths, accidents and illnesses which had smitten the family and said she was responsible. That she had had only one child was, as is usual, attributed to her own witchcraft: she had "eaten the children in her belly".

Progress

When she next came, bringing her sacrificial cow, she was much better. When I later visited her home both she and her mother had gone to the mother's "village".

Commentary

Gonococcal "one-child sterility"—less common since the advent of "smoggri" (smuggled) and other illicit penicillin.

Her anxiety, dreams and hysterical blindness seem to have preceded her family's imputation of witchcraft. As is usual in those few cases where the rôle of witch is thrust upon, rather than irrationally embraced by, the patient, the first suggestion was made by a drunkard. She is probably afraid that her husband will take another wife.

CASE 66. AKOSUA E. of Wenchi district, Ashanti. F. *c*. 28.

Shrine
Mframa at Mframaso.

Reason for referral
Dreams.

Family History

Parents: Not cross-cousins. The father, an illiterate Christian cocoa-farmer in a village near Wenchi, died three years ago. The mother's home was near Wenchi. The mother is still living.

Siblings: Eleven born, eight surviving. Only one went to school. He is now a lorry-driver.

Personal History

Childhood: N.a.d. disclosed.

Schooling: Nil, but she is a Christian.

Work: She was a cloth trader in Sunyani for five years.

Marriage: She married about eleven years ago. Her husband, a literate lorry-driver and native of the Kwahu district, was driving his own lorry based on Wenchi when he met the patient and she continued for several years to live with her mother in the traditional manner. Then her husband's family in Kwahu bought a lorry and sent for him to drive it for them. The arrangement was financially unsatisfactory, so the husband went to drive for a European for about five years. Then the husband took six months' "leave" and went home to Kwahu, taking the patient with him. It was there that she fell sick. The patient says her husband's relatives are disagreeable to everyone, but her they especially dislike. She gives as the only reason that she is a stranger. After six months the husband went to drive for a firm in Kumasi, where he still is. She has never joined him there. She says she and her husband love one another, but both want more children. He treats her well. The husband had another wife beside the patient but has divorced her now.

Children: One miscarriage, then one healthy child now nine years old. The patient thinks that someone has made bad medicine to prevent her bearing more children.

284

Present Illness

This began about a year ago when she was with her husband's family in Kwahu. She felt something rolling about in her belly and rolling up into her chest. She had giddiness, palpitations and pains in her backbone. She also dreamt that she went to the latrine and that one foot slipped and became soiled with faeces. She had out-patient treatment at the nearest hospital but the trouble grew worse. When her husband left Kwahu she came home to her mother near Wenchi where she had further bad dreams, mostly recurrent, as follows:

(1) A snake chases her.
(2) Two cows chase her.
(3) She is in a graveyard jumping over the graves.
(4) Someone (unknown) is dead in a coffin and the dreamer jumps over the coffin.
(5) A dead brother is near her.
(6) A church congregation ask her to go with them.
(7) She finds herself dead and unable to move.
(8) A strange European man stands over her and tells her that her intestines are decayed.
(9) She dreamt once that she was weeding the cemetery. A coffin containing a corpse was there and something made her open the coffin and give food to the corpse.

She then went into hospital as an in-patient, but felt that the sickness was getting worse, so she discharged herself and came to Mframaso complaining of the ubiquitous cow-dream. (Hospital records destroyed. Probably gonococcal "one-child sterility".)

At Mframaso the *obosom* told her that there was no witchcraft involved, but someone had made a bad *suman* or *adutu* against her.

Interview

A pretty, well-turned out, healthy-looking young woman, fully conscious of her attractiveness. She was full of her aches and pains. There is no self-reproach: she is sure that her husband's family are to blame.

Progress

She stayed in Mframaso for nine months, going often to Wenchi to see her mother. There is only small improvement. She is still full of aches and pains and not free of bad dreams.

COMMENTARY

Anxiety reactive to marital stress and sterility. She is probably worrying lest her husband take another wife to bear children.

With regard to the dream of the European: a European (especially with Christians) usually means judgment and censure. I recall a frenzied woman whom I met years ago in a medicine-man's compound. At the sight of me she cowered in terror, crying, "You are white, like God. You have come to judge me, like God."

CASE 67. KWABENA F. of Wenchi district. M. *c.* 20.

Shrine

Mframa at Mframaso.

Reason for referral

"Big" dreams.

Family and Personal History

No information, patient was seen only for a few minutes as he was about to leave.

Present Illness

A few weeks ago the patient's wife, a sturdy, young woman of roughly his own age, bore her first child which almost immediately died. Both parents were normally disappointed. I saw the wife at the time, for she came complaining that lactation did not stop and her breasts were engorged and painful. She was otherwise quite well and took her loss with composure. The husband, however, had several dreams which were so vivid that he could not forget them and felt he must tell the *obosom*.

Dreams

(1) The dreamer saw a big water-butt full of water and saw his wife weeping.

(2) The dreamer was weeping and saw two women who asked him why. They said he must stop crying for they had put honey in his wife's belly and she would have another child.

(3) The dreamer found a big water-butt containing a dead body in his sleeping-room. He was frightened and told his wife that they should leave the dead body and sleep elsewhere. She agreed, so they left it and slept elsewhere.

At the shrine the *obosom* reassured him that the death was natural ("God's death"), told him to kill a fowl for Mframa, make his request for another child and go.

Interview

Both parents seemed cheerful, friendly, healthy young people, but the husband had been drinking palm-wine with his friends after his *abisa*, which may have obscured anxiety.

COMMENTARY

The loss of children is so common and, as a rule, so stoically accepted, that this man's anxiety must be regarded as unexplained.

CASE 68. ADWOWA D. of Bekwai district, Ashanti. F. *c.* 36.

Shrine

Mframa at Mframaso.

Reason for referral

Fear of becoming a witch.

Family History

Parents: Not cross-cousins. Both alive. Non-Christian, illiterate cocoa-farmers. The father had three wives. The mother left him when the patient was an infant. She married again and had four more children. The mother was "caught" by the *obosom* Tigari for witchcraft nine years ago, talked "*basa-basa*" and was wild and "mad". She went to Tigari and confessed and the madness left her, but it is presumed that she did not confess everything for she is still "caught". At first she was mute, but now talks a little, though she will not converse freely and if any caller comes she locks herself in her room. She spends most of her time lying down, but has lately begun to walk occasionally to the farm.

Siblings: Nine born, two died. Eldest sister was "caught" by an *obosom* for witchcraft a year before the mother. This sister bore ten children, of whom seven survived and had children of their own before their mother's illness. This illness lasted three years, with "madness", weeping, inability to work and affirmations of having killed many people.

Personal History

Childhood: The patient and her mother lived in the grandmother's house in a cocoa-"village" with three uncles and their wives and children. Each had his own cocoa-farm. Patient continued in this house after her marriage.

Schooling: Nil. Non-Christian.

Work: Has her own cocoa-farm and is successful. She thinks her prosperity provokes envy. She says many people don't like her and quarrel with her because of her cocoa.

Marriage: Cross-cousin. Patient is the only wife. The marriage was happy till husband developed leprosy and patient left him about a year ago. Since then she has consorted with a lover who has another wife, but she says she doesn't want to marry him.

Children: One born sixteen years ago. Died aged one week.

Present Illness

Three years ago the patient and her husband came to the shrine to put themselves under protection, presumably because the husband had begun to show signs of leprosy. Before the patient left the husband she dreamt that a cow had been killed and that many people had gathered round the dead carcass. As a dead-cow dream is widely supposed to mean that the dreamer is to be given an *obayi* she was much frightened and went to the town rubbish-heap and there prayed to Mframa. Recently the same dream has often recurred and the patient feels that her mother, who is not wholly cleaned of witchcraft, is imparting the power to her.

She is able to do her work, but is restless, seldom sleeps, and when she does has either troubled "*basa-basa*" dreams which she cannot remember, or the dead-cow dream, which is always vivid.

Interview: 16.6.57

I could see her only briefly as she did not appear till evening *abisa*, had some cleansing rites to do after it and was leaving at daybreak the next day. At the shrine she told her story fluently and indignantly, saying that her family was full of witches and that she was afraid they wanted to make her one of them. The *obosom* subscribed to this. At interview she seemed very near to tears although she shed none. Her face was drawn, anxious and frightened. She talked excitedly, was loudly indignant, but was friendly towards me and gave a good account of herself. She seemed an intelligent and active type.

COMMENTARY

Anxiety and fear, reactive to events, in a woman with a bad family history of affective illness. The dead cow—i.e., a large piece of "meat" —is so universally associated with witchcraft that anyone afraid of becoming a witch expects to dream this, and does.

Though I did not ask her, it is likely that she feels that her witchcraft gave her husband his leprosy. As her house contains self-confessed witches, it is highly probable that both her husband and his kinsmen hinted at this.

CASE 69. ADWOWA W. of Akwapim. F. *c.* 30.

Shrine

Mframa at Mframaso.

Reason for referral

Fear of becoming a witch.

Family History

Parents: Not cross-cousins; both are dead. They were illiterate non-Christians. The father was a senior chief in Akwapim. The mother came from Akim. The father had several other wives.

Siblings: Four born, all living. The patient and a sister are farmers; one brother stays in the chief's house and does no other work. One trades in soap in Kumasi. The soap-trader alone is literate.

Mother's sisters: One was "caught" by Tigari for witchcraft six years ago. The patient was absent and does not know how long the illness lasted, or its nature, but the aunt is now well. The son of the mother's other sister drinks heavily and was brought by his mother to Mframaso several years ago, but refused to put himself under the *obosom*, saying that he knew he could not desist from drinking and would someday do something punishable and be "caught" for it.

Personal History

Childhood: She was about eight when her mother died, thereafter was cared for by her grandmother, who died about fifteen years ago.

Schooling: Nil, but she went to the Presbyterian Church, and still does.

Work: Food-farming.

Marriage: Her first husband was a native of her home-town, but she divorced him because he failed to support her. She then married her cross-cousin. He has no other wives. He has his own cocoa-farm and also farms for absentee farmers on the *"busa"* system. He was unable to stop drinking, so he became a Mohammedan about four years ago, since when, the patient says, he has abstained. She says he is a good husband and insists that they are happy, but she is clearly apprehensive lest he should relapse.

Children: Two children by the first husband, five by the second. The eldest died. The eldest survivor, aged ten, is at school.

Household: In an Akwapim colony in Akim Aboakwa. Husband, patient, children and some of the husband's labourers. Two of the mother's sisters live in the same colony but in different households.

Present Illness

Two months ago the patient dreamt that she saw "many black mushrooms". In her dream her mother's sister (the one whose son drinks) asked her to help pick these mushrooms. She picked two and then was afraid, threw them away and refused to pick any more. The next night she had palpitations and could not sleep. She consulted a medicine-man, who said the dream meant that someone wanted to give her an *obayi*, but her spirit resisted it. He made some "medicine" for her but she got no better, so went to a dispenser and had one injection. After that the palpitations were so bad that she had no sleep at all, so she went to a second medicine-man, who said the same as the first. The patient's aunt, the one who figured in the dream, advised the patient to come to Mframaso and said she would come with her. At Mframa's shrine she was again told that someone wanted to give her an *obayi*, the implication being that the person she dreamt of was that "someone". She was instructed to present a sheep and receive ritual baths for seven days.

Interview: 5.1.57

I was not able to interview her till a few days after the baths had begun. She said she was much better for them. She was a healthy-looking, well-nourished young woman with well-cared-for children and seemed of very good intelligence. She was over-talkative, chattering in a very rapid gabble, vivacious and smiling in conversation, but in repose she looked very anxious. She said she was a close friend of the aunt she dreamt about. I asked her what she thought the dream meant and she said evasively that she thought it meant that she and the aunt were both going to die because mushrooms meant danger, and black meant death and sorrow. I had no doubt, however, that she had accepted the reiterated interpretation concerning the *obayi*.

21.1.57. She is no longer talkative, but subdued and looks anxious. She has been joined by the aunt whose son drinks. This aunt is already under Mframa's protection. She also looks anxious and depressed.

1.2.57. She is trying hard to persuade herself that she is better, but she still looks extremely anxious and apprehensive. She is no longer worried about the attempt to thrust an *obayi* upon her, but she had not told the *obosom* of her worry concerning her husband.

10.2.57. She went away as soon as she had completed the short course of ritual bathing but she looked no better.

COMMENTARY

The patient's mushroom dream can be interpreted in two ways. The first refers simply to the dreamer's refusal to admit that she may have to partake of her aunt's black and bitter lot. The second explicitly involves witchcraft (as, indeed, the various *abosomfo* said), mushrooms being one of the traditional dream-symbols of sorcery. Drunkards are virtually the only people who ever accuse others, point-blank, of witchcraft. They insist that the witches have put the drink-craving into them "to bring them down into poverty and disgrace". Both the women figuring in this case had almost certainly considered the possibility of their being the unwitting cause of their menfolk's drunkenness: if so, they must have deemed it obvious that the younger woman would receive her *obayi* from the older.

CASE 70. KWAKU T. of Anum district, Trans-Volta. M. *c.* 26.

Shrine
Tigari at Suhum.

Reason for referral
"Useless" arm.

Family History
Father: Alive and well. Illiterate, non-Christian cocoa-farmer, colonising Kade in Akim. He has two wives, the patient's mother being the junior of the two. He had three children by the senior wife before he married the junior.

Mother: Alive and well. She brought the patient to the shrine.

Siblings: The patient is the third of his mother's eight children. There were twelve half-siblings—six of whom died—by his father's other wife.

Household: In the home-town the father and the two wives live in three different houses, but when cocoa-farming in their cocoa-village near Kade they are all together. The house in which the patient was born belonged to his mother's family and housed also the mother's sister and her children and the mother's brother.

Personal History
Childhood: At the age of about four the patient fell sick. He does not know the nature of the sickness. Shortly after this a woman relative of his mother, previously regarded with affection and respect, also fell sick and surprised everyone by saying that she was a witch, had killed seven out of her own ten children, numerous other children besides, and was also the cause of the patient's sickness.

The patient and the woman were taken to a medicine-man: the woman was cleansed and sent home, the patient stayed on for treatment.

The patient conceived a great affection for the medicine-man, was reluctant to leave and stayed on for ten years, virtually adopted as a son. His duty was to sweep his foster-father's room, lay his table and generally wait on him. This he did with devotion. At the end of ten years the medicine-man died and the patient was disconsolate. He was taken home to his father's house where he wept a great deal. His father's house contained also his father's sister and her son. The father's other children often visited the house but lived in their respective mothers' houses. The father's sister was kind and her young son friendly, but the patient continued to grieve.

School: When the patient returned to his father's house he was then about fourteen and at that age he began school at the bottom, the other children laughing at him. He stayed at school till the age of twenty-two (sic), attaining Standard IV (top is VII), and then his father, having other children to educate, removed him from school.

Work: Six months after leaving school he was apprenticed to a lorry-driver, and worked as driver's mate. His father paid the driver a guinea, a bottle of whisky and a tin of cigarettes, and promised £5 at the end of the course. The patient conceived for this master the same kind of devotion he had had for the medicine-man. He fetched water for his bath, swept his room and helped his wife to cook his meals. He says the master was "good" and that he loved him.

He remained a driver's mate for four years, failed his driving-test three times, but passed at the fourth attempt. He then got a post as "spare driver", at £5 a month.

Another driver's mate, who had failed his test at the time when the patient passed, was jealous of him—or so the patient thought—and wished him ill. The patient was afraid he might make a bad medicine against him so that his lorry would run into the ditch and be wrecked.

Marriage: The patient has never considered it.

Present Illness

The onset was over a year ago, about four weeks after starting to drive alone.

His fear of the machinations of the jealous driver's mate made him very nervous of driving. One morning as he was dressing to go to work he had a sudden pain in his right arm from shoulder to elbow. He was unable to bend the elbow and unable to drive. He went to a qualified doctor who gave him—he says—purgatives and two injections, but without effect on the arm.

His father then sent him to stay with a medicine-man near Kade. This practitioner confirmed that the sickness was due to bad medicine by an enemy. The patient did not take to this medicine-man, felt no confidence in his treatment, failed to improve and ran away to his mother.

His mother brought him to stay with a Tigari priest at Suhum. This priest is a very good personality, kindly and reassuring, a good psychotherapist and much respected. He agreed that the sickness was caused by the envious rival and said he could both cure the patient and give him Tigari's permanent protection from harm.

Interview: 12.12.55

When first seen the patient had been seven days with his new protector, had bathed his arm every day in Tigari's consecrated water, had regained the power of bending his elbow and had lost his pain.

There were no neurological signs, no weakness in hand or arm, no loss of sensation or muscle-power, and no wasting. The patient was slight in build, diffident and complying. He looked considerably less than his age. He was languid and apathetic, but said he was beginning to feel better. He described himself as "never bold" and seemed a gentle and inadequate personality.

10.1.56. He has much improved in vitality and is smiling and talking spontaneously. He has become attached to the Tigari priest and plans to bring his lorry to Suhum and drive it from there in order to be near this new protector, whom he now speaks of as his "father". He says he is now satisfied that no harm can come to him.

1.6.56. I had news of him that he is happily at work, keeping well and still clinging to his new "father".

COMMENTARY

This is a conversion hysteria in a timid, inadequate personality, never happy without a sustaining "father-figure". I do not regard his outlook as morbidly paranoid. The driver who failed to pass the driving-test probably was indeed jealous of the patient's success and would have liked to see him come to grief. The patient was not, like the true anxious paranoid, impervious to reassurance.

CASE 71. AMA K. of Akwapim district. F. *c.* 50.

Shrine

Mframa at Mframaso.

Reason for referral

Patient thinks someone has made her into a witch.

Family History

Parents: Cross-cousins. The father is dead. He was an illiterate cocoa-farmer colonising Akim: he was very prosperous and built large houses. He became a Christian towards the end of his life. The mother is alive and well: she is a cocoa-farmer. She became Christian with her husband. She married again after his death, and had more children.

Mother's sister's daughter: She is a witch (see Adwowa S., Case No. 13).

Siblings and half-siblings: The mother bore ten children, of whom four died: two sons and four daughters survive. All are cocoa-farmers. One son is a literate Christian, the others are illiterate non-Christians. Two daughters are Christian, two are not.

Personal History

Childhood: N.a.d. disclosed. No schooling. Non-Christian.

Work: The father gave her a prosperous cocoa-farm. She has also corn-farms and markets the produce. Financially she is extremely well-off.

Marriage: The husband is a non-Christian, illiterate cocoa-farmer.

Children: Six born, three survive. One son is a literate Christian post-master. The elder daughter, about thirty, is married but has no children. The younger daughter is a witch (see Afua N., Case No. 12).

Katamenia: Menopause not yet reached.

Home: In the home-town in Akwapim the house (built by the dead father) contains the patient, one of her sisters, their grown-up children and grandchildren and some other relatives, including Afua N., Adwowa S. and Kwaku D. (Case No. 55).

In the Akim "village" (near Asamankese) the house (built by the patient's father) contains the patient and her husband, the patient's brother, brother's three wives and children, patient's daughter and mother's sister's daughter, which latter two go everywhere with the patient. (Afua N. and Adwowa S.)

History of Present Illness (from husband)

Onset eleven years ago. Patient complained of "pains all over" and said she was "caught" by Tigari because "someone had given her a bad thing". She went to the shrine of Tigari, said she had killed various people and was purified. The pains went away, but she then started to complain of a lump like a foetus walking through her body into her head. She went to innumerable medicine-men, who removed the lump, but it always came back and walked into her head. She complains of "burnings all over like pepper" but has never been sleepless, has never wept and never lost weight.

She has spent the last eleven years in travelling round from one medicine-man to another, staying with them for periods of two years, one year and six months. She always takes with her the daughter who was "caught" by Tigari at the same time as herself, and since her niece was "caught" has taken her too. She herself has spent on her illness more than £350 of her own cocoa-fortune, her sister has given her £100 and her husband about £150.

The husband is a gloomy, long-suffering, thin, worried, laconic man, nearly in tears himself—the antithesis of the patient. He says she talks without ceasing about her ills and he is wearied out by it.

Interview: 21.11.56

A mountainously fat woman who can just carry her weight around with a slow waddle. She talks about her troubles with a vivacious, bright smile and never stops. She takes her witch-daughter and witch-niece everywhere and overpowers them. I had difficulty in getting them alone to hear their stories: neither they nor anyone else get a chance to speak in her presence. They are genuinely depressed: she shows no sign of depression. There is no self-reproach: she says, "Someone has given me a bad thing".

Progress

10.2.57. Patient has settled down in Mframaso and shows no sign of budging. Afua N. and Adwowa S. are with her. The two latter look anaemic as if they might have helminthic infestation, but she will not allow me to estimate their haemoglobin and will not let them join the flocks of people who come to me to be de-wormed. (There are some very effective and safe vermifuges on the market now and the other villagers come and ask for them and have great fun counting the worms expelled).

21.1.58. The two young witches are now being made to plant a food-farm near Mframaso for the patient, who stands over them while they do it. This implies a proposed long stay.

10.2.58. She is still in Mframaso. She has become, on Ashanti diet, less fat, but is still much overweight. A few months ago the *obosomfo* told one of the younger women, Afua N., that she was now cured and must go home. She went, whereat the mother looked depressed for the first time.

COMMENTARY

Hypochondriasis in a non-depressive personality who affirms defect of body rather than defect of character and blames other people. Her influence has adversely affected three weaker characters in her household in addition to her husband, who is himself not far from reactive depression.

IV

THE PARANOID REACTION

In a country where nobody looks twice at a lorry announcing in big letters, "Enemies all about me", or "*Suro nnipa*" (Be afraid of people), it is clear that our ideas of what constitutes a morbidly paranoid attitude must be revised. We have seen, in examining the general outlook of ordinary people who bring their everyday troubles and desires to routine *abisa*, that successful men are full of fear lest they provoke the envious malice of the unsuccessful and that the latter are convinced that spiteful bad medicine is the cause of their failure.

Most rural people, however, accept what they regard as a heavy risk, insure themselves against it at the shrine and then go their way in much the same spirit as people in our own society quietly accept, with no more than a passing shudder, the statistical evidence that they have a high chance of dying by cancer. But just as, in our own society, we are able to recognise as abnormal the man from whom no reassurance can shift the groundless conviction that he has cancer, so we are able in rural Ghana to recognise the morbidly ineradicable paranoid conviction. The man who comes to *abisa* complaining that his "old wife" has, by means of bad medicine, made him impotent with his new wife, is usually *not* paranoid: he is amenable to reassurance and goes home the same day, returning in due time to say that he is cured. But the man who comes and makes a lengthy stay at the shrine, though often less definite about whom or what he suspects, usually has an obstinacy about his suspicions that puts him in a different class. In deciding upon a classification for case-histories I was at first minded to place the milder of the disabling paranoid reactions among the disabling anxieties and those which showed marked impairment of appreciation of external reality among the paranoid psychoses, but have now put into one category all those cases which exhibit in any degree that peculiar recalcitrant obstinacy, whether the distortion of outlook is very slight or whether it amounts to a paranoid schizophrenia.

The universality of the "normal" paranoid attitude makes it necessary to diagnose a paranoid schizophrenia only with caution. Any early schizophrenia which produces subjective interference with the thought process in a setting of clear consciousness may move the patient to indignation: "Someone is putting something into my head." Even a schizophrenia of relatively insidious onset that causes the patient to lose his job through inefficiency will not often prevent him from attributing the loss to witchcraft or bad medicine. This attribution is not an inherent part of the illness: it implies the retention of some insight into it.

CASE 72. CLARENCE KWAME A. of Bekwai district, Ashanti.
M. 18.

Shrine
Mframaso.

Reason for referral
Conviction of supernatural persecution.

Family History
Parents: Illiterate, Christian cocoa-farmers. Cross-cousins.
Siblings: Patient is the youngest of nine. One sister dead. All illiterate cocoa-farmers except patient.
Maternal grandmother: She was "caught" by Tigari and confessed to killing patient's sister who died pregnant. She then became "mad" and cried and said she had done immense wrong. Then she became mute and lay "dead" till she was taken to Tigari's shrine where she revived and recovered speech. The illness lasted two weeks. She is still in the patient's house and he is afraid of her.
Mother's brother: He went to school and did well. On leaving he became interpreter to the District Commissioner. When the District Commissioner went on leave, the interpreter, thereby unemployed, went one day to his farm. A short thunder-storm occurred while he was there and in the storm he heard voices talking to him. This frightened him so that he fell down "with weak legs" and had to take the Sixth and Seventh Books of Moses out of his pocket and read aloud before he could get up. Shortly after this he died. Later a man was "caught" for witchcraft and confessed that he was one of the witch-company whose voices made the victim to fall down in his farm.

Personal History
Childhood: N.a.d.
Schooling: He reached Standard VII at the age of sixteen. Good scholar. Games Captain. The school fees were paid first by the sister who died, and after her death by the uncle who died. The patient

believes that both these benefactors were killed by envious people because they were assisting him to become a rich and famous man.

Household: The occupants are the patient's parents and maternal grandparents, all cocoa-farmers. The house belongs to the patient's great-uncle. The mother's sister and her children are present. One is a schoolgirl, another a drug-peddler who went to school up to Standard V. The drug-peddler and the patient are friends.

Marriage: Unmarried. He shuns marriage, he says, because he has erotic dreams of terrifying affect.

Work: On leaving school he became a pupil-teacher for a few months at Takoradi but was told to leave because he insisted that he was sick. Then he came home and did some drug-peddling. He says he made £30 in two years. He has the idea of going someday in the vague future into the Army and becoming very important.

Present Illness

While teaching in Takoradi he became convinced that he had "a very bad disease" sent to him by family witches determined to kill him before he could fulfil his illustrious destiny. He felt something going round and round inside his head. The literate uncle with whom he lodged in Takoradi—who is an army-trained dental assistant—took him to hospital and to several European doctors who could find nothing wrong. He then returned home at the instigation of his uncle's wife, who resented the money his uncle was spending on him. Various cocoa-farmer brothers then paid for him to visit various shrines and medicine-men in the intervals of desultory drug-peddling.

About seven months ago he became worse and felt "heaviness" in his head and "darkness" in his eyes. Every morning and every evening he both saw and felt insects "like lice" walking on him. No one else could see them, but he saw them plainly. Every night he heard a snake walking under his pillow, but on lifting the pillow it vanished. He also felt an animal walking inside his head. In his dreams he was chased by a crowd of people, a snake and cows. Sometimes he dreamt of fighting with someone who ran away and when pursued could not be found. His cocoa-farmer brothers have been generous and have spent £150 on various treatments. One brother brought him to Mframaso. There the *obosom* agreed that witches were after him and advised a course of ritual bathing.

First interview: 20.5.57

He looks physically well, brisk and active. He talks in nervous, stammering jerks and shows over-much of the whites of his eyes. Fully accessible, but has an incessant inappropriate smile. His story took several sessions to elicit because he has the schizophrenic habit, when asked to clarify a point, of making it more obscure. He is intensely hypochondriacal: said he never had a bowel action, but on pressing admitted that he had one to-day, yesterday and the day before. He says he has improved since coming to Mframaso but there is still a snake in his head. Intellectual tests very good. No insight.

21.5.57. Given some writing materials and told to write his life history, he produced a well-constructed and coherent story, but full of grandiose ambitions and denunciations of envious kinsmen who want to kill him because of his approaching greatness and riches.

30.5.57. His landlord (a sensible, kindly man) thinks he is "getting mad", mainly because of the number of times a day he goes to the river to wash. His room is meticulously neat and clean. He works quite hard helping his landlord on his food-farm.

10.6.57. No change. Still hears the snake in his head and under his pillow at night. Thinking this might be a misinterpretation of the sound of his own carotid artery I gave him a demonstration of arterial pulsation, both on himself and on other people, and pointed out that it was normal to hear the sound of the artery near the ear when the latter was pressed against a pillow. He took this in with intellectual appreciation and interest, but said, "My arteries are full of poison which the witches have put there."

31.9.57. There was no change till a few weeks ago when he said the snakes were troubling him less. He wrote for prospectuses of correspondence colleges and plans to take a commercial course. His drug-seller kinsman visited him and brought him money with which he paid the entrance fee for a course of study. The kinsman seemed a stable personality but made an *abisa* at the shrine saying that he was not prospering and wanted protection and help.

10.10.57. Patient has much improved, but is still not confident enough to leave Mframaso.

20.2.58. Relapsed after a short improvement. He is secretive and evasive, but I have met him at other shrines in the district reiterating his tale of persecution. He now seems permanently "hospitalised" at Mframaso.

29.2.58. He disappeared from Mframaso, taking leave of no one, but carefully taking all his possessions.

COMMENTARY

Paranoid schizophrenia with hypochondriacal features in an intelligent young literate.

CASE 73. KWAKU K. of Bekwai district, Ashanti. M. *c.* 18

Shrine

Mframa at Mframaso.

Reason for referral

He came alone to the shrine seeking protection from his mother whom he believed to be trying to kill him by witchcraft.

Family History

Parents: Cross-cousins, illiterate non-Christians. The father is a cocoa-farmer. He has two farms, a small one near home and a large one far away in the Wiaso district of the Western Province. He lives on the latter and comes to see his wives and children only about once a year. The profits of the smaller farm are used for the children's education. The second wife is in her own household in the home-town. The patient is on better terms with her than with his own mother and says that she is honest and that she looks after his cocoa-money for him. The patient's own mother was "caught" by Tigari when the patient was "a very small baby" (puerperal depression ?) and volunteered that she was a witch and was trying to kill the baby. The patient knew nothing of this till one day, when a small boy, he was travelling with his father and said he wanted to go home to his mother. The father said, "No. Your mother is quite willing to kill you. If it were not for the family ghosts of my people, who defend you, she might have succeeded." The patient says his mother is "always getting angry" and that she hates him, especially now that the cocoa-profits are being used for his education. She hated his elder brother—whose education is now finished—when he used the profits. Two years ago she was elected Queen-mother in her town. (This implies that she has lived down her witchcraft and is respected.)

Siblings: The patient has one elder brother, who is a telephone operator in a distant town, and five young sisters.

Personal History

Childhood: He says he was always afraid of his mother. The disclosure made by his father bit into him deeply.

Previous Illnesses: 1951—Pneumonia. Out-patient treatment at a hospital. In-patient treatment was impossible because there was no one to look after him. (In-patients in most hospitals have to be accompanied by a relative to supply their meals.) 1953—Severe "stomach-ache". Out-patient treatment.

Education: He attends a Presbyterian school but goes to a Roman Catholic church and says, "I am a Catholic", though he has not been baptised. He has always been top of his class and is now in Standard VII. He says, quite matter-of-factly, "I was always a clever boy." He intended to go on to a secondary school, but since his illness he has decided that he cannot catch up, either financially or scholastically, and now intends to be "a merchant".

300

Home: Household consists of maternal grandmother, mother, her brothers and sisters and their children. The patient says that the grandmother, the eldest uncle, the mother and her children all hate him, bu the others like him.

Present Illness

Nine months ago, the patient was very ill for three weeks and "was nearly for death", so that his mother sent for his eldest brother. His headache was intolerable, he was soaked with sweat, had diarrhoea, severe abdominal pains, and eyesight disturbances. He was treated by a Nigerian medicine-man, who said the illness was caused by witchcraft, but did not say whose. The patient was sure that it was his mother's, but he also ranged his grandmother alongside the mother. He had frightening dreams, of which he told the medicine-man, who then gave him medicine to put under his pillow. He narrated two of the dreams to me: (1) "My grandmother and my mother were chasing me to kill me", and (2) "My grandmother and my mother boiled yam and many eggs to make *oto*. A snake came and took the yam. I could see the witches who sent the snake watching to see what I would do. I said, "I will never eat such yam", and I threw it away. That angered the snake and it came to bite me. A spirit (*sunsum*) was standing beside me helping me. This *sunsum* cut off the snake's head but the headless body rushed at me. This *sunsum* cut the body into many pieces. I don't know whether the *sunsum* was from the land of ghosts or whether it was the medicine-man's *sunsum*, but I knew it was a *sunsum* because it wasn't someone I knew well and it was invisible."

The brother who came when the patient was expected to die shared the opinion that the witchcraft was his mother's. He said he would take the patient to finish his education away from home, but he has not kept his promise and the patient has begun to think that his brother also hates him and only came in the hope of his death. When the patient was near death his mother looked after him, but when convalescent he had to prepare his own food or go without. Ever since the illness the patient has had a headache which has interfered with his school-work and convinced him that his mother is still trying to kill him. When he decided to come to Mframaso he did not tell his mother, but said he was going to stay with a friend at Agogo.

At the shrine the *obosom* confirmed his belief that witchcraft was the cause of his illness, said he would be able to cure the headache in about six weeks by means of daily ritual baths and promised him future protection.

Interview: 28.5.56

He is a rather tall, limp youth with tiny circular ears and a timid irresolute face, but his determination to come to Mframaso without anyone else's knowledge bespeaks more self-reliance than his manner conveys. He looks depressed and apathetic, smiles weakly and is full of self-pity—"I am only a poor lonely one." He takes a realistic view of his scholastic situation and has abandoned the idea of secondary education without railing against fate. He has no inflated ideas of his own importance or the grandeur of his thwarted destiny. He seems to be of a kindly, complying disposition without aggressiveness, though he thinks himself the victim of aggression. He goes into great detail about the headache. At first it was like the pain of "a sore" on the vertex, but whenever herbal medicine is applied to the head the pain spreads out and covers it like a cap. He says, "I think that means that the medicine is fighting the sickness."

2.6.56. He sits about in dispirited dejection, taking no interest in anything except the daily application of the *obosom's* sacred herbs to his head.

10.6.56. He dreamt that he was walking along a road and was chased by his mother and his grandmother. These changed into an elephant and continued chasing him. When he was tired of running he met his father's spirit (*sunsum*) which ran beside him. The dreamer said, "Let us hide in the bush on the left side of the road", but his father's spirit said, "No, let's hide on the right side." The dreamer said there was hardly any cover on the right side, but plenty of bush on the left. They contradicted one another about four times and then hid on the right. The elephant passed by and didn't see them, but it nearly trod on the dreamer's foot. When it had gone the dreamer's father said, "Have you seen? Have you seen? Have you seen?" many times. The dreamer woke up sobbing. He then got up and burnt some incense and said some prayers.

17.6.56. He sits about doing nothing, looking very dejected and depressed. He says his headache is not improving.

30.6.56. He has cleared a little grove in a thicket where he has a fireplace and warms the water for his medicated baths. He goes sometimes to his landlord's farm to help him bring back foodstuffs and also does a little cooking.

17.7.56. He asked me what he could do to hasten his recovery. I said work, and suggested mud-bricks, which are easy to make and sell at six shillings a hundred. He disliked the idea of work and every day found a new excuse not to begin, but at last he did.

25.8.56. He has an order for several thousand bricks, is working quite well and has already received some money which has encouraged him. He pays someone to carry the water required for the mud-making, saying that his head pains him if he carries water.

13.9.56. He now says he feels better. He dreamt that he was in the little grove where he brews the *obosom's* herbs for his bath. Some women came from his home-town having bad intentions towards him. They stood about in circles talking about him. They wanted to approach and do him harm but he stood in his little grove and said, "You can't come in here", whereupon they went away. A few days later he dreamt that a man sent by the *obosom* came and said, "You will soon be well." He woke up very happy, and on that day his head stopped giving him pain. He says he is thinking of going home.

25.9.56. He keeps postponing plans for going home.

4.10.56. To-day he asked the *obosom* if he might go home to sit for his Standard VII Certificate and then return for more treatment. The *obosom* assented. He persists in describing himself as friendless. He now describes his brother as "cruel". He says his school-master is also cruel. He admits, when challenged, that his father's people are kind, honest and helpful, but repeats, "I am only a poor lonely one." He seems confident of passing his examination, though he has done no school-work for nearly a year.

8.11.56. He returned to Mframaso saying that his application to sit the examination had been too late and he had not sat. The school-master had asked his mother for his address but she did not know it. Nevertheless, he looks astonishingly better—blacker, firmer, more manly, confident and cheerful. He says he will sit next year. No doubt he found his mother less frightening in the flesh than his nightmares and broodings from a distance had pictured her. He says he shall go home in a fort-night's time.

20.11.56. He departed, seemingly recovered.

15.1.57. He returned to render thanks, and seemed brisk and well. He has given up the idea of further schooling but is taking a Bennett College commercial course by correspondence. He has used some cocoa-money to start in trade.

16.6.57. He came to the shrine again yesterday. I happened to see him passing on his arrival, and called him in. He looked extremely miserable and apprehensive but said perfunctorily that he was quite well, that he had left his mother and had set up in trade in another town and that his trade was prospering. He said he must hurry and find some lodgings and would come back. He clearly did not want to talk. He did not come back, but the next day at *abisa* he told the *obosom* that he had prospered and married, only to find that he was impotent. Before coming to the shrine he took steps to ascertain whether he was impotent with all women or only with his wife and found that the former was the case. After making his *abisa* he disappeared quickly from the town without spending another night and I had no opportunity of discovering whether the anxiety concerning his mother's supposed designs on his life had been renewed or whether some new anxiety had arisen.

COMMENTARY

This is rather more than a paranoid anxiety exacerbated by a febrile illness. Though there must be innumerable Africans whose mothers confessed to witchcraft in their childhood, this is the only one I have met whose attitude to his mother has been significantly affected by it. In view of his feeling that many people beside his mother hate him and are "cruel" to him, I think the prognosis is sinister, and that he is a candidate for a paranoid psychosis.

CASE 74. YAW A. of Begoro district. M. *c.* 30.

Shrine
Mframa at Mframaso.

Reason for referral
He came alone complaining that he was going mad because an enemy was making bad medicine against him.

Family History
Parents: Cross-cousins, both now dead. The father was a non-Christian, illiterate cocoa-farmer of the Begoro district, the mother a native of Akim. The father was an elder of his home-town. The patient says both his parents liked him.

Siblings: One sister and two brothers. Four others died. The sister is married to her cross-cousin in Akim.

Personal History
Childhood: Brought up in a country-town in his father's house away from his mother's family.

Schooling: Reached Standard III (top is Standard VII). Then his father died and his uncle declined to pay for more schooling.

Marriage: One wife. Satisfactory.

Children: Four, none dead. The eldest, aged eight years, goes to school.

Home: He lives in his late father's house with his wife and children in town, not in the cocoa-village.

Work: Cocoa-farmer. He has three farms. He is litigating about the ownership of one. Before his illness he "liked hard work".

Religion: Christian. He was a regular communicant till nine months ago when he became sick. The minister visited him and prayed, but this did him no good.

Present Illness (*from patient*)
About a year ago the patient had a law-suit about the ownership of one of his three cocoa-farms and became sleepless and worried. Judg-

ment was given against him. The case cost him over £100, which he did not possess, but the head of his mother's family, his sister and his brothers clubbed together to lend him the money. He has two other farms, which should easily enable him to pay the debt when the cocoa is harvested in a few months' time.

When the case was in progress he lay awake night after night worrying, and when the verdict was given he "felt his mind going *basa-basa*". His relatives protested that he was not "*basa-basa*" but he was convinced of it, and was also convinced that an enemy had made a bad medicine against him.

Shortly after this his foot swelled up and burst into "a sore", so that he was laid up for three months. At length he went to a doctor who gave him two injections. The sore healed but he remained convinced that an enemy had sent it. He often dreams that he is walking in the forest, gets lost and wanders distractedly trying to find the way.

Interview: 2.8.56

At the shrine he simply said that he was going mad because a friend had made a bad medicine against him. He promised a cow if the *obosom* would cure him. He was told to kill a fowl and go home with a bottle of consecrated medicine.

I was able to talk to him only very briefly as he was in the house of an unfriendly elder and left Mframaso the following morning. The niece who came with him had gone to market. He was well set up and well nourished and seemed a self-respecting person. He was correctly orientated, fully accessible, and with no inappropriate affect. He sat looking dejected and deeply anxious, occasionally grimacing and saying he could not stop thinking about his troubles nor listen when people talked to him; indeed, many of my questions had to be repeated before he took them in, but his answers were always clear and to the point, and he gave all the above information himself.

Asked why he thought he was going mad, he said that his mind made him want to go and work on his farm, but when he got there he could do no work and came home. Asked whether anyone disliked him, he said that many people did "because people always envy a hard-working man who has property". (This is the prevalent view and is not regarded as morbid.)

COMMENTARY (*written on* 2.8.56)

Anxiety reactive to stress with secondary depression but no self-reproach: blame is projected. Few Africans would regard this man's situation as stressful enough to account for his anxiety and depression. Most Africans would cheerfully run far more deeply into debt than he has done. Nor would they be worried by litigation, which is the national sport. To lose a case fires them with zeal to appeal and go on fighting till they are completely destitute. This patient must be regarded as unusually vulnerable.

20.12.56. He returned to Mframaso with his sister. He is now unmistakeably schizophrenic. Not agitated, not depressed, affect entirely inappropriate. He says smilingly that he cannot go back to his town again because people always take away his money out of his room, that people come in the night and tie his legs because they envy him, that everyone who sees him says he is a policeman, that Dr. Dankwa sent to arrest him because he had worked for the Americans, that he cannot go and work on his farm any more because people have arranged that his cutlass shall injure him if he does.

His sister says that he did not lose the land-case but it was adjourned because he was too much agitated and too incoherent to plead. It is not true that he has other cocoa-farms: he has only one and it is newly planted and not yet yielding. He worked as a paid labourer and earned good money till lately. He was a bricklayer's labourer for the Americans during the war. It is not true that he left school because his father died: he left before his father died, after attending only one year, when he himself declined—without reason—to go any more. His wife has abandoned him since he became "mad", so his sister has taken him to her home in Akim. The other brother—by the sister's account—sounds like a simple schizophrene. He was clever at school, reached Standard V, but has never done any work: he just sits quietly about. He had nine children, of whom four survived, but his wife has left him because of his indolence. He often got her into debt by buying food at the stores and crediting it to her. He is never "rough", does not drink, but says he is not strong enough to bestir himself, which the sister says is untrue.

21.12.56. The patient is socially acceptable in the village, pleasant and affable, superficially normal, but cannot do the simplest memory and attention tests which his sister and other illiterates do easily. He says he is sleeping in Mframaso because the *obosomfo* is going to give him the money to open a store here. (The last thing the *obosomfo* would do.)

1.1.57. He comes to see me to tell me he has no money for tobacco (which is true) and goes away happy with the price of a few cigarettes. There is no depth of affect. He goes smiling from one group of people to another. He has now no insight. He says he came here to open a store but takes no steps to do so. He refuses to take ritual baths: says there is nothing wrong with him. His habits are deteriorating: he does not wash and says he is not dirty.

10.1.57. The sister has lost patience and heart because he refuses ritual baths and is getting worse. She is taking him home to-morrow.

The Paranoid Reaction

COMMENTARY

Paranoid schizophrenia, beginning with some insight, in a man with a schizophrenic sibling.

CASE 75. KWAKU S. of Akwapim. M. *c.* 35

Shrine

Mframa at Mframaso.

Reason for referral

Fear of enemies.

Family History

Parents: Both dead. They were cross-cousins: non-Christian, illiterate cocoa-farmers.

Siblings: Eight born, two died. All illiterate, non-Christians. An elder brother was a drunkard who was "caught" by Tigari. His belly swelled up, he vomited all the time, then he became "*basa-basa*", ran away to the bush and shortly after died.

Personal History

N.a.d. A non-Christian, illiterate cocoa-farmer. He married his cross-cousin and has two children, aged about ten and six.

Present Illness

Three years ago he began to sleep badly because he thought people hated him and were plotting to take away his farms. This has become worse lately. He dreams he is chased by dogs and by people with sticks, and that people stand around threateningly. He says everyone hates him and wants to kill him because they envy him his big farms. He is under the *obosom* Tigari, but he thinks that people have found a way to weaken Tigari's power so that it can no longer protect him.

Interview: 20.1.58

A well-built, physically healthy-looking man. Wild-eyed, deeply anxious, fidgeting and restless, convinced that his enemies have determined to do him harm. He was unable to give a coherent account of himself. His general distraught aspect recalls that of Yaw A. (Case No. 74) at the onset of his paranoid schizophrenia.

Progress

Unknown. He went home after putting himself under protection.

COMMENTARY

This may be the onset of a paranoid schizophrenia.

CASE 76. KWABENA P. of Bekwai district, Ashanti. M. *c.* 40.

Shrine

Mframa at Mframaso.

Reason for Referral

Impotence, presumed to be due to malicious sorcery.

Family History

No information.

Personal History

Childhood: No information.
Schooling: Nil.
Religion: Christian communicant.
Work: Cocoa-farmer and peddling trader.
Marriage: He has two wives, the younger a Christian of his own Church. There are six children by one wife and three by the other. The wives are on good terms with one another and are united in wanting to leave him. It is the younger wife—contrary to the common pattern—whom he suspects of bad magic.

History of Present Illness

About a year ago he was on a peddling journey and slept with a prostitute. Shortly after that he developed "*babaso*" (gonorrhea) and had swellings in the testicles, groins and penis. He went to hospital and started a course of out-patient treatment, but feeling sure that the trouble was of supernatural origin he abandoned hospital treatment and went to various medicine-men but did not improve. His sleep became very poor and he lay awake night after night brooding in fear upon the wrong that had been done him. Finally he came to Mframa, who told him to go home and fetch his two wives. The wives' families would not allow them to come.

Interview

A pleasant, gently-smiling, unassuming little man, but his face in repose is deeply anxious. Intellectually, he is perfectly capable of appreciating that his illness is due to his own act, but maintains that the only possible reason for it is either witchcraft or bad "medicine". He does not, however, accept the priest's reassurance. His conviction of persecution has a peculiarly unshakeable quality.

COMMENTARY

I place this patient in the morbidly paranoid class because he will not accept the *obosom's* view that his illness is amenable to hospital treatment now that he has dealt with the supernatural aspect, and remains impervious to supernatural reassurance.

CASE 77. KWAKU B. of Asamankese district, Akim. M. 25.

Shrine
Mframa at Mframaso.

Reason for referral
Patient thinks that envious persons who want to kill him are sending him illness by sorcery and witchcraft.

Family History
Parents: Not cross-cousins. Father died when patient was very small. Mother, who is still alive and well, did not marry again but farmed cocoa and sent her sons to school with the profits.
Siblings: Four sisters and one brother alive. Four died. Patient is the ninth child. Patient says all his sisters have been "caught" for witchcraft but recovered quickly. The brother is a timber contractor and also owns a store. He is very successful and rich and very generous to the patient.

Personal History
Schooling: The patient says he was twelve when he started school. He spent nine years there and gained the Standard VII certificate. He says he was clever and second in his class. He left in 1953.
Marriage: He married, while still at school in Standard V, a girl whom he seduced. His mother and brother paid the marriage expenses and supported the young wife. Patient says he is happily married. His wife has guinea-worm but he shows no concern for her. He made no arrangements for her when he came to Mframaso.
Children: Two born, both died. One was almost walking, the other crawling.
Work: He did no work till two years after leaving school. Then the elder brother gave him £450 to start a modern beer-bar with a refrigerator, etc. He ran this for a year and says he did well, but does not know what profits he made as he "never made account".

Present Illness
Patient says that as soon as he opened the beer-bar he knew that people were envious and would try to kill him by sorcery and witchcraft. He knew there were witches in his family for some had been "caught" by Tigari but were quickly cured: one of them came to Mframaso. The patient had palpitations, pains in neck, head, arms and chest,

which he knew were due to sorcerers' poison because the poison in his chest was like a snake walking round. He dreamt that cows were chasing him: he fled from one up a tree. Once he found himself surrounded by a herd of cows. One cow said, "Now I will catch him", but another cow said, "No, leave him alone." When his child was ill he dreamt that the child was sitting on his chest and a cow came and attacked it. The next day the child died. He continued in fear till one night when he woke up with asthma. He went to various doctors and to a hospital where he had a chest X-ray, but reassurance failed to satisfy him. "The poison that people had sent had come to my chest and was eating my chest." He sold up his beer-bar and spent two years going to all kinds of doctors. The asthma came at intervals of two weeks to two months and lasted three days. Sometimes "the poison" goes to his shoulders and joints and he hears it "making cracking".

First Interview: 2.1.57

Well built, muscular, well favoured. Vigorous and active. He speaks better than average English for his kind of education. He shows a great deal of the whites of his eyes and recounts his bodily afflictions with relentless volubility and broadly-smiling cheerfulness. He insisted that I should examine his chest: it revealed no signs of asthma.

3.2.57. He has had no more asthmatic attacks. He is very sociable and cheerful, with an almost boisterous vigour. He brings home heavy head-loads of yams from his landlord's farm, helps in the *obosom*'s drumming, did some bush-clearing round my quarters with great gusto, but insists that he is very ill and weak and full of "the poison".

16.4.57. He still cheerfully insists, in the face of all the evidence, that he is very ill. When I said he looked well, he replied, "The sickness is all in spiritual form, so it isn't visible." I asked him whether he felt safe now that he was under the *obosom*'s protection. He said he was satisfied that no *new* harm could be done to him but a residue of the "spiritual poison" that the witches had put into him still remained, and until the *obosom* had taken it all out it could still "eat into him" and would do so if he went home prematurely.

20.6.57. Still in Mframaso and is most inappropriately content to stay. He has written several times to tell his wife to come and join him, but he gets no reply. Only himself is surprised at this, as he has not supported her for months nor sent her the means to come.

31.7.57. He came to me with a mild attack of asthma. His brother has written to him that his wife has left him, adding that women are plentiful and he will easily get another. But the patient's fears are renewed because he is certain that witchcraft or some other sorcery has been used to "turn her mind against him".

1.10.57. He shows no signs of going home. I asked him when he pro-

posed to go. He said he thought he might be ready at the end of another year. He seems permanently "hospitalised".
2.2.58. No change.

COMMENTARY

This is probably a developing paranoid psychosis.

CASE 78. KOFI T. of Berekum district, Ashanti. M. 26.

Shrine
Kyinaman, at Bredi.

Reason for referral
Sleeplessness and fear of witches.

Family History
The parents are not cross-cousins. The father is a non-Christian, illiterate cocoa-farmer. He is a chief's *okyeame*. He separated from the patient's mother two years ago. He had five wives when the patient was a child and has three now. The mother was the father's senior wife. She now lives in a house of her own. The father's elder brother is known to the patient as his "senior father". He is a Christian, lives in a mission compound and the patient spends much time with him. The siblings are two brothers and two sisters. The brothers are older than the patient and are illiterate. The sisters are young and at school.

Personal History
Childhood: N.a.d. disclosed. Household consisted of mother and her children only, the co-wives being elsewhere.
Schooling: Nil. Non-Christian.
Work: Farmer.
Marriage: One and a half years ago. One child.
Previous Illnesses: About eight years ago the patient cleared a farm to plant cocoa but has never planted it because annually when he is about to do so "a sickness like darkness in front of the eyes" attacks him. He thinks this is sent by witches among his kin and people who envy him because he will someday become rich through cocoa. There have been many witches in his family and some have been "caught" by *obosom* Mframa, who killed one about two years ago, and by *obosom* Kwaku Firi, who killed another about four years ago. For years he has had recurrent dreams of a pursuing cow, of someone chasing him with a cutlass to kill him, of someone trying to push him into a hole and of people wanting to tie him up with a rope.

Present Illness

A year ago he decided to fell more trees and make a bigger farm, so he procured a *suman* from a Kramu to protect him from witches and envious people. Recently he went to the Kramu again and had a bad magic made against his enemies. He knew that it was wrong to make bad medicine because his elder brother had drunk at the Bredi shrine on behalf of all the brothers. Since then his dreams have become worse and he has hardly slept at all. Then he developed pains in his eyes, ears, head, neck, arms, chest, etc., and thought himself about to die. He came to the shrine, and immediately all the pains vanished except for discomfort in his ears. Sleeplessness, however, has not improved.

Interview: 21.1.57

A strapping young man, healthy-looking except for nasal catarrh, probably with slight Eustachian involvement. Very anxious and frowning. Tremulous hands. He fidgets in his seat. Bites his fingers. Slight stammer and blinking tic. Heavy-eyed, sleepless look. Pleasant and ready to talk. Fully accessible. Extremely worried because people want to harm him. No thought-disorder, hallucinations, etc., elicited. All mental tests well done. No relative was with him.

Progress

I saw him only once as he went home the next day. I wrote for news to his Christian uncle but had no reply.

Commentary

Recent exacerbation of chronic anxiety with a strong paranoid trend. The *suman* is an ominous feature.

Compare with Clarence Kwame A. (Case No. 72), of whom he is reminiscent even to the blink and stammer, though his affect is warmer. His illiteracy probably gives him a better prognosis than that of Clarence.

Case 79. KWESI B. of Akim district, Ashanti. M. *c.* 23.

Shrine

Mframa at Mframaso.

Reason for referral

Frightening dreams. He thinks sorcery is being practised against him to prevent his prosperity. He is afraid of death.

Family History
  Father: He died a few years ago. He was an illiterate non-Christian.
  Mother: She is alive and well—an illiterate non-Christian.
  Siblings: Two brothers, one a cocoa-labourer, the other a boy at school. No sister. (This is a great misfortune.)

Personal History
  Childhood: Normal.
  Schooling: He only reached Standard III (Standard VII is the top of the Primary School). He left because his parents could not afford to keep him at school. He now feels very inferior to and envious of his school-mates who completed their course and are doing literate jobs. He dislikes meeting them.
  Work: A timber-labourer. Earns £5–£6 a month. He is fined if absent from work. He thinks the work too hard and the wages too low. He wanted to be either a store-keeper or a motor-mechanic. He contrasts his lot with that of his literate school-mates.
  Marriage: Unmarried.
  Home: He lives with his maternal grandfather and his wife, and various uncles, their wives and children. The grandfather and uncles are farmers; some have cocoa.

Interview
  I could talk to him only very briefly as he was catching the next lorry home on the same day he made his *abisa*. (Probably much more to tell.)
  He was a healthy-looking, muscular youth with a pleasant though somewhat vague manner. He was not overtly anxious. He had no English, but nevertheless regarded himself as a valuable literate.
  He described his dreams:

  1. Recurrent dream of people gathered together for the purpose of "catching" him.
  2. Recurrent dream of the Kramu medicine-men arranging their Koran to make him die.
  3. There was a crowd of people, and among them a man who ate three cats. The dreamer also ate two cats but could not manage to eat the third. A man climbed a palm-tree, and the dreamer climbed another palm-tree. The man fell from the tree, and then the dreamer jumped down from his own tree. There was a row of palm-trees and a river. A young girl told the dreamer that because he could not eat all three cats he must climb a hill and she would follow. He told the man who had eaten the three cats that he would race him up the hill, each carrying a fallen palm-tree. As they raced he found tears in his eyes. Then he found that a river was carrying him away. When he reached the top of the hill

he met some people who showed him some money. These people were going to do him harm and he woke up terrified.

COMMENTARY

Frustration anxiety in an ambitious semi-literate. A potential paranoid.

I am told that some people eat ritually sacrificed cats because "a cat is food for the soul". The Ashanti word for cat is *okra*, the same word as the word for soul. Whatever the symbolism of cat-swallowing in the dream, it is clear that the man who ate three achieved something that the dreamer fell short of. The young girl possibly symbolises either marriage or mercenary sexual liaison, and the girl's dictum that she would follow when he had climbed the hill—possibly the Hill Difficulty—refers to his delayed achievement of an attractive status as a bridegroom or monied casual partner.

V

NEW CASES OF SCHIZOPHRENIA

General Remarks

Probably there is no culture in the world which has not the concept of "madness", and no language which has not a word for it. And if the stranger asks to be shown a madman he will probably be led to a florid schizophrenic. On the other hand, so long as a schizophrenic is accessible, talks coherently, is not destructive or aggressive, and has only such delusions and hallucinations as are within the bounds of culturally determined credibility, he may fall a long way below social approval without being accounted mad. He may be thought idle, dirty, Solitary, callous, heedless or perverse. In short, if his friends say that a man is mad (*obodam*), he is usually a schizophrenic, but he may be the latter, particularly of the *simplex* type, and "get by".

But on the whole, Africans are shrewd at diagnosing madness and often know the main differential diagnoses—epilepsy, mental defect ("not clever"), trypanosomiasis and "spirit-possession". On several occasions when they declared a patient to be "becoming mad" I at first disagreed with them, but later found that they were right.

Madness is spoken of as a sickness (*oyare*) and, like other sicknesses, it is usually regarded as the result of either the patient's own wrong-doing or someone else's malicious sorcery. Sometimes, however, it is believed to be "from God" and nobody's fault. In no case is the patient dreaded or shunned, unless, of course, he is dangerous or destructive. The general attitude towards him is much more sensible and kindly than that which prevailed towards madmen in our own society till recent times.

Assessment of Schizophrenic Reaction Types

Very often at the onset of schizophrenia the African patient has a good deal of insight. He feels that something has gone wrong with his mind ("Something keeps catching hold of my thoughts"). This realisation distresses him and he may weep with bewilderment, fear and exasperation. Such weeping should not be taken as indicating a schizo-affective illness: it is a protest against, not an integral part of, the illness. Often at this stage he thinks someone has maliciously sent something bad into his head to make him mad. This attitude should not be regarded as paranoid, for people do in fact buy *suman* designed to make others mad, and he is making, according to his lights, quite as sober a guess at the aetiology of his illness as one of ourselves who might say, "I must have caught this cold from Smith in his car on Tuesday."

Relation between Schizophrenia and Inbreeding

The Ashanti and other Akan peoples of Ghana have for many generations practised that form of first-cousin marriage whereby a man gives his daughter as bride to his sister's son and waives the marriage-fee which would be demanded from a non-kinsman.

Among the parents of ninety-five undoubted schizophrenics (combining acute and chronic cases) it was found that the incidence of cousin marriage was 40%, whereas among the general population (taking 1,200 marriages) the incidence of cousin marriage was only 19%.

This correlation does not *necessarily* imply that cousin marriage is the operative genetic factor. A young person of schizoid personality, lacking self assertion and "drive", is of the type to accept passively the marriage partner offered by senior kinsmen. The more spirited and enterprising seek the stimulus of new contacts. The same principle of passive acceptance of tradition by schizoid personalities would equally apply if the favoured tradition had been to marry, say, someone born on the same day of the week.

Relation between Schizophrenia and Bad Magic

It has been mentioned that one of the activities specifically forbidden to those under the protection of shrine deities is the making of bad magic or "medicine" against others, that disobedience to this injunction frequently brings the offender to the shrine in a psychotic frenzy, and that classical schizophrenia often eventually follows. Experience has further taught the writer that secret ritual with "bad medicines" and other magical apparatus often ushers in a frank schizophrenia without any inaugural episode of transient frenzy. The making in secret of bad magic against others is, in fact, a schizoid type of aggression as distinct from a healthy, quarrelsome type of aggression. Into the same class of schizoid personality would have fallen a celebrant of the mediaeval Black Mass, performing his sinister rites in solitude at midnight.

Of many a long-standing chronic schizophrenic it is said, putting the cart before the horse, "He became mad because he made bad medicine. The *suman* (apparatus) were found hidden in his room." This does not imply that *only* potential schizophrenics make bad magic against others, but merely that this type of aggression is particularly favoured by schizophrenics.

Rôle of Schizophrenia in Primitive Belief

It has already been postulated (Part 1. Chap. 2) that the fantastic self-accusations of the Depressive—in modern Europe taken as one criterion of illness, but in rural Africa and mediaeval Europe taken as statements of fact—are largely responsible for keeping alive in present-day Ghana the concept of malevolent witchcraft. By a similar postulates many of those schizophrenics who, by retaining their accessibility in a setting of clear consciousness, escaped popular dismissal as madmen, probably had a profound influence on the tenets of primitive belief.

The predilection of the incipient schizophrenic for ritual with traditionally magical objects has already been mentioned. It should now be added that a well-preserved schizophrenic frequently produces, sometimes to his own distress, *original* fantasies in which concrete objects and the manipulation of these have, for him, a mysterious association with persons and events. One well-preserved and outwardly normal woman was plagued with a great variety of such fantasies; she confessed at the shrine—and was naïvely believed—that her spirit (*sunsum*) actually carried out these rites. She said, for instance, that she had an invisible bottle in the roof of her house and when, in spirit, she corked it, she caused all women in labour to be obstructed: when she uncorked it they promptly delivered.

It may well be that many traditional magical procedures were thus invented by schizophrenics of sufficiently normal aspect to make their statements acceptable to their fellow-men. The so-called "primitive mind" may thus be merely the credulous mind, able to accept—albeit with awe, wonder, fear and, above all, frank incomprehension—more bizarre notions than would have occurred to itself.

This gives a new slant to such "primitive" ideas as lycanthropy and to the question of the origin of animal totemism.

Regarding the latter, I can recall instances, not only in rural Africa but in modern England, of objectively normal schizophrenics who felt that certain animals had a special significance for them. One such patient, a London woman, said that when she walked in the parks all the birds seemed to be trying to bring her mysterious messages. Another

English patient said that the thrushes in the hospital grounds seemed to be, in some strange way, identified with his wife and the sparrows with his children.

It is probably not correct to say that such patients "revert to primitive modes of thought". It seems more likely that schizophrenic modes of thought are specific to schizophrenia and are independent of cultural background. It is their assessment and acceptance by others that is culturally determined.

Lilliputian hallucination is another mental disfunction frequently associated with—though by no means confined to—schizophrenia. This phenomenon, combined with traditions of a real but departed race of small people, seems to have created a mythology of fairies.

Apparent Relation between Schizophrenia and Education

Whereas the incidence of literacy among the overall population of Ghana is usually estimated at 10%, I found the incidence of literacy among the forty-five new cases of schizophrenia at shrines above 40%. I wish to stress that this correlation is, for several reasons, highly misleading and does not point to a conclusion that schizophrenia is ever caused by literacy.

Firstly, we have no census figures telling us the incidence of literacy *in the various age groups*. But we do know that in the last twenty-five years the number of schools has increased so rapidly that the great majority of literate people are *young* people. It so happens that the great majority of new schizophrenics, probably the world over, and certainly among illiterate African males,★ are young people. In other words, literacy and schizophrenia tend to fall into the same age-group.

Furthermore, young literates tend to have wealthy kinsmen, for schooling is one of the things on which wealth is spent. Another thing which requires wealth is extensive treatment at distant shrines. Most of the literate schizophrenics whom I saw at shrines had come from a distance, some had been to a succession of shrines and some were making long stays. In other words, had they not been wealthy I should not have met them, and had they not been wealthy they would not have been literate, but (as will later appear★) they would probably have developed schizophrenia all the same.

In England, Ghana and Nigeria, at the present time, concern is being expressed about the large number of young Africans who go to Britain for study-courses and there suffer mental breakdown. But it is not

★ See chap. XIII, on Chronic Schizophrenia.

appreciated how high is the breakdown rate among young literates of only primary-school standard who remain in their own country in their own homes. They are less conspicuous than those who break down in Britain, but they are probably no fewer.

The reason for the literate breakdown appears, in rural Ashanti, not far to seek. In any village or small country-town, on any morning of the week, are to be seen numerous able-bodied men sitting under trees drinking palm-wine or playing draughts while other idlers look on. They are all farmers, but only during planting, harvesting and weeding need they do any active work, and even then, if they feel disinclined, some kinsman or wife will usually take over. No demands are made on most men in the way of regularity or punctuality. Simple schizophrenia may thus go unnoticed. Other potential schizophrenics may never meet any stress severe enough to precipitate an acute attack. The literate's life, however, is more exacting. Its demands begin before the adolescent leaves school. Often the young schizophrenic simply gives up going to school, saying that he does not want to continue. Teachers are well aware of this leakage of adolescents from schools. But perhaps the young schizophrenic scrapes through his primary-school leaving examination and takes a job. He does not keep it long, and sooner or later he drifts home again, unemployed and unemployable, a permanent loafer, but not conspicuous, accepted with little resentment by his easy-going kinsmen.

Yet we must perhaps look a stage deeper still. These slightly educated young schizophrenes in their own country break down *less* conspicuously than the highly educated ones abroad, but *more* conspicuously— because more disappointingly—than those who have had no education at all. It may well be that the ultimate plight of a predestined schizophrenic is not affected by his literacy. We shall return to this question in the chapter on Chronic Schizophrenia.

Another point to bear in mind concerning young Africans in Britain is that a certain type of young literate schizophrene is just as likely to embark on an ill-judged, over-ambitious programme as another type is to subside quietly and early into educational inactivity. I recall one such who in the nineteen-thirties walked from Nyasaland to the Gold Coast because he had heard of the great educational opportunities there offered. His feat of endurance and apparent enterprise evoked such admiring interest that he was given facilities to achieve his ambitions, but he turned out inattentive and withdrawn, took to wandering vaguely about the countryside when he should have been at work and was eventually recognised for what he was.

Case 80. KOFI A. of Offuman, Ashanti. M. *c.* 16.

Shrine

Oboo, at Offuman.

Reason for referral

Self-accusations of witchcraft. Voluntary confession of planning to kill his uncle with bad magic.

Family History

His mother is a depressive (Ama A., Case No. 1).

Personal History

Childhood: N.a.d. disclosed.

Schooling: Nil. Illiterate non-Christian.

Work: He has a cocoa-farm of young trees but has done no work of any kind for a year.

Marriage: Unmarried.

Present Illness

Just over a year ago he went one day to the farm with his sister. The sister fell and severely damaged her foot. The patient did not help her, though she could not walk, and left her to hop home with the aid of a stick. She reviled him for his callousness. Shortly after this he began to feel that it was he who had caused her accident. He also ruminated guiltily about a plan he had made to kill his uncle with a bad *suman* because the uncle had not kept his promise to give him a gun.

The uncle and the patient's father had both drunk at Oboo's shrine, the father on behalf of all his children as well as himself, so the patient began to fear that Oboo would "catch" him for his sins against his sister and his uncle. He began to dream that people were standing over him threatening him with sticks and other weapons. He developed a headache and "fever" and felt "a great weakness all over his body", but was not laid up.

He went to the shrine and confessed and was purified but did not feel much better. Ever since then he has felt no interest in doing any work and has, in fact, not done any, saying that he feels "weak". His appetite has remained good throughout and there is no objective history of confusion, abnormal behaviour or speech, or any physical incapacitation. He has spent a good deal of time ruminating on his "weakness" and has been to various medicine-men. When the lorry accident happened (*vide* Case 1), he was on his way to another.

Interview

The patient is of stocky, muscular build and has a very low hair-line. He looks physically extremely well and noticeably fatter than anyone else; no doubt because he eats more and does not work.

The interview was short and inadequate and held in the presence of a gaping crowd of relatives and neighbours. The patient was a good informant on the subject of his mother's illness but his manner changed to anxious self-concern when he spoke of his own. He said he often felt "shakings" in his eyes, but apart from that dwelt only on his "weakness" —meaning probably apathy and disinclination for work.

Progress

I only saw him once as he went away to a distant village. Two years later I heard that he was unchanged, still doing no work.

COMMENTARY

Deterioration of initiative with hypochondriasis and marked indolence in an adolescent. Good physical condition rules out trypanosomiasis. This is probably a developing simple schizophrenia and an example of the common association of bad-medicine-making with the onset of this disease. The illness set in at the age when, had he been a schoolboy, he would simply have dropped out of school.

CASE 81. PATIENCE S. of Akwapim (patrilineal section). F. *c.* 32.

Shrine

She has been only to various medicine-men. She has never drunk at a shrine. Seen in her own home.

Reason for referral

She complains that people have made her into a witch.

Family History

Mother: The mother married the patient's father after divorcing her first husband. She died when the patient was about sixteen. She was an illiterate cloth-seller and became a Christian in middle age. She left the patient's father when the patient was five, taking the latter with her. She married again but left the third husband before her death because he wanted her to live in a "village" from which she could not trade. The patient's husband has recently heard that "she also was a witch and was caught. If I had known that, I would never have married her daughter."

Mother's sisters: Three illiterate Christians. One was denounced by her husband on his death-bed for causing his last illness. These are strong-minded women who defied both a paramount chief and his "great oath".

Father: Died fifteen years ago. Illiterate. Christian cocoa-farmer. He had two other wives concurrently with patient's mother, the latter being the most junior. He lived mostly in his "village", which village, now occupied by one of his widows, his sons and their wives and children, is now always open, by right, to the patient if she wants to stay there.

Father's sister: She is childless and always willing to play a mother's part to the patient, giving her a home if need be.

Siblings: One half-sister by the mother's first husband was grown-up and married when the patient was born. She is good to the patient, gives her a home when necessary and supervises her deserted children. There were two half-brothers by the father's first wife. One of these is dead, the other is now head of the "village". There are one half-sister and one half-brother by the father's second wife. This brother and his children are also in the "village". There are no full siblings.

Personal History

Childhood: The patient lived mostly in town in her mother's family house owned jointly by the mother's siblings. These were usually absent in their "village", leaving the patient and her mother alone

Schooling: She is said to have passed Standard VII at a Mission school but has forgotten all her English. She is a full church member.

Work: She has a sewing-machine and before her illness made good money as a seamstress, helped with her husband's food farms, did the marketing of food crops and made good profits. She was hard-working and he regarded her as a financial asset.

Marriage: She married at about eighteen. The husband, then about twenty-eight, was a literate Christian. He was a cocoa-buyer in a large Akwapim colony-town in Akim and was an absentee cocoa-farmer with labourers running his farms in Kwahu and Ashanti. Since the death of the cocoa in Akim he had taken various odd jobs. He is even-tempered, cheerful, hard-working and patient with his wife's illness. He says the marriage was very happy till she fell ill.

Home: On marriage she came to live in the Akim town with the husband, who rents part of a house.

Children: Five born, no deaths. Eldest fourteen, youngest twenty months. The eldest three are at school. The fourth, aged six, is a bed-wetter and very anxious, imagining she sees ghosts round the house at night.

Present Illness

Onset was when the fourth child was a few weeks old. The patient became irritable, tearful, restless and complained of itching skin and burning feet and wept when spoken to. One day her husband returned from work and found she had gone away taking the youngest child but deserting the others. He sought her among her relatives and found her in the elder brother's "village" where he was told that she had "fainted" but had revived. (Possibly this was a stupor: possibly she was exhausted by the journey.) When her mother's sisters heard of this "fainting" they went to visit her but she flared up and slapped them, saying that someone was making her into a witch, and it was they whom she suspected because one of them had come to visit her when the baby was a few weeks old and had stayed several days. Immediately after this, the patient said, she found herself crying because she had become a witch and witchcraft did not agree with her spirit. She called down upon the three aunts the conditional curse (*ntam kese*) of the town chief if they did not appear before the chief to defend this charge of making her a witch, but when summoned they refused to come, sending a "pocket-lawyer's" letter demanding to know on what grounds she accused them.

She consented to go home with her husband but ever since has been restless and never stays long in one place. She goes to her father's sister, her own half-sister and to her brother's village, stays a few weeks and then goes away without warning. Or she may say she is going and then not go. She does no work and takes no interest in anything. She scolds, slaps and neglects the children. She is particularly restless at night, walking about, opening and shutting boxes, shifting the sleeping children's pillows and disturbing everyone. On one occasion she woke her husband and demanded that he should throw away her necklace and waistbeads (the traditional abode of a witch's *obayi*). When he did so she reviled him. She has never accused herself of wrong-doing: on the contrary, she resentfully asserts that wrong has been done to her. She quarrels with all sorts of people and calls them witches, so improbably that they think it merely absurd. She once hit her father's sick sister, spat in her face and said she was old and ought to be dead. This aunt is very patient with her, saying, "She was good till the witchcraft spoilt her".

Though grossly unreasonable in her fits of irritation she has never talked "*basa-basa*" or been suspected of madness. There was no exacerbation of the illness at the birth of the fifth child. The husband has taken her to various medicine-men but never to a hospital or qualified doctor though he once had part-time employment with a doctor.

Interview

I saw this patient only once for a few minutes on one of her brief visits to her husband and children. She was thin, languid and exceedingly pale with colourless conjunctivae. She was fully accessible, polite and well behaved, with a watery but appropriate smile on shaking hands, but she was vague and inattentive. She was restless and fidgeting and looked actively unhappy, anxious and discontented. Of her illness she would say only that "something had spoilt her".

The prominence of irritability and restlessness, absence of self-reproach, presence of "burning feet" made me think this illness less likely to be a puerperal depression or psychosis than a hookworm anaemia and vitamin deficiency, exacerbated by the call of childbirth on depleted blood and vitamin reserves. On the other hand, the poor physical condition may have been the result of self-neglect since she fell ill.

Progress

Though I did not see her again, I heard two years later that she had greatly deteriorated, become more and more vague, wandered more from place to place and engaged in promiscuous sexual intercourse.

COMMENTARY

Probably schizophrenia beginning in the puerperium.

CASE 82. AMA D. of Akwapim. Living in cocoa-village near Mangoase, Akim. F. *c.* 15.

Preface

I saw this patient only once, and very briefly, as I paused at the shrine in travelling. She was mute at the time, but the *obosomfo*, an exceedingly intelligent and friendly Akwapim, said that she had talked on previous days and that he had called a scholar to take down in the vernacular a verbatim record of her statements, which he showed me. As this contained a great deal more than the stereotyped "confessions" given by most witches I asked him to have a copy made and posted to me. This he did.

Shrine

Tigari, at Adawso.

Reason for referral

Self-accusations of witchcraft.

Family History

Parents: Illiterate, non-Christian cocoa-farmers. Father died a few years ago.

Siblings: One brother, aged about eight.

Personal History

Previous Illness: There was a period in the patient's childhood when her behaviour was strange and her mother thought a bad spirit had got into her. An Ewe medicine-man was called in to remove it, which he successfully did. The patient remembers the episode and now says the bad spirit was not wholly removed.

Home: After the father's death the patient's mother and her two children went to live with the patient's maternal grandmother in her "village". Two children of the patient's uncles are there also.

Schooling: Nil.

Katamenia: Has not reached menarche.

Previous Personality: Happy and hardworking. She trades in the market. She has a sewing-machine and makes good profits.

Present Illness

Onset about a month ago. She began by being irritable and "disrespectful", refused work and sat about moodily, weeping both by day and night. She lost weight, became dirty and lousy, and said she was "caught" by Tigari for witchcraft.

Interview

Weedy, thin, immature figure. Mute, miserable, anxious, almost immobile except for twisting her hands and the corner of her cloth. My impression was of a schizo-affective illness.

Patient's statement dictated to obosomfo's clerk:

The patient had talked on seven different occasions and her statements were written down verbatim in the vernacular.

"The beginning was that my mother had a sore throat. That was caused by us [the coven of witches]. Then a herbalist gave my mother a dressing for her sore leg and we made up our minds to take it away [extract its virtue] but we couldn't catch her properly. My witch's pot [*bayi-sẽaa*] is a frog, but one day when I went to dig koko-yam I lost it."

"When I was a child someone [among the witches] killed my grandfather and that part of him which was given to me [to eat] I got by means of an iron trap which I set to catch him."

"I have a bit of old rag, and when I want to fly I fling it round my neck and turn into a bat and fly away."

"When I was very young my mother saw that the spirit [*sunsum*] that was with me was not a good spirit, so they brought an Ewe man to take it away. He took all my trinkets except my broken ear-rings which I kept back [this is fact] and that is why the bad spirit is with me still."

"When the cocoa-disease came, the place where they put my bad spirit sprouted koko-yam and when I went to dig koko-yam I took the bad thing again."

"The place where they [the witches] cut up flesh is X.'s village and the place where they eat it is Anheam."

"In their clay fireplace they put a human finger for firewood and they pour blood on it, but what they do to make it catch fire I don't know."

"Now, the big toe, the heart, the liver and a crab's claw. The work of the crab's claw is to go and take any money that my grandmother gets. The work of the big toe is to press upon the money of people who buy soap from my mother, so that they do not pay her promptly. In the heart there is a needle and when I want to kill somebody I hold it and call the person's name and then it goes to kill the person."

"I have lice in my hair [this is fact]. My witch company put it there and they say they won't take it away till I give them a kinsman [to eat] so I made up my mind to give them my mother. My mother should bathe in *anumum* leaves thrice daily [to protect herself] and should also drink some."

"The killing of people is the reason why I went back to find the frog again."

"Also I called my brother Kwaku to come and be killed, but he didn't come, so I put an itching leaf on his skin and that is why he has always had skin trouble. To cure it he should bathe with cassava leaves and *nyanyera* leaves and rub them into foam. And he should take *anumum* leaves and char them in a pot to black powder and rub on his skin mixed with palm-kernel oil."

"When they [the witches] share out meat they give me a rib and I eat it, then I too get a pain in my own ribs."

"It was I who killed Kwabena A. I killed him because a woman [fellow witch] gave him to me for killing. It was I too who killed Kofi B., but I did it because he was unkind. He has money, but when people ask for some he refuses: I killed him so that he should know what it is to suffer."

"Also we went to a certain silk-cotton tree, and when we got there I was the first to take off my nose [*sic*] and then all the others took off theirs."

"I killed my uncle's wife because she reviled me, saying I was a devil [*abonsam*] and had killed her child."

"I have two snakes in my belly. One is *okyerebeng* [very poisonous]. After cooking the [human] flesh we sing the snake's song, which goes, 'Oh come! Oh come!' and then those who like come. When the meat is cooked we pour it into a brass bowl and shout out our passwords [*mmran* = passwords ?]. When I go to the tree the name I go by is 'Odi akese' [She eats grand people]."

"There was a wanton woman named Abena X. who had a child and when they performed its coming-out ceremony she became jealous [of the gifts brought to it] so I killed the child's mother. I did it by sticking into the heart the needle which I have."

"When I was under the silk-cotton tree there was also a tortoise, a snail and a sea-crab. And there Tigari caught me."

"A woman named P. was hanged in the tall palm-tree. An antelope was her horse and it was Kwesi S. who shot her antelope."

"Now this is the way Tigari caught me: I changed myself into a lizard and walked on the ground and when Abena was coming from the farm she saw it and thought it was a bush-rat and flung her load of firewood on it and broke its leg so that she was able to catch it. At that time I had an iron tunic [*batakari*] and my spears were not playthings."

"Also they brought some bush-meat from Mamfe and my mother bought some, but when it was cooked it was so bitter that only I could eat it, because it was human flesh."

"My uncle N. lost £6. They [the witches] are the people who took it. I wanted my witch company to kill my uncle N. but because of his strong spirit we couldn't, so we have given him something that makes him lose £100 as soon as he gets it. When my grandmother sells shea-butter I cause her to lose the money."

"I know I have done wrong and that the time I shall stay in this world is very short, and yet I am spending that short time in doing wrong."

"My grandmother B. gave me some more [witch-power] to add to my own. She gave it me wrapped in a red cloth."

"The reason why I am not married is that I am a woman during the day but a man at night. Also my genitals smell nasty so that no man likes me and because of that I am a virgin."

"When my uncle's wife became pregnant I spoilt the pregnancy, but I have forgotten how I did it."

"My grandmother is still alive, but because she never gives me clothes I resolved to kill her."

"One day my grandmother sent me to market to sell 12s. 0d. worth of palm-kernels. She told me to buy 2s. 8d. worth of fish so that the remainder should have been 9s. 4d., but I kept back 3s. 4d. and gave her 6s. 0d. Then she gave me back some on top of what I had already taken, so I saw I had done very wrong. Also I bought a shillingsworth of fish at the market and didn't pay for it, so I see I have done wrong. Also I sold some palm-kernels to a woman for 1s. 0d. so I didn't want to give her any change, but I did give her change, and because of that I resolved to kill her."

"When I go to market the first person whose goods I touch is able to sell very little. Because of all this the people in the market watch me. So when I go to the market I don't pay for all the things I buy and this also is very wrong."

"There is a Hausa-man in our village. His wife took me to court because I stole palm-nuts from their trees. For this I have resolved to kill her so that I can enjoy the fruits of her land."

"The people who help me to spoil pregnancies are Ama X., Adzoa Y. and Effua Z."

Progress

I lost sight of the patient for some months, after which I sent a messenger to see her. She was found in the market, selling her wares and looking very clean, plump and smiling.

COMMENTARY

Schizo-affective illness in a young adolescent who had a mental illness in childhood. Features include:

1. Legitimate guilt-feelings for factual misdemeanours.
2. Ideas of reference.
3. Fantasies of revenge following normal resentment.
4. Fantastic self-blame for actual events.
5. Fantastic presentation of actual events.
6. Stereotyped fantasies (traditional).
7. Original fantasies.
8. Depressive convictions (e.g., going to die soon).

CASE 83. KWESI A. B. of Techiman district. M. *c.* 32.

Shrine

Oboo, Techiman district.

Reason for referral

"Madness."

Family History

Parents: Not cross-cousins. Non-Christian, illiterate cocoa-farmers. Father has a nephew and niece (the latter seen, the former died) who both became schizophrenic in their teens.

Siblings: Seven born, two died. The others are all well.

Personal History

Schooling: Nil, but he became a Seventh-Day Adventist for a time about ten years ago and then lapsed.

Work: Farmer.

Marriage: Normal marriage, four children born, one died. The eldest son is about fifteen. The wife is a good personality.

Present Illness

The onset was sudden, about six weeks ago. He came home from his farm one day and said that someone there wanted to kill him. He was terrified and "mad" with fear. He became quieter but sat about shedding tears and saying that persons and a *sasabonsam* wanted to come and kill him in his sleep.

On Examination

Looks physically very well and active. Correctly orientated, accessible and co-operative, but his manner is vague and preoccupied and he never smiles. He says he hears talk and the preaching of the Gospel going on inside his head, and he himself then feels that God has given him the power to preach. Sometimes he hears God talking. He says this has happened before: long ago he often heard a *honhom* talking in church and now it has come back. It says, "Get up and do God's work as you did before." It also tells him that he will become a great man. Asked if anyone hated him, he said he couldn't tell who did and who didn't. (This is a normal attitude.) Asked about his work, he said he had not been able to do any since the voices began, but he cannot explain why. He says he sometimes feels giddy.

COMMENTARY

Acute exacerbation of paranoid schizophrenia with delusions of grandeur in a man who appears to have had sub-clinical manifestations for years. There is a family history of schizophrenia.

CASE 84. KWESI D. of Wenchi district. M. *c.* 20.

Shrine

Mframa at Mframaso.

Reason for referral

Recurrence of madness.

Family History

Paternal grandmother: She became mad.

Father: He became mad and hanged himself. He was an illiterate, non-Christian cocoa-farmer.

Mother: She was not the father's cross-cousin, but it is the mother whom the patient strikingly resembles in appearance—a big, strong build, low, thick level brows, eyes deep-set though large, unusual for West Africans, who have mostly arched brows, and eyes shallowly set and wide apart.

Siblings: Six born, three survive. A sister is married with children, a brother is a literate working in Kumasi, his mother does not know at what.

Personal History
Childhood: N.a.d.

Schooling: Attended for a short time and then gave up. He can speak some English. Christian.

Work: A carver of wooden *fufu* mortars. He is interested in all the herbs of the forest and learnt all their names from a herbalist relative, but has never practised.

Marriage: He has never had any inclination.

Home: A remote cocoa-"village" with only a few relatives.

Previous Illness: Two or three years ago he had a similar illness and came to the *obosom*. The latter said that it was not good for him to live in a remote village and he must come and live in the *obosom's* town and be a drummer, helping with the drumming on three days in the week. This he did and quickly recovered. About a year ago, however, he left and went back to his mother. A few weeks ago the illness returned.

Interview: 25.9.56
I saw the patient for the first time during an Afahye festival. I took him for a possessed *okomfo*, for that was how he was behaving—dancing in the street, going round shaking hands with everyone with his left hand and with an abstracted expression of face. The next day he was walking vaguely about the town, was accessible to greetings, but walked off in the middle of conversations, looked around at the sky, crossed himself and came back. He told me, when asked where he lived, that he had come to the *obosom* because he was sick. He said he would come and inspect my house and if it was not properly built would put it right.

Progress
The next day he helped with drumming as the *obosom* recommended but had to be told not to drum when the other drummers were silent. Then he came and visited me and said he wanted to make me a present of a cat. Later he brought me a present of a sheath-knife in a sheath and some fruit and various herbs. He saluted and said he had been a soldier in East Africa—which was not true.

He stayed in the town for a few weeks drumming and I met him when I was taking a walk one evening and he told me the names of innumerable plants and trees and what they were used for. Now and again he made some quite successful attempts to speak English. He seemed exceptionally intelligent. A few days later his mother appeared, weeping, and said he had disappeared from home and had been seen in Techiman. She accepted the reassurance that everyone in Techiman knew him and would not let him come to harm, which in fact was so: someone brought him home. He stayed then in his mother's village, settled down gradually and resumed his wood-carving.

1.10.57. He has been socially quite well ever since but very silent and withdrawn. I saw him once on his bicycle, doing an errand for his mother. He dismounted and greeted me gravely, looking infinitely sad.

1.2.58. He continues wood-carving in his mother's village, silent, vague, but gentle and amenable.

COMMENTARY

Schizophrenic descendant of a schizophrenic father and schizophrenic grandmother. He is an example of the schizophrenic schoolboy who abandons school.

CASE 85. KODZO P. of Wenchi district, Ashanti. M. *c.* 20.

Shrine

Owusantowa at Awisa, and others.

Reason for referral

"Caught" for making bad *suman.*

Family History

Parents: Not cross-cousins. Father died recently. Illiterate Christian cocoa-farmer and produce-buyer. Successful. He had a lorry. Mother a non-Christian, illiterate trader.

Siblings: Patient is the second of four. One brother is an illiterate tailor. Younger brother and sister are at school.

Personal History

Childhood: N.a.d.

Schooling: Nil, but is a Christian.

Work: Six years ago he was apprenticed to carpentry. He served one year and then set up for himself. He did well: obtained some Government contracts.

Marriage: One wife. One child.

Home: Great-uncle's house with great-uncle and various other relatives.

Present Illness

Fairly rapid onset four months ago. No fever, headache or physical illness. He stopped going to work and sold his carpenter's tools. He took people's money and took wares out of stores without paying. He tried to drive away his father's lorry though he knew nothing of driving. He produced a *suman* and asked his father to kill a fowl on it to make it work. It was then found that he had bought three bad *suman* from Kramu medicine-men and said that he had made up his mind to kill his great-uncle and various other relatives. He was taken to the shrine at which the great-uncle had drunk and there confessed. He was fined a cow and ritually cleansed, but became worse—noisy, destructive, aggressive and unmanageable. If confined in a room he smashed himself out. He was again taken to the *obosom*, who said he had more to confess. He then confessed to having stolen trinkets from his father. The father searched and found that this was true. As the father had drunk at another shrine he was taken there. The *obosom* said it was not he who had "caught" him but the ancient State-god. The relatives, however, particularly the great-uncle, said they could endure no more from him and that if the *obosom* killed him they would be glad.

Since then he has been confined to one room with his foot shackled to a heavy log. His great-uncle says his habits are degraded and that he defaecates into his food-dishes. Asked whether the patient was ever released and taken for exercise, he said no, because he always became unmanageable and did damage.

First interview: 2.8.57

I did not see him till he had been ill for four months. He was in a shuttered dark room, shackled, but able to stand, sit and lie down. The floor was strewn with the silk-cotton stuffing of his pillow.

He was a tall, weedy type with long, limp hands. He was bleached and wasted and appeared to have a mixed vitamin deficiency with dermatitis, alteration of texture of hair and glossitis. He was accessible, shook hands in a tremulous, fumbling fashion, responded to greetings, told me his name when asked, but was quite bewildered when asked if he were ill. Asked if there was anything he would like, he said cigarettes. While these were being fetched he stood up and sat down alternately, singing to himself and smiling at the ceiling. Asked to show his tongue he obeyed, and it was seen that his mouth contained a large gobbet of chewed green cotton from the cover of his pillow.

31.9.57. He has now been released from the log and could come out into the yard if he wished, but spends his time lying down with his face covered in the dark room. He gets up when told to and says "Thank you" for cigarettes. Movements are very unsteady and uncoordinated. He cannot be persuaded to emerge from his room: he seems afraid. He is physically very weak. No other youths can be found to take him for short walks out of doors. His mother (who lives in another house and brings him his food) has been given a supply of vitamin tablets but I doubt if she administers them regularly.

10.1.58. I have seen him often. He does not change much but is sometimes shackled to the log.

COMMENTARY

Another example of the association of bad medicine making with the onset of schizophrenia.

CASE 86. KWAME T. of Kwahu. M. *c.* 20.

Shrine

Mframa at Mframaso.

Reason for referral

"Madness."

Family History

Parents: Not cross-cousins. Illiterate, non-Christian cocoa-farmers in a "village" in Kwahu. Formerly the father had a store in Kumasi, made money and was able to build houses and buy a lorry. The lorry crashed into a ditch: its owner consulted Tigari, who said the accident was caused by witchcraft and advised him to go back to cocoa-farming. This he did and shortly afterwards Tigari "caught" a woman relative who became "*basa-basa*" and died. It was assumed to be she who had sent the lorry into the ditch. The mother brought the patient to the shrine. She seemed a good personality.

Siblings: Seven born. Two daughters and three sons survive. The patient is the youngest son. One brother finished primary school and is now at a commercial college. The other brother is an illiterate tailor. A younger sister is at school, the elder is married with children.

Personal History

Childhood: N.a.d. disclosed. The home was in Kumasi where the father had two wives living together, the patient's mother being junior, but the senior left later.

Schooling: Nil. The maternal uncle had intended to send him but died.

Marriage: Unmarried.

Work: He travelled in Togoland selling sandals for an uncle who is a sandal-maker in Accra. After this first illness he went back to his parents in their cocoa-village and did farm-work.

Previous illness: Two years ago he came back from Togoland and told his uncle he would travel no more. His behaviour was strange, so the uncle sent for the mother, who took him home. So far as the mother knows, there was no associated physical illness. He quickly became mute, restless, wandering and unwilling to take food. His mother brought him to Mframaso where the *obosom* said he was the victim of witchcraft in the family. No one, however, became "caught". He stayed four months, recovered and went home, but refused to go back to trading and worked on a farm previously given him by his father.

Present Illness

A year after recovery he should have returned to Mframaso to give thanks, but he refused to come. For that reason—his mother said—the trouble returned.

First interview: 30.12.56

He looks physically well but is inaccessible, mute, and walks about restlessly. He is difficult to restrain from wandering away.
7.2.57. He is still mute and becoming more restless, resistive and troublesome. He seldom eats or drinks and has lost much flesh.
1.3.57. He has gone home unimproved.

COMMENTARY

Second acute attack of schizophrenia. The first, two years ago, left much deterioration of personality.

CASE 87. AFUA B. of Mampong district, Ashanti. F. *c.* 38.

Shrine

Kyinaman, at Bredi.

Reason for referral

Self-accusations of witchcraft.

Family History

Parents: Illiterate, non-Christian cocoa-farmers. Not cross-cousins. Father dead, mother alive.
Siblings: Eleven born, three died. N.a.d. disclosed.

Personal History

Childhood: N.a.d. disclosed.
Schooling: Nil. Non-Christian.
Work: Food-farmer.
Marriage: Husband is a weaver. Cross-cousin. Has two other wives

junior to patient. No friction disclosed. Husband brought patient to the shrine. Pleasant, kindly man.

Children: Nine born, three died. Eldest survivor about twenty.

Household: Husband, patient and children. Other wives elsewhere.

Present Illness

Onset about one month ago. No fever or other physical illness. Patient says that she felt her mind was becoming *"basa-basa"* because she could hear her thoughts loudly talking and saying, "Do this, do that". She also felt that her mind "was being taken out of her head so that she wouldn't have any thoughts again". This worried and upset her and made her often to cry. She could not sleep and thought she must be a witch and was being "caught" for it. Her husband said she had talked *"basa-basa"* and he had thought she was going mad.

First interview: 8.1.57

I did not see her till after she had been to the *obosom* and been cleansed and reassured. A well-nourished, healthy-looking woman vigorously pounding *fufu* in a mortar. She welcomed me in a casually friendly fashion, told me the above and then suddenly became reticent and wary and would say no more. She silenced her husband sharply when he said he had thought she was going mad. She was fully accessible, not apparently depressed but was anxious. She said she was sleeping again since the *obosom* had begun to take her trouble away. Attention, memory and other mental tests very well done.

30.1.57. Seen several times since. She is specious and evasive, but I think quite deliberately so. Says perfunctorily that she is quite well but smiles warily and won't go into details.

5.2.57. Patient has gone home.

COMMENTARY

Hallucinations and disturbance of the thought-process with full insight in a setting of clear consciousness with secondary anxiety and depression, the two latter removed by the *obosom's* reassurance.

CASE 88. JOHNSON KOFI D. of Akwapim (now living in Ashanti). M. 20.

Shrine

(1) Kyinaman, Bredi.

(2) Mframa at Mframaso.

Reason for referral

"Basa-basa" talk.

Family History

Parents: Cross-cousins. Both alive and well. They are non-Christian, illiterate cocoa-farmers. The father is now a minor chief. He had four wives, of whom all died except the patient's mother.

Siblings: The mother bore twelve, of whom five died. The patient is the youngest survivor. The eldest brother is secretary to a Co-operative Society in an Ashanti town. He is an able, sensible, successful owner of cocoa-farms and passenger-lorries which latter his three younger brothers drive for him. Another brother is a clerk in Government service. All are literate Christians.

There are seven half-siblings by the father's other wives, all literate Christians in good positions. One is an assistant education officer, one a police inspector, some are teachers.

Personal History

Childhood: N.a.d. disclosed.

Schooling: Standard VII certificate.

Work: On leaving school he spent two years in a "typewriting school". His mother's sister then bought a lorry which he drove for her. Later he left and drove for his eldest brother in Ashanti. He talks of going into the police-force.

Marriage: He had a wife for one year but the marriage broke up, ostensibly because of the wife's infidelity. There is one child.

Present Illness

The patient was driving his passenger lorry from Cape Coast to Techiman when he picked up, at an intermediate town, a woman-passenger whose destination was not far away. She was attractive and dressed in black velvet. The patient put her on the front seat between himself and the driver's mate, and judging her—as also did the driver's mate—to be a prostitute, told her that he loved her and suggested taking her on to Techiman to sleep with him. She declined, but he nevertheless sped through the town of her destination without stopping and took her to Techiman where he spent the night with her. In the morning, instead of reporting to his elder brother (the lorry-owner) as usual, he took the lorry and the woman to Kumasi, right off his beat. She left him in Kumasi and he returned to Techiman, giving his brother only a vague and unsatisfactory account of his behaviour.

A few days later, on a Saturday, some fellow Akwapims, also working in Techiman, approached the lorry-owner and said that one of them had died and they would like the lorry to carry the corpse home to Akwapim—some 250 miles. At first he refused, for a corpse is dangerous cargo: the spirit of the dead man, if uneasy, may wreck the lorry. They

336

persisted in their entreaties, so the owner asked the patient whether he was willing to drive. He consented, so the funeral party set off. On the way he suddenly stopped the lorry and told the mate that he could see the women in black velvet. He shouted to her, "If you are going I will go with you." No one else could see her, and he was restrained from following her, persuaded to drive on, and reached home in Akwapim.

On the next day, Sunday, he was apparently hallucinated again and kept shouting, "If you are going, I will go with you." An elder of his family said that the spirit of the corpse was troubling him and that such a young driver should not have been made to drive a corpse. This elder made some medicine for him to bathe in.

The next morning he appeared quite well and set off with his lorry to Techiman. On the way he again saw the woman in black velvet, shouted and stopped the lorry. The mate then found another driver in the next town to take over. When they reached Techiman the patient was talking *"basa-basa"* and his elder brother took him to the Mission hospital. Nothing physically wrong could be found, but he was asked to report again in three days.

The next day he was taken to the shrine of Kyinaman at Bredi, under whose protection he had previously put himself, and it was on that occasion that I first saw him. No one told me that he had been to hospital. Only the two younger brothers were with him. They told me only that he had been taken ill while driving a corpse, had had pains in his head and chest, had talked *"basa-basa"* and been unable to finish the drive home.

First interview: 8.1.57

He was lying on a mat looking ill, distressed and dazed. At first sight I thought of a febrile confusional state, but was puzzled to find no fever and normal pulse and respirations. However, his replies to questions were partly correct and partly confused. He gave his name correctly, but when asked the name of the shrine village, looked bewildered and said, "All this travelling troubles me." He repeatedly said, looking deeply worried, "Something is being put into my head", but could not make it clear whether he was complaining of thought-blocking. At the shrine, when asked whether he had done wrong, said he had often cheated his brother out of lorry profits but could make no other coherent statement. He was led away, looking bemused and muttering about Jesus Christ, to take his ritual bath.

9.1.57. When I went to Bredi the following day he had gone. I later called on his elder brother, who said that he had sent him home to Akwapim as he was no better. The two other brothers had gone with him.

20.7.57. Six months later he appeared in Mframaso, brought by all three brothers. They said that in Akwapim he had been taken to a succession of *abosom* and medicine-men, one of whom had said that the woman in black velvet had been a ghost and that by sleeping with her he had taken a mortal sickness.* (Ghosts are believed to be, when visible at all, indistinguishable in appearance and behaviour from ordinary people.)

He then, his brother continued, became completely mute, except for intervals of talking in which he said his business had been spoilt by his illness. He became entirely dependent on his mother, but when he was mute he always wrote down on paper what food he wanted her to give him and she took the paper to a scholar for elucidation. On one occasion the brothers took him for a few days to Accra to see a doctor. When they were all resting in their lodgings he disappeared. They eventually went to the police, who had in fact picked him up and taken him to the Mental Hospital. There he made signs that he wanted a pen and paper, wrote his name and address and a request to be taken home, with the result that he was pronounced "not mad" and sent home with his brothers. When he arrived in Mframaso his brothers said he had been continuously mute for a month.

20.7.57. He was fat, sleek, black, shining and physically healthy except for a discharging ear brought about by some potion put into it by a medicine-man. His behaviour was infantile. His brother washed, dressed, fed him, brought him a chamber-pot when necessary, and made him into a whole-time job.

He seemed to me perfectly accessible but wilfully mute. He sat smiling, not the empty or preoccupied smile of the schizophrenic but the self-conscious, mischievous smile of a coquettish little girl who has grown-ups exactly where she wants them. His eyes were fully aware and expressive: they were rather large, lustrous eyes with long, curled lashes, and he used them girlishly. One of his brothers always laughed loudly at this "act" and the patient's grin would then widen in mocking childish triumph. He never returned greetings but put on the shy "knowing"-little-child "act" and hung his head. Even in walking he required to be led by the hand and took little, toddling steps, and if his cloth fell off he stood like a helpless baby until one of his brothers replaced it for him. However, if he wanted a cigarette he mimed the action of smoking, and if he wanted toilet or any other attention

---

* The belief that sexual intercourse with a ghost results in death was once held in Europe; *vide* "Ballad of Clerk Saunders and Maid Margret":

> "My mouth it is full cold, Margret,
> It has the smell now of the ground.
> And if I kiss thy comely mouth
> Thy days of life will not be lang."

unanticipated by his brothers he beckoned one of them and then whispered into his ear very competently.

18.8.57. During the past few weeks the two younger brothers have been caring for the patient in Mframaso, the eldest brother coming in one of his lorries on Sunday visits. The patient made no statement to the *obosom*, who having heard of the ghost theory, subscribed to it, and ordered a course of baths to wash away the ghostly influences.

There was no change till a few days ago when the patient lost his knowing smile and childish ways and sat huddled, bemused, wretched and inaccessible. He has even ignored food and is said to have eaten nothing for two days. He has lost his sleek, glossy look and is thinner.

21.8.57. He is now an unmitigated schizophrenic. He stands all day leaning against a wall, inaccessible, with a faintly smiling hallucinated look. He seldom eats and is getting thinner.

7.9.57. He now alternates between coquettish hysteria and a bewildered oppressed schizophrenic demeanour. He does not talk in either phase.

8.9.57. As the *obosom's* course of treatment is now completed, without any improvement, the elder brother has asked me for "injections"—the universally approved panacea.

Amytal and Methedrine Abreaction. I.V.I.

Before the injection the patient was in the childish, hysterical phase. Immediately after injection he looked worried, bewildered and frightened. He started talking at once, saying, "I think I have been dreaming for several days. Once when I was a very small child I was very frightened because I looked into a very deep hole" (water-well?). He could give no further details of this, but on questioning revealed himself as an intelligent young man, frightened and distressed by the onset of thought interference and hallucinations which he was aware were abnormal. He said again, "Something has been put into my head to spoil it." He said he could hear all sorts of languages being talked in his head and that they prevented him from thinking and reading the newspaper. He also said that he heard a perpetual singing of birds, and that the birds followed his lorry and came and sat on his head. They were friendly birds, but he could not say of what kind.

Asked whether anyone wished him ill, he said No. Asked further about his feelings, he said, "I feel as I am a thief and want to burgle people's houses", and also, "I feel as if I want to be circumcised." He could not follow up these topics. Asked whether he had done any wrong, he said No. Asked concerning the woman in black velvet, he could not recall her.

Most of his other responses were vague, elusive or irrelevant.

Further progress

When I left the district in February, 1958, he was no better and had gone home to his mother in Akwapim.

COMMENTARY

I cannot tell whether the headstrong determination to consort with the prostitute was normal for him or not. If it was, then the illness began during the driving of the corpse and may have been precipitated by fear—as psychosis often is in Africans.

The hysterical behaviour should probably not be regarded as an integral part of the schizophrenia, but as a refuge from the fear and stress of the thought-interference and hallucinations which began in a setting of clear consciousness. Reversion to an infantile dependence on his mother and elder brothers brought temporary relief to his distress and panic. If schizophrenia is a metabolic disease, comparable in its inevitability with, say, diabetes, it will, when its time arrives, strike the neurotic and the well-adjusted personality indiscriminately. But the two will receive it differently.

CASE 89. SAMUEL KOFI M. of Sunyani district, Ashanti. M. 20.

Shrine

Kyinaman, at Bredi.

Reason for referral

"Madness." Smashing up the house, attacking people.

Family History

Father: Farmer. Some cocoa. An illiterate non-Christian, alive and well.

Mother: She died about six years ago: an illiterate non-Christian.

Siblings: One older brother. Literate. A tax-collector in another town. One younger sister: a schoolgirl.

Personal History

Childhood: Father lived in a different household. Mother's household contained three other children about the patient's own age, several men whom he cannot recall, a woman and her son and several other people, filling an eight-roomed compound. When the patient started school he left home and lived with his father's nephew.

Schooling: He reached Standard VII of the Mission School with ease. "You couldn't in all my town find twelve boys more clever and obedient than me." (This is probably true.)

Work: 1952–1955. Apprentice motor-mechanic. He only received two shillings a week and tips from drivers. He did not live at home but had to pay for a room and his food. A fellow-apprentice who had been a school-friend became very jealous of his cleverness as a mechanic and the patient became afraid that he would find a way to do him harm. He denies, however, that this was the reason why he left the job: he could not live on the pay. He had been ambitious to go to England to study motor-engineering, but had to give up the idea. He seems to have shown no initiative in seeking a better job.

1955–1956. Cocoa-farming with his father and father's nephew. They have three or four very old farms, not yielding much. The patient has planned to plant a new one but is finding that clearing the forest single-handed is very heavy. He has bought a Government subsidised sprayer, £2.

Home: The father has two houses, an old one inherited from his uncle and a new one built by himself. The father lives in the old one together with two Fante lodgers. The father's wife lives in her own people's house. In the new house live the patient, the father's two nephews and several strangers renting rooms. The patient's young sister brings in his meals. She lives in the late mother's house together with the "small grandmother" (great-aunt) whom the patient dislikes.

Marriage: Financially out of the question, but he does not seem to desire it.

Religion: Christian, but he drank at the Bredi shrine a year ago for protection against enemies and for prosperity.

Present Illness

Onset two months ago. Began with severe toothache. One day on returning from his farm at noon he told his father he had seen "something like an electric light" in front of him on the path. He saw it four more times in the same place and then made a new path and did not see it again. The toothache became worse and he had little or no sleep. One evening he wrote an article entitled "Let God be true" and sent it to the *Accra Evening News*. It was not printed. He has not slept since that night and has had several disturbed episodes—smashing things, attacking people and accusing them of making him into a witch to bring about his downfall. His father brought him to Bredi and immediately left him there and went home to borrow money for his treatment. There was one outbreak of violence in Bredi on the day before he appeared at the shrine. He ran to a town on the main road, some three miles away, pursued by his custodians, and attempted to seize and drive away a lorry that was standing there. The driver thrashed him.

Interview: 24.8.56

When I arrived the patient was sitting composedly in the yard, and I did not notice, till I attempted to shake hands with him, that he was in handcuffs.

His manner was pleasant, friendly, sensible and unassuming. His English was good, and free from the usual flowery adornments. His statements were all clear, brief and to the point. Their paranoid content was in startling contrast to his unresentful, quietly matter-of-fact style.

He told of the onset of his illness with great exactitude as to dates, etc., and then said, "I have not left off thinking since the night when I wrote the article and I haven't slept since that night. My toothache has been too severe. That night I dreamt I saw a python [*onanka*] under the bed. It was the snake that started the whole thing." (It is probable that in African dream symbolism a snake symbolises simply a sly, dangerous enemy.) "I got to know in dreams that my small grandmother is taking my valuable cloth and is using bits of it to make bad medicine against me. My relatives find that I have changed: someone is making me into a witch, but I have never flown in the night. All my teeth must fall out before I die and the person who is doing it must be punished. Evil spirits as well as people are checking me [impeding my progress] because in future I will be a great man. Envious people don't want me to succeed to the stool in my house. The man now on the stool and two others are against me. They want to kill me. They want to put something into my head so that I shall kill someone and be hanged."

Questions concerning his family and personal history he answered briefly and accurately.

He realises that he is ill, that his violent behaviour has been intolerable, but he has no other insight. He denies any hallucinations other than the "electric flashings" on the path from the farm. (As these were always seen in the same place they may well have been the sun striking an old tin canister or bottle thrown away in the bush.)

In reply to a question about dreams, he said, "All my life I have dreamt about eggs. Sometimes some are broken and some are good." (It may well be that eggs symbolise potentialities, promises of achievement, ambitions to be fulfilled.)

He told me that three of his teeth had big holes in them. He pointed to the lower molars, only one of which had a hole in it. He had a greatly swollen face in the parotid region and a gum abscess beginning to point but not yet burst.

Before the shrine he was docile and matter-of-fact, giving the orthodox perfunctory account of his witchcraft. He named three men whom he said he had killed. His *obayi* came, he said, from God, it abode in his fingers and its name was "S.K.". "It dances like electric and sings and then I kill the victim. It sings: *Kuma no sesese, Kuma no sesese.*"

Here the patient danced and sang, desisting obediently when called back to the railing. Asked if he would stop killing people after his purification, he said he would. He was co-operative throughout his purification ritual.

30.8.56. The first time I saw the patient I had offered to take him to have the offending tooth extracted. This was declined, but a few days ago the abscess burst and is still discharging into the mouth. This has greatly relieved the pain and his landlord says he is having good nights.

Mentally he is much worse, though quiet and docile, grimacing and posturing, and cannot remember how long he has been in Bredi. I asked him to listen to an adapted version of the Cowboy Story and tell it back. He smiled fatuously, appeared to listen, but when asked to repeat it he looked at the palm of his hand and said, "Community Centre, here at the centre of my hand", in a typically schizophrenic manner.

6.9.56. I could talk to him only for a minute as I was walking through to another village, and he was on his way to the *obosomfo's* farm to help with the work. The abscess was still draining into his mouth and the swelling was less. He said he was sleeping well and his house-mates confirmed this. There had been no more violence and he was leading a normal, quiet and helpful life.

He was correctly orientated, remembered my name, but was slow in response. He spoke of the *obosom* as "my great lord who is curing me" and referred several times to God. He kept gazing at the sky and screwing up his eyes. Asked what he was looking at, he said he was trying to remember the date of his arrival (which in fact he achieved correctly). He hesitated and grimaced when asked questions, but always returned to the point of the question.

20.9.56. They said in Bredi that he had gone home quite well. I doubted the latter and wrote to him.

12.10.56. A good, brief, straightforward letter in reply. I wrote again urging him to have the tooth out and saying that I thought the abscess was sending poison into his brain.

12.11.56. Returned to Bredi with his father. He looks strikingly different—now fat and sluggish. His sister has been plying him with food and he has done no work. He is indolent and emotionally flattened, and does not speak at all unless addressed. Quite accessible, he has no delusions and is not paranoid. He has accepted the suggestion concerning the "abscess poison" as the cause of his illness and says his father and the *obosomfo* are now willing to allow the tooth to be extracted. The tooth was extracted at Techiman Mission Hospital and penicillin given over several days.

24.11.56. He is about to leave Bredi for home. His mouth has healed, but he sits about inert and uninterested, in contrast to his first visit when he worked hard. The illness appears to have left a marked deterioration in personality.

19.1.57. He writes, in reply to a letter, that he has still done no work.

10.1.58. He writes, in reply to a letter, that he is doing some farming.

COMMENTARY

Paranoid psychotic reaction to frustration in an able, ambitious young man, precipitated by pain, sleeplessness and toxaemia. The episode left considerable deterioration of personality.

CASE 90. KODZO T. of Bekwai district, Ashanti. M. *c.* 17.

Shrine
Mframa at Mframaso.

Reason for referral
"Madness."

Family History
Parents: Not cross-cousins. The father is a non-Christian, illiterate beer-store keeper, cocoa-buyer and cocoa-farmer.
Siblings: Eight born, two died. Patient is the eldest son. The mother is pregnant now.

Personal History
Childhood: At the age of two he was given to his grandmother and has lived with her ever since. She brought him to the shrine. Household consists of grandmother and her sister and some tenants.
Schooling: Nine years at a Mission School. Patient is the only Christian in the family and is a full communicant. He is said to have been clever at school and wanted to be a clerk in the Department of Agriculture.

Present Illness
Onset eleven months ago shortly before Standard VII examination. He began by talking in a jumbled fashion. He sat the examination but failed. Two days after the examination he became quite mad. At first he was violent and noisy and kept running away to the bush. Then he became quiet, but difficult to manage, because he wandered away if left for a few minutes.

First interview: 14.11.56
A small-boned, plump boy, smiling constantly and inappropriately. He is restless, keeps getting up and walking away. Not wholly inaccessible. When asked a question he usually replies rationally but immediately slides off into disconnected sentences, in English if first addressed in English.

344

Q. "What school did you go to?"

A. "Roman Catholic, then something told me to go to the cemetery. A bad sponge is not used to take a bath. I only drink palm-wine. Someone gave me a watch. Someone gave me a lorry-address. I have something in my hand, but an aeroplane will take it."

Q. "I hear you have been ill. How do you feel now?"

A. "I feel something knocking in my eyes. Somebody kicked my head. I have written Tamale, Accra, Takoradi . . . 100 pence is 8s. 4d. . . ."

30.12.56. The grandmother finds him very difficult to manage as he cannot sit still and wanders away.

5.2.57. The restless wandering has stopped. Talk getting more disorganised. He does not finish one sentence before beginning another. He still smiles unceasingly.

25.4.57. He has become very fat and settled into sluggishness. He no longer smiles. If addressed, he talks a completely disorganised word-salad.

17.5.57. He seldom moves unless urged, seldom speaks and does not smile.

26.6.57. He is mute, inert and difficult to persuade to eat. The grandmother has sent for the mother to take him away as he has become worse.

1.7.57. The mother has come. Sensible and pleasant. She says she would have come before but was pregnant. She has delivered her child, which died. The mother asked the *obosom's* permission to take the patient home. The *obosom* says the patient will die.

COMMENTARY

Schizophrenia, onset coincident with scholastic stress. His remark about going to the cemetery suggests that he may have made magic with the Sixth and Seventh Books of Moses, but he could give no further information and the grandmother disclaimed any knowledge.

CASE 91. KWAME P. of Trans-Volta. M. *c.* 18.

Shrine

Mframa at Mframaso.

Reason for referral

Self-accusations of witchcraft.

Family History

Parents: Cross-cousins. Non-Christian illiterates. The father was a cocoa-farmer who died a few months ago. He had three wives, of whom the patient's mother was the senior. She and one other wife divorced him a few years ago because he did not fulfil his obligations. The mother trades in cloth. She brought the patient to Mframaso. She is a pleasant, friendly woman but not a good witness.

Siblings: Nine born, three died. Patient is the seventh child. The older survivors, except a younger sister about twelve, are grown-up and married. The patient is the only literate.

Personal History

Childhood: N.a.d. The mother and other wives and their children all lived in the father's own house in his cocoa-"village".

Schooling: Attended for six years and was always top of the class. Reached Standard III and then left because of illness. Before starting school he drank at Tigari's shrine to bring scholastic success.

Present Illness (from mother)

There have been three episodes in all, the first during the Coronation (over four years ago). Onset was sudden, during the night. The patient woke shouting in fear, "I am caught! Tigari has caught me for witchcraft! My grandmother [maternal] has given me an *obayi*!" He further declared in great agitation that he had already killed ten people and was "caught" because he had resolved to kill his father with whom he had always been good friends.

He was taken the next day to Tigari's shrine, where he and all the family had drunk, but became rapidly worse, though he never appeared frightened after the first night. He said he could actually see the witches, thirty of them, standing round him and that at night they took him to their meetings. Sometimes he was severely disturbed, banged his head on the wall, tried to put his head in the fire and rolled on the ground. At times he lay down all day, inaccessible, and at others stood motionless out in the rain, was mute and neither ate nor washed. His habits were degraded with both wetting and smearing.

All the household except his mother left home because he had said he had made up his mind to kill them by witchcraft. The mother is hopelessly vague about the length of this illness but it seems to have lasted only weeks rather than months. The patient can remember nothing of it except a prodromal headache and fever.

Two similar episodes have occurred since. It is now a year since recovery from the last.

When Tigari failed to help, the mother took the patient to a woman at Somanya whose reputation for supernatural powers of healing rests on her having once "died and come back to life". His mother also took him to the out-patient clinic of a government hospital where she was told that there was nothing physically wrong with him. He has made no attempt to resume his schooling, though he has had three year-long remissions.

Interview: 21.8.57

Apparently quite well, mentally and physically. He smiled pleasantly and appropriately. No complaint of thought interference, hallucinations, etc. Memory, attention and other mental tests well done, and he has none of the typical schizophrenic evasion of the point when asked a question. He is quiet, gentle and unassuming but seems over-docile, lacking in drive and without any indignation or other emotional concern about his situation. When asked of his future he discloses no special ambition and does not feel that his illnesses have damaged his prospects. He says he will resume school when he is quite sure that he is cured and will afterwards take any suitable work that is offered him. He says casually, "I know I have a mental disease and I would like my mother to send me to a mental hospital." When reminded that he had been well for a year and need not assume that he would ever be ill again, he said indifferently, "It doesn't seem so to my mother."

COMMENTARY

Probably a simple schizophrenia with three atypically short, acute episodes possibly precipitated by malaria. Trypanosomiasis is made unlikely by the length of time since onset, the remissions and the good physical condition. Probably a trypanosomiasis investigation was done in hospital.

Trans-Volta men are different from Ashanti. A self-reproachful rather than a paranoid reaction would, on general grounds, be expected of them. (See also Case No. 32.)

CASE 92. KWABENA D. of Sunyani district, Ashanti. M. *c.* 16.

Shrine

Mframa at Mframaso.

Reason for referral

"Madness" because of using bad *suman.*

Family History

Parents: Cross-cousins. Illiterate, non-Christian cocoa-farmers and market-gardeners. The father went to school up to Standard II (the top primary standard is VII) and had to leave because of money. He is an intelligent, pleasant, sensible man. In build and facies the patient

347

resembles him. Responsibilities include his own dead uncle's children and grandchildren. He treats the sick boy with endless patience and devotion. The mother is intelligent and composed.

Siblings: The patient is the eldest of six, of whom one died on the day of birth. The youngest is eighteen months. The mother is pregnan now.

Household: In the home-town the patient stays with his father in his grandfather's house with two of the grandfather's brothers and two of the father's brothers, but for the most part the patient's parents and children live together in their isolated cocoa-village.

Personal History

Childhood: N.a.d. disclosed.

Schooling: He attended school for six years. He enjoyed school and was clever and ambitious to study in Europe to be a lawyer. He was keen on football.

One day more than a year ago he came home and said he was not going to school again because he had quarrelled with the teacher who coached football. During the game the teacher had accused him of taking no part in the game. He admitted that this was true and said he felt tired and no longer interested in football. He said he was going to work on his father's farm. He did this, apparently forgetting all his scholastic ambitions. His father says he worked quite well, but as cocoa-farm work is intermittent he may well have idled a good deal without exciting comment. He often got up early in the morning and went off into the bush to set traps. (The father gave this part of the history without realising that it was probably the insidious onset of the illness.)

Present Illness

About November, 1955, the patient, his father, mother, mother's brother and some friends made up a lorry-party and visited Mframaso to make *abisa* for prosperity in their farming. They went home the same day.

About a fortnight later the father sent the patient one day into the bush to find some *tosa* bark to make gun-wads. The patient returned home saying he had seen "something like an *obosom*", and they must take him to Mframa because the *obosom* was about to catch him. He did not, however, appear appropriately frightened. Asked why the *obosom* should be after him, he said that he had obtained some bad *suman* and had planned to use them to kill his uncle, his parents and a small sister. His uncle he wanted to kill for the sake of his cocoa, but could give no reason for wanting to kill the others. Another *suman*, he said, was to make women admire him. As he was a good-looking and manly youth, these supernatural aids to courtship were inappropriate.

When asked where the *suman* were, he disclosed their hiding-place, and they were found to be a fact.

He also said that he had ordered "The Sixth and Seventh Books of Moses" and had planned to dress himself in white clothes and perfume, take the book to the cemetery at night, together with an "altered" crucifix and finger-rings, and there make bad medicine by reading from the book and "uttering words". He did not in fact ever obtain the book.

He was immediately brought to Mframaso together with the bad medicines which were there detoxicated.

He did not, according to his parents, who were good witnesses, appear in any way physically ill or feverish. He remained quiet for about two months, usually refusing to talk, sometimes refusing to eat and sometimes sitting with his tongue hanging out. It was unanimously agreed that he was "mad", and both his parents sometimes shed tears at the spectacle. Later he became restless, talkative and mischievous, and gave much trouble by wandering away and getting lost.

Interview: 5.3.56

When I first saw the patient he and his parents had been staying in Mframaso about three months. The first time I saw him his feet were being fettered to a post in the landlord's yard because his parents were exhausted by keeping him out of mischief, especially that of running away. He was fighting, spitting, hurling mud from the ground at his captors and then weeping. When I approached him, knowing that he had been to school, I greeted him in English and he shook hands and replied politely, but immediately began a rambling mixture of English and vernacular, interspersed with cackles of loud, irrelevant laughter.

Q. "When did you come to this town?"
A. "When we framed a charge against Queen Elizabeth and took £1,500 from her, I and Lawyer Taylor. My father bought a gun for five shillings and gave it to me. I have ordered the Sixth and Seventh Books of Moses because with it you can work wonders and without it you can't go to England."

Physically he was a broad, heavily-muscled youth, looking in excellent physical condition.

15.7.56. He continued without much change till July except that there always seemed to be a slight improvement on the days when the *obosom's* servants had given him ceremonial baths. These officials were, however, slack and neglectful and the patient's father became dissatisfied with them. The patient then began running away nearly every day, and on one occasion got into the hands of the police for seizing a stationary lorry and running it down a hill into a bank. The police were satisfied that the patient was mad and, though glad to be rid of him, did not hand him to his father (so the father said) till he had given them a much bigger "dash" than he could afford. The father then decided to take him home.

10.12.56. In December, 1956, the patient and his parents returned to Mframaso to give thanks for his perfect recovery. The parents said that he had recovered about two months after returning home and had been working well on the farm ever since. He looked physically in excellent condition and his behaviour was perfectly satisfactory. They stayed only one day and I had no opportunity of testing his concentration, etc., but in superficial conversation in the presence of a group I thought his replies to questions eluded the point and that his affect was shallow. His father said he was content to work on the cocoa-farm to help recoup the expenses of his illness—a total of £250, in addition to £300-£400 worth of cocoa spoilt because it went unharvested at the onset of the illness.

COMMENTARY

Schizophrenia. The patient's consistently good physical condition and the insidious onset rule out trypanosomiasis. The use of bad *suman* and the intention to make magic with the Sixth and Seventh Books of Moses frequently herald the onset of schizophrenia.

He is another example of the young schizophrenic who drops out of school.

CASE 93. KWAKU P. of Domeabra district. M. 27.

Shrine
Oboo, at Offuman.

Reason for referral
"Madness."

Family History

Parents: Cross-cousins. Father died ten years ago. Illiterate, non-Christian cocoa-farmers. Father had six wives simultaneously, but later left them all except the patient's mother. The latter is a composed, sensible woman who has tackled her present misfortune with quiet resolution and fortitude

Siblings: Eleven born, four brothers and three sisters survive. Patient is the only literate. One brother is a tailor, one a farm labourer; the youngest, aged twelve, went to school for a time but disliked it and left. The sisters are all married and have children.

Personal History

Childhood: The patient's mother and her children lived in a large house belonging to her husband, together with all the other wives and their children. On his death the patient's mother and her children all went to her people, where they are now.

School: From age nine to eighteen. Reached Standard VII. He says he was a good scholar.

Work: On leaving school he was a pupil teacher for four years at £2 13s. 4d. per month. He says he left because the pay was poor, but one would have expected a good candidate to obtain promotion within four years.

He then became a store-clerk in Kumasi. He insists that his work was very good and that his employer, a European, loved him, but his fellow employees hated him for thus finding favour. He cannot produce any reason for leaving except that witches spoilt his work and "brought him down".

Marriage: Married five years ago. One child. His wife left him because he failed to support her.

Present Illness

Nine months ago the patient went home to his mother with a leg so badly swollen that he could not walk. He said that a tsetse-fly had bitten it, but added, however, that he saw the tsetse-fly settle and when he raised his hand to smite it his arm "broke and became weak" and could not be moved. There was no fever or delirium associated with this swollen leg. His mother took him to a local *obosom* who said a witch had sent the tsetse-fly. He was given herbal dressings for the leg and recovered. He then went back to Kumasi. A few months later his mother went to *abisa* to ask how he was faring as she had not heard from him. The *obosom* told her to go to Kumasi and see him, which she did. She found him doing no work and "becoming mad". He said that witches had tied a rope round his waist. He also said that because he thought the swollen leg was caused by someone using a bad *sumam* against him, he had in turn made another, for which he was "caught". The mother took him to another *obosom*, who said that his trouble was madness. He denied madness, was resentful of his mother's solicitude and said she was the witch who had spoilt his work. He was, however, reasonably amenable in the daytime but disturbed and shouting at night and needing restraint to keep him from running away to bush. His mother took him patiently round to some half-dozen *obosom*, and finally to Offuman, where I first met him. Offuman people were all agreed that he was mad, often beat up his mother and kept running away.

First interview: 10.5.57

Well built, tall, muscular, healthy-looking. Clean and well dressed. Intellectual tests satisfactory. He gives an unintelligible story of his illness, has no insight and insists that he is persecuted by his mother and other witches. Argumentative, incoherent, he cannot keep to the point. Incongruous smiling alternates with indignation. He says, "I cried because of the witchcraft, and the crying and the sorrows brought the disease."

12.5.57. His mother brought him to see me at Mframaso to ask what to do next. Remembering the tsetse-fly, I told her to take him to Kintampo Field Unit for trypanosomiasis investigation. He agreed to submit to this. He was very hostile to his mother, blaming her for his illness and misfortunes, but was more forthcoming about his symptoms and feelings. He also said he sometimes heard voices in the roof reviling him for having done wrong. He admitted having used a bad *suman* and then been frightened and "caught" for making it.

21.5.57. His mother brought him to me again, together with a report from Kintampo that blood, gland puncture and C.S.F. were all negative. On this day the patient was floridly schizophrenic. He described "visions" as well as voices, the latter harping on the bad *suman*. He described thought-blocking, saying that witches and spirits put poisons into his head to make him forget what he began to talk about. They also put poisons into his arms and legs. His mother and his kinsfolk were all witches and wanted to kill him. "It all began by witches bringing me down in my work in Kumasi."

9.6.57. Patient's mother came to me to enquire whether he had come to me, as he had run away without any money. She said that latterly he had been sitting inert and speechless for most of the day. She said that she had spent all she could borrow (about £250) on the illness and had promised many *abosom* three cows each if they would cure him.

16.6.57. At Offuman the *obosomfo* said that the patient had returned after running away, and that his mother had taken him back to her town.

COMMENTARY

Schizophrenia in a young literate, but some part of his resentment is soundly based on tiresome visits to a succession of shrines. The use of bad *suman* is a common feature of the onset of schizophrenia.

It is probable that the paranoid colouring of the illness is chiefly an attempt to explain it. He appears to have lost his job through bad work before he postulated the witches who made him lose it.

VI

MENTAL ILLNESS RESULTING FROM PHYSICAL ILLNESS

The mental illnesses which I have put into this group are those for which the physical illness seems to be the single cause.

By far the commonest mental illness arising out of physical illness is depression, and the illnesses which generate it are many and various.

Surprisingly, one meets at the shrines relatively few mental illnesses which are an integral part of the physical illness. Trypanosomiasis is the outstanding example. Other febrile illnesses classically able to produce delirium and confusion are tolerantly regarded by the patient's house-mates, save when they are accompanied by expressions of fear and guilt and the patient says the illness has been sent to punish and kill him.

In addition to the sample which I now present of physical illnesses with mental sequelae, others met at the shrines include two cases (one fatal) of cerebro-spinal meningitis which had both had some hospital treatment before they discharged themselves, one case of trypanosomiasis (or so I opined) with a motor aphasia and resulting alarm, one case of ascariasis with gross anaemia, worm-vomiting, avitaminosis, neurosis and death,* one case of sudden blindness with neurological signs, and several cases of tuberculosis.

CASE 94. YAW K. of Konongo district, Ashanti. M. 40+.

Shrine
Mframa at Mframaso.

Reason for referral
Self-accusations of witchcraft.

Family History
No information.

* Shortly before death this patient consented to go to hospital, where the diagnosis was confirmed.

Personal History

Childhood: N.a.d. disclosed. He had measles, since when he has been blind in one eye. He cannot remember a time when he could use it.

Schooling: Nil. Non-Christian.

Work: He farms foodstuffs for market. No cocoa, but he has charge of the cocoa-farm of an absentee farmer and gets one-third of the profits. He says the farm-work prospers.

About two and a half years ago it appears he became restless and decided to go and work as a diamond-mine labourer. He came to Mframaso first to put his wife and children under the protection of the *obosom* and to ask for prosperity for himself. He stayed at the mines only a month: he says he disliked the work.

Marriage: He has two wives, the first a cross-cousin.

Children: (a) By his first wife: six born, of whom the two eldest died, one at the age of one month, one at the age of one year.

(b) By his second wife: four born, two died in infancy. One came with him to Mframaso, aged about ten.

Household: The patient lives with his elder brother in a house built by the latter out of cocoa-profits. One of the brother's three wives and her children also live there. The patient's two wives and their children live elsewhere.

Present Illness

About six months ago he noticed that when he closed his eyes to sleep at night he felt himself being swung into the air. He also saw bright lights in the night. He had pains all over and "burnings", especially in his feet. He had very little sleep and when he did sleep he was unrefreshed, "as if he had done work in the night." He became unable to go to his farm because he was tired by his "night-work". Then he found that he was a witch. "No one knows what kind of soul is behind him and I found that I was a witch. I knew that I had had it from birth: no one was forcing it on me. I found that I was going to kill my elder brother and my younger brother, though I have always been on good terms with them." Questioning elicited no compulsive urges.*

He came to Mframaso, confessed, was cleansed and went home, but other members of the witchcraft coven, he supposed, did not assent to his giving up witchcraft and began to trouble his nights again. He felt that his young son was also a member of the coven and was a witch from birth. He furthermore felt that he had sent this child to go and do evil. The boy then fell sick, whereupon the father knew that

---

* I have many times heard people say that "one doesn't know his own soul" in contexts where this can fairly be translated "one doesn't know his own Unconscious, or unconscious motivation".

both he and the boy were "caught" for being witches. He took the boy to a local *obosom* who agreed with this view. They then came to Mframaso accompanied by the patient's maternal uncle (= wife's father), who was paying the expenses.

Interview: 4.3.56

Well-built muscular man. Thickened facial features—possibly either incipient acromegaly or leprosy. I could not decide whether his hands were thickened, as many Africans have markedly slender hands which would thicken up to about "normal". There were signs of pellagra—phynoderma, red smooth tongue, burning feet.

Pleasant and friendly. No signs of thought-disorder, etc. Concentration and memory tests satisfactory. Dispirited, lethargic and anxious, but able to smile appropriately if provoked. He says the most miserable feature of his illness is the inability to work or sleep.

At the shrine his "confessions" were not extravagant. He said his coven met at the back of a school and sat on a felled tree. The *obosom* reminded him that this was his second offence, and further that he was now leading his young son into evil, and that his purification fees would therefore be doubled.

The son was with him, a thin, feverish, languid little boy of about ten, with a cough, docile and ready to assent to anything. He was in no mental distress, but said matter-of-factly that he would not have known he was a witch if his father had not told him. At the shrine he was not embarrassed. He said he had not killed anyone and was not a member of a coven, but he confessed to a desire to kill his father's niece, about nine, who often came to visit the house. He probably was in fact jealous of this child, who no doubt often invaded the compound and was indulged and given food by the boy's father.

Progress

Unknown. The family party went away to collect more money, chiefly because the *obrafohene* was unreasonably avaricious about fees for ritual baths. They did not return.

COMMENTARY

Depression in a middle-aged man of good personality, probably secondary to organic changes.

CASE 95. YAA D. E. of Konongo district, Ashanti. F. *c*. 35.

Shrine

Mframa at Mframaso.

I am setting out the facts of this case in the order in which they unfolded to me, as this illuminates the deceitfulness of appearances.

In mid-June, 1956, a tall, weedy, stupid-looking man appeared at the shrine accompanied by a tall, weedy, stupid-looking woman. Both were poor, tongue-tied witnesses: the woman, in particular, seemed of low-grade intelligence, gaping open-mouthed when asked questions. The man said that she was his sister and was not well, supposedly because she had broken one of the *obosom's* rules. She and her husband had placed themselves jointly under the *obosom's* care in order to have more children. The woman had subsequently divorced her husband for neglect but had failed to come and acquaint Mframa with the separation. The husband, however, had not so failed.

The pair irritated the *obosom* by their poor witness and had to appear four or five more times before it was wormed out of the woman, by leading questions, that she had, since divorcing her husband, consorted sexually with a number of other men, been to a Kramu-man and made a bad medicine against her former husband and had finally had sexual intercourse with the Kramu. As this tale of sin was unfolded the woman became less tongue-tied and oppressed, but I still thought her a near-feeble-minded promiscuous type: so did the *obosomfo*, and he told her one day, in exasperation, that she had the face of an antelope.

She was fined, for her sum of sins, a cow and a sheep. These her brother brought and then went home, leaving her to complete her week of ritual baths.

Before the week was out, the patient's sister arrived and at the shrine asked help for herself, because her husband had refused intercourse with her for two years. This sister seemed another stupid woman. I did not seek an interview with either of them but relegated them to the limbo of adultery cases which are heard by the score at all the shrines.

The sister went away and the patient settled inconspicuously down in Mframaso for several months—as indolent patients and delinquents often do when they are reluctant to face their homes again. Now and again she appeared at the shrine making additional confessions and complaints of a trivial nature. She was nearly always kept waiting till a later session as the *obrafohene* thought her a tiresome time-waster. Once she complained of amenorrhea, but this was naturally attributed to her extra-marital encounters. Once, after standing in the queue for an hour in the sun, she slithered to the ground in what seemed a vaso-vagal fainting fit of very short duration. Her house-mates said casually, "Yes, she does have fits". And, indeed, she seemed a typical near-feeble-minded epileptic and I still did not seek an interview with her.

One day in October, my cook, a kind-hearted Moslem, said he had given some of his own money to three women who were starving. I followed this up and found that the mother and the sister of the patient had joined her in Mframaso to fetch her home, were waiting till the *obosom's* next session to take formal leave, and were meanwhile destitute except for their lorry-fares home. The avaricious old man in whose house they lodged was quite indifferent to their plight.

All three women came to my quarters for an interview. Neither the mother nor the sister seemed very intelligent but were at their wits' end, distressed and weeping. Over £30 had been spent on the patient in Mframaso alone. They declined to let me take her to hospital but said they would take her when they got back to Konongo. The mother gave me the history as follows:

Family History

Father: Dead. An illiterate, non-Christian farmer.

Mother: An illiterate, non-Christian trader.

Siblings: Eleven born, six died, two grown-up sons died about eighteen months ago within a month of one another. One was knocked down by a lorry while drunk after a funeral. The other woke one morning with pains in his ribs, spent a fortnight and a week in Konongo and Agogo hospitals respectively (costing £11 in all) and then came home because the hospitals said they could do no more for him. This shattered the family's faith in European medicine.

The surviving sons are farmers, the daughters traders: all are illiterate, non-Christians.

Personal History

Work: Successful trader.

Marriage: Satisfactory till about eighteen months ago. The patient and her husband came to Mframa to ask for more children. The mother and sister came to put themselves under Mframa's protection mainly because of the death of the two brothers. Shortly after this the patient divorced her husband for neglect.

Children: Three born, all living. Eldest is fifteen, and the youngest twelve. The patient earned the money for their schooling till she became ill, when they had to leave.

Previous Personality: Clever and imperious. "People were shy to look at her."

Present Illness

About a year ago the patient fell suddenly sick. She wept aloud, crying "My head, my head, my neck, my neck", was prostrated on her mat and fell down if she tried to walk. The illness was much worse at night: she talked "*basa-basa*", sang, danced and behaved like an *okomfo*. When she lay down she thrashed her head about. In the daytime she was quiet, shivered and said she was cold.

She went to various shrines. At one she stayed six months, at another one month. (I do not know why she was not brought straight to Mframaso. Her family did not, according to their own lights, behave intelligently.) The illness subsided, but she still felt poorly and was brought, at the end of about nine months, by her brother to Mframaso. It was during this nine months that her moral standards deserted her.

Interview: 25.10.56

The patient, though she walked to my quarters and took a seat with social competence, was unmistakably approaching the terminal stage of trypanosomiasis, and kept falling asleep as she sat. Her lower lip was swollen and drooping, her hands were tremulous. She could not co-operate in examination of the cranial nerves, for her eyes rolled about uncontrollably. When stimulated she had bursts of intelligence—she did simple, mental arithmetic about money very well, but fell asleep in reciting the days of the week backwards.

30.12.56. The patient must be still alive or a message reporting the death would have been sent to the *obosom*.

16.1.57. Messenger from Konongo says the patient is dead.

COMMENTARY

According to Dr. Geoffrey Tooth, eighty per cent of *hospital* cases of trypanosomiasis have mental symptoms. According to Dr. Djoleto, who worked with Dr. Tooth in Accra Mental Hospital (the only mental hospital in the country),* trypanosomiasis accounts for the great majority of patients who are brought in "raving mad", the parasites being found in the cerebro-spinal fluid.

But probably a far greater number than those who ever appear in hospital are, like Yaa D. E., mentally *disturbed* only at the onset of the illness, and never severely enough to be deemed unmanageable at home.

CASE 96. ADWOWA A. of Saltpond district, Western Province.
F. *c.* 60.

Shrine

Kyinaman at Bredi.

Reason for referral

Self-accusations of witchcraft.

* 1957. There may be more now.

Family History

Mother: She died two years ago. She was a non-Christian, illiterate trader.

Siblings: Several sisters, non-Christian, illiterate traders. (Two seen.) No other information.

Personal History

Childhood: No information.

Schooling: Nil. Non-Christian.

Previous Illnesses: Nil.

Marriage: Married twice, both marriages dissolved, the last ten years ago. The informants do not know why.

Children: Barren.

Work: Successful trader, working industriously till the day of the onset of her illness. She and two sisters have been living together in Kumasi for the purpose of trading.

Previous Personality: Popular and generous. She had recently given £30 to a sister in Cape Coast who had got into debt through unsuccessful trade.

Present Illness

The onset was sudden about three weeks ago on Election Day. She rose early in the morning but staggered and fell down. She did not lose consciousness and there was no paralysis. She got up and went with her two sisters and cast her vote, but said she felt giddy. On reaching home in the afternoon she said she was tired and was very silent. Asked why, she said she felt as though she was tied up with a rope, and could not get loose. When they ate their next meal she said she had pains in her jaws and could not open her mouth.

The next day, while sitting silently, she suddenly called her absent sister's name (Kakra) and said, "I have done very wrong. I have offended Kakra and harmed her and made her get into debt." Then she became agitated, walked to and fro unceasingly and took no food or drink for four days. During this time she said she was a witch and had killed all the children in her own womb. She also said she had caused a nephew to get into debt.

The other two sisters were astonished, "because she had always been a good woman". On the fifth day they decided to bring her to Bredi to confess and be cleansed, believing that the *obosom* there had "caught" her for directing her witchcraft at Kakra who had put herself under his protection because her trading was not prospering.

During the lorry-journey from Kumasi to Bredi (about eighty miles) she became mute and at intervals stuporose. On arrival she spoke, telling the *obosomfo's* uncle that she was very wicked and had done wrong.

Then she relapsed into silence and stood, bowed down, with her head nearly touching the ground. She refused to eat or drink but during the night became restless again and walked about muttering. In the morning her two sisters left her while they went to the stream to fetch water. On their return she was lying on her mat, dead.

She was buried immediately in the bush graveyard reserved for dishonourable deaths, without a coffin, without mourning or weeping, or any kind of ceremony.

When I reached the village just after the burial (having had a message the previous night that a witch had arrived) the two sisters—vivacious, vigorous Fantis—were cheerfully preparing to go home. They were friendly and smiling and readily gave me an account of their sister. No one would have guessed that they had just had a harrowing experience. A part of their resignation must be attributed to their being spared the enormous financial burden of a normal respectable funeral.

COMMENTARY

This may have been a "little stroke"* followed by a major vascular accident.

Though I did not see the patient, I consider the case worth recording as the witnesses were all good and their testimony given while the events were still fresh in their minds.

A sequel to this case is that of Georges Dubois (Case No. 61).

CASE 97. AFUA Z. of Bekwai district, Ashanti. F. *c*. 30.

Shrine

Mframa at Mframaso.

Reason for referral

Self-accusations of witchcraft.

Family History

Parents: Cross-cousins. Illiterate non-Christian cocoa-farmers. Mother alive and active, still bearing children. Father died two years ago. Only one wife.

Siblings: Patient is the eldest of nine, of whom four died. Two young brothers are now at school. All the others are illiterate. Youngest survivor aged six. No one in the family has ever been "caught" before.

Personal History

Childhood: N.a.d. Home was in father's house, built by him. His mother and her children were also there.

Schooling: Nil.

* Alvarez, "The Little Strokes", *Jour. Amer. Med. Assn.* (1955), vol. 157, p. 1199.

Marriage: Married her cross-cousin five years ago. Husband illiterate cocoa-farmer. Christian.

Children: Three born alive. One died aged one week. Youngest is suckling. One miscarriage.

Work: Helps husband with cocoa.

Home: Cocoa-village with husband. All the other relatives in town. Several other households in the village.

Present Illness

Began with pains in her belly and head when she was working on her farm. She came home sweating and hot, and lay down. She became worse and thought she was "caught". Her dreams became "*basa-basa*". She heard someone calling her name. She dreamt that people wanted to kill her mother and that she (the patient) offered a young sister (aged about ten) instead. Then she saw an *obosom* who hit her in the ribs with his fists. After that she couldn't sleep at all, but rolled on the ground crying with pain. She vomited and felt "burnings" in her belly. (Her mother volunteered the information that her urine changed colour.) She was taken to hospital, had two injections, but as these did not immediately cure her she discharged herself and hurried to a local *obosom* who told her that Mframa—at whose shrine a senior kinsman had drunk on behalf of all his juniors—was involved. So she came to the shrine with her mother and husband.

Interview

At the shrine she said she was a witch, had killed her own child and many other people, had planned to kill her uncle and had caused her aunt to stop menstruating. At interview she looked ill and languid and it was clear that she had had a sharp attack of cholecystitis with biliary colic. She was much depressed, but she talked freely though anxiously. She said that not only had she no milk in her breasts but that she never had had—which was not so, for her suckling child was thriving and contented. She still thinks she is going to die and that she deserves it.

Progress

Good gradual recovery, both physically and mentally. She went home after a few weeks.

Commentary

Transient depression reactive to physical illness.

CASE 98. EKWIA E. of Bekwai district, Ashanti. F. *c.* 25.

Shrine

Mframa at Mframaso.

Reason for referral

Her husband thinks she is a witch.

Family History

Parents: Not cross-cousins. Illiterate, Christian cocoa-farmers. The father died about five years ago. The mother is alive and well.

Siblings: Eight born, six survive. All are grown-up and married, except two schoolboys.

Mother's sister: She was "caught" by an *obosom*, south of Kumasi. Said she was a witch, talked "*basa-basa*", became mad, but she recovered after six weeks' residence with the *obosom*.

Personal History

Childhood: N.a.d. No schooling, but she is a Christian.

Marriage: Cross-cousin. There are two junior co-wives. The husband is a native-court police constable and has also a cocoa-farm. He attended school up to Standard IV and speaks English. He has two young children of his own and claims that he supports a nephew at secondary school. He is talkative, cocky and always on the defensive. He came to the shrine some months ago complaining that he was not prospering and that someone had "made his hand into a sieve"—unable to hold money. The *obosom* subscribed to his belief that witches had done this. A few months later an elderly woman—kin of his mother—became ill and restless, said she was "caught" for witchcraft and then talked "*basa-basa*", tore off her clothes, became mad and presently died. The patient's husband came back to the shrine to thank the *obosom* for finding and killing his enemy. He also said that all was not well with his wife, that she had lately appeared to have been "caught" and had talked "*basa-basa*" and, furthermore, "her children always died". He was told to go and fetch her.

Children: Three born. Two died, one at the age of about six months and the other of diarrhoea while beginning to walk. The survivor is a suckling which the patient's sister is nursing because the patient, though she fed the other two, has now no milk. The husband argues that the dead children were big and strong when born, therefore evil must have been done to them. He says he has spent much money on medicine-men. *abosom*, and additional wives, trying to acquire children.

Home: Patient lives with her mother and sister in a maternal kinsman's house. The husband lives in his father's house.

Present Illness

The onset was sudden—four weeks ago. She had fever, sweating, shivering, pains in right rib, vomiting. She sometimes vomited worms.

She had pins and needles in her feet and could not walk. Her sister said she was only slightly "*basa-basa*" and kept repeating herself. The patient said she had "*basa-basa*" dreams in which people chased her. Her mother and sister at first thought she had a "strong fever" and treated her with herbs, enemas and two illicit injections from renegade dispensers, but as she did not improve they took her to a local *adunsini* who said that her husband's *obosom* was involved.

Interview

The patient was thin, pale and ill, and said she was still vomiting worms. She was depressed, was not self-reproachful, and seemed a good personality. She was inclined to be reticent and referred me to her husband. She declined treatment for the worms.

Progress

I was not allowed to see her again, her sister always saying she was asleep. The husband had almost certainly imposed his veto.

COMMENTARY

Heavy ascaris infestation with secondary pneumonia, anaemia, and avitaminosis with peripheral neuritis. The patient's illness was evidence, welcome to the husband, that he himself was not to blame for not prospering.

It is not generally appreciated how severe can be the effects of a heavy ascaris infestation. Another young woman in Mframaso, after months of anaemia, vomiting and all the stigmata of vitamin deficiency, at length consented to enter hospital where the diagnosis was made. Treatment was too late to save her life.

CASE 99. KWESI A. of Akwapim. M. 42.

Shrine

Semina Boni, owned by private practitioner from Dahomey, settled in his own remote "village" in Akyim.

Reason for referral

Severe physical illness.

Family History

Father: Fante man. Mother left him eight years ago. Alive and well.

Mother: Aged about sixty. Akwapim woman. Petty trader, married twice. She left both husbands. Patient's father was her second husband. She left the first after the birth of her first child.

The mother was with the patient in the practitioner's village. An anxious, irritable, indignant woman but not depressed: vigorously repudiating insinuations that she was a witch. She complains of *odai* (leucorrhea) consistent with either syphilis or gonorrhea (*vide* heading "Siblings") and says she has not felt well since her last miscarriage. The practitioner says, "There is a [physical] sickness in the mother's belly which has caused the same to the patient."

Siblings:
(1) Half-sibling by mother's first husband. Died aged three days.
(2) Patient. By mother's second husband.
(3) Died aged three days.
(4) Died aged three days.
(5) Died aged three days.
(6) Died aged twenty days.
(7) Miscarried.
(8) Miscarried.

Mother's elder brother: Patient's mother has lived with him in Fante country since the separation from her second husband. He is a farmer but lives in a town and goes to his farm. This brother's wife—his cross-cousin—and his one child left him six months ago. He and the patient's mother are on bad terms, and she refuses to cook for him. She maintains that this ill-will is only because she reproached him for ill-treating his wife. The only people in the house beside the patient's mother and her brother are strangers lodging there.

Family Religion: Mother is a Seventh-Day Adventist. Mother's brother is a Presbyterian. Patient was brought up as a Methodist but taught in a Roman Catholic school. None of the relatives had drunk at the shrine of Semina Boni or any other *obosom-brafo*.

Personal History

Childhood: N.a.d.

School: Methodist Mission school. Reached Standard VII in his early twenties. (This is not unusual: children often do not start school till ten or later.)

Work: On leaving school he became a pupil-teacher, then joined the Army and served for seven years. On leaving the Army he taught in Akwapim and then was persuaded to go to Ashanti where there was a great shortage of teachers. His work was good and he was sent to take a special teacher-training course. During this course he fell ill and has not worked since.

Marriage: He married after leaving the Army. The wife is a native of his own town in Akwapim. She returned there when he fell ill.

Children: Three. Ages seven, four and two. All are said to be healthy. The eldest is at school in Akwapim.

Previous Illnesses: He had a course of injections while in the Army, but no details are available.

Present Illness

No very good witnesses. Onset about six months ago when he fainted while standing in a drill-parade during a teacher-training course. He became rapidly worse, was delirious, violent and attacked people with a cutlass. He was admitted to a Kumasi hospital, where a course of injections was started, but the relatives removed him against medical advice, believing the illness supernaturally caused. He went then to his uncle's "village" where he was treated by native practitioners. He became worse: the mother describes epileptiform fits. The uncle then decided that the illness was caused by the mother's witchcraft and brought him a great distance to the village where I found him, telling the medicine-man that if the mother came near the patient, he (the uncle) would wash his hands of the whole matter. The patient did not improve and became unable to talk.

Shortly after this, in spite of her brother's injunctions, the mother travelled to visit her son. The next day he was unable to walk and the practitioner accused the mother of causing this deterioration. She stoutly denied it, saying, "He is the only child I have left to bury me when I die, so how should I want to kill him?"

Interview

The patient was extremely ill, lying semi-stuporose in a dark hut and was not easy to observe. When stimulated, he smiled and unsuccessfully attempted to speak. His lips were swollen, his tongue, lips, hands and facial muscles were tremulous. The eyelids were drooping, the joints spastic, and there was dermatitis. Witnesses said, however, that he rose with help on most days, took some food but did not speak. His illness was certainly organic, trypanosomiasis and syphilis being among the possibilities.

Progress

I saw the patient once more about a week later. (It was a very long walk to the "village".) The patient was unchanged. An incident had, however, occurred which convinced everyone that the patient's mother was a witch. A bird—probably a night-jar—had flown into the room in which she and some other women were sleeping. It blundered against the lighted lantern several times before it made off. The other women were terrified. The bird could only have been another witch turned into a hawk and come to call its fellow-witch to the night's assembly. The practitioner then insisted on shaving the mother's head and performing

the rest of a witch's purification ritual. He insisted that she should confess—which she reluctantly and resentfully did. I then left the district
and only later heard the sequel. The mother became more and more
irritated by the medicine-man's nagging till one day she seized a stick
and beat the patient. The medicine-man then said he would have no
murderous assaults in his village so he expelled both the patient and his
mother. Some labourers carried the patient in a litter to the main road
where he and his mother were put on a lorry and not heard of again.

COMMENTARY

This witchcraft case contrasts sharply with the usual run of Ghana
cases in that the witch is not a depressive, voluntarily affirming irrational
guilt, but is aggressive and stoutly denies it when accused. This is the
pattern which Europe popularly associates with witchcraft and to which
most anthropologists subscribe when they state that "the function of the
belief [in witchcraft] is that it provides an outlet in action . . . for the
anxiety and distress aroused by things going wrong".* The "action"
taken within this pattern is against the obvious person—one who is on
bad terms with near relations and against whom there is also what is
regarded as incriminating evidence.

Since I saw this sick man I have seen several cases of trypanosomiasis
and now incline to the opinion that that was his illness, basing this
mainly on the sudden onset with delirium and violence, the subsequent
quieter slow course with fits, swollen lips, tremor, somnolence and
aphasia.

CASE 100. ADWOWA P. of Bekwai district, Ashanti. F. *c.* 20.

Shrine

Mframa at Mframaso.

Reason for referral

Self-accusations of witchcraft.

Family History

Parents: Both alive and well. Not cross-cousins. Illiterate, Christian
cocoa-farmers. Mother drank at the shrine on behalf of herself and all
her children.

Siblings: Twelve born, seven survive, all adult; only one male, who
is a fully-trained teacher in a Mission school. Only one sister went to
school: she was seduced by a teacher at the age of sixteen. All the sisters
appear to prefer casual unions to marriage.

* M. Fortes, *op. cit.*

366

Personal History

Childhood: N.a.d. A house built by the father is still the home of his wife, daughters and grandchildren.

Schooling: Nil.

Marriage: Nil.

Children: One only, aged about sixteen months. Its father (another teacher) supports it.

Present Illness

Onset ten days ago. No headache, but felt cold and shivering and wanted to lie in the sun. Then became yellow and vomited profusely. Cough and pains in chest. Went first to a *"smoggri"* (practitioner dispensing smuggled drugs) and had several injections, but becoming no better went to a medicine-man who said she had offended Mframa and been "caught" by him. She then declared herself a witch.

Interview

Extremely ill, weak, wasted, deeply jaundiced. Very tender liver and spleen, impaired respiratory excursion right lower ribs, shivering and feverish. No mental confusion but aware of the gravity of her illness. Whimpering, moaning and frightened. She was carried to the shrine, where she was capable only of saying that she was guilty of witchcraft. The *obosom* ordered her to be taken back to her lodging and there to make a detailed confession to his clerk. This confession contained no original fantasies except that she had not one but three *obayi*, one hidden under her father's bedstead, one in her own farm and one in her own best dress. She gave a reason for having resolved to bewitch and kill her father, viz., that whenever she brought him bath-water and did not remove the bucket after his bath he reviled her, saying that she would never have a father for her children. She arrogated to herself the blame for all the family misfortunes: it was she who had prevented her teacher-brother from having children and had turned his hands into "sieves" incapable of holding money: she had also changed her young sister's tongue into two tongues. (This child was in the family party at Mframaso and was found to have a large ranula beneath her tongue.)

The teacher-brother, who had come with her, though an intelligent, unaggressive personality, subscribed to the view that his sister's witchcraft was the cause of his having begotten no children.

Progress

The *obosom* consented to pardon the patient's sin and remove her evil powers. However, as her physical condition deteriorated, she continued to think up new confessions. When a little girl in her landlord's house fell ill with pneumonia the sick woman blamed herself for this. From the first she declined to be taken to hospital, insisting that she was "caught" for wrong-doing. A fortnight after her arrival she died.

COMMENTARY

Cholaemic depression with irrational self-reproach.

CASE 101. ABENA G. of Bekwai district, Ashanti. F. *c.* 30.

Shrine
Mframa.

Reason for referral
Self-accusations of witchcraft.

Family History
Parents: Not cross-cousins. Non-Christian, illiterate cocoa-farmers.
Siblings: Patient is younger of two sisters.

Personal History
Childhood: Mother died when the patient was about two. She was brought up by the mother's sister, who was always kind.
Schooling: Nil. Non-Christian.
Work: Farmer.
Children: Five born, eldest died. Eldest survivor is about ten, the youngest about twelve months.

Present Illness
Began with influenza which all the household had about five weeks ago. When convalescent she felt very miserable and sleepless and felt that she was a witch with special designs upon the life of her two-year old child—a *mpese-mpese* in the care of the *obosom*—and was "caught" for it. She dreamt that she was chased by cows and people with cutlasses, and also felt, when sleepless, that an *obosom* was standing behind her to punish her. Relatives say that she was at no time "*basa-basa*", only miserable and frightened.

Interview: 10.10.57
When seen, she had been to the shrine and had been promised pardon. She was thin, languid and miserable, but no longer self-reproachful or frightened.

COMMENTARY

Transient post-influenzal depression.

368

Case 102. AFUA A. of Fomena—Adanse, Ashanti. F. 50+.

Shrine

Mframa at Mframaso.

Reason for referral

"Caught" for witchcraft.

Family History

No information.

Personal History

Little information, but son and daughter seen. Both intelligent literates, son a watchmaker, daughter married and with children. Another son drank at the shrine three years ago.

Present Illness

About six months after the son first drank at the shrine the patient became suddenly wretched, said she was a witch and that the *obosom* had laid hold of her for trying to injure her son. Shortly after that she was struck down with paralysis and speechlessness and has been helpless ever since. She was taken to hospital, where her family were told that nothing could be done for her. (I do not know why she was not brought to Mframaso till more than two years after the stroke.)

When I first saw her she had been several weeks in the village, had been taken to the *obosom* and had signified assent to the suggestion that she was a witch. Her son had gone home to collect money for the purification ritual.

Interview

I saw her several times while she was awaiting her son. She was a typical speechless hemiplegic of long standing with severe pressure-sores and leg drawn up into permanent flexion. When addressed she appeared quite accessible and shed tears as hemiplegics often do.

Progress

When the son arrived with the sacrificial cow the purification ritual was performed. Immediately afterwards she was able to speak, haltingly, but quite intelligibly. I myself on several days spoke to her, she returned greetings and replied to a few commonplace questions. About a week later she suddenly deteriorated, refused to eat and again became speechless. Her son and daughter thought (probably correctly) that she was dying and took her home.

COMMENTARY

The only explanation that suggests itself is that the loss of speech, initially organic, was later functional and that a fair degree of speech recovery and possibly motor recovery would have been made had the patient consulted the *obosom* earlier.

It would seem that a "little stroke"* preceded the major one, bringing loss of all sense of well-being and consequent conviction of sin. This conviction determined her own and her relatives' attitude to the major stroke.

CASE 103. ADWOWA E. of Techiman district. F. *c.* 55.

Shrine

Dimankoma, Akrofrom.

Reason for referral

Self-accusations of witchcraft.

Family History

Parents: Not cross-cousins. Non-Christian, illiterate yam-farmers.

Siblings: Six born, three died. A brother is a grey-headed elder considerably older than the patient.

Personal History

Childhood: N.a.d.

Schooling: Nil. Non-Christian.

Work: Farmer.

Marriage: Not cross-cousins. Husband, a cocoa-farmer, died nine years ago.

Children: Nine born, five died. The two youngest are youths, one at school. The others, illiterates, are all married with children.

Katamenia: Menopause eight years ago. Uneventful.

Home: Elder brother's house.

Present Illness

Three months ago she became sleepless and had no appetite. Now she often sheds tears, and dreams of travelling to a far-off place where people prepare food and ask her to join in eating. Sometimes she accepts and sometimes not. Recently she dreamt that she met an *obosom* with a small boy: the latter had a knife and made as if to attack her. She then told her relatives that she was a witch, had killed three people, and resolved to kill five others.

* Alvarez, "The Little Strokes", *Jour. Amer. Med. Assn.* (1955), vol. 157, p. 1199.

Interview

She looks ill and exceedingly wasted. She has no cough, but says she sometimes has fever. She complains of her belly and has a palpable mass in the lower abdomen. She has a simple goitre of the kind common in the district but says she was not thin till four months ago. She is depressed and miserable but not retarded, and is well-disposed and pleasant. Asked what her trouble was, she said, "I have found that I am no good."

Progress

Her mental state did not change and a few weeks later she died.

COMMENTARY

Wasting disease accompanied by sleeplessness, depression and self-reproach.

CASE 104. AFUA E. of Wenchi district, Ashanti. F. 14.

Shrine

Mframa at Mframaso.

Reason for referral

"Caught", presumably for witchcraft.

Family History

Father: Alive and well. He lives in his cocoa-village.

Mother: When the patient was about four, her mother became thin and coughing and spontaneously declared herself a witch, "caught" for her sin by the *obosom*. Shortly afterwards she died, the popular assumption being that she had incompletely confessed.

Maternal uncle and aunt: The patient's guardians since her mother's death. The uncle is a Christian but put himself and his potestas under the protection of Mframa because all his nephews died young, though he himself has five children. The maternal aunt is not Christian. Both these people seemed sensible, quiet and kindly.

Siblings: No information.

Personal History

Childhood and present home: After her mother's death the patient was brought up by her mother's sister in the house of this woman's husband, a prosperous cocoa-farmer who has several other wives, children and grandchildren, all living in the same compound and numbering over thirty. One room in the compound has ambitious "lounge" armchairs and an asbestos sheet ceiling under the universal sheet-iron. The elder members are all prosperous cocoa-farmers, several of them are Christians—though the patient's foster-parents are not—and several of the younger ones go to school. The patient's maternal uncle is a near neighbour.

Schooling: Nil. but she is a baptised Christian.

Previous Personality: Always shy—"She doesn't like to talk. She can't talk to seniors, only to other children." Before her illness she was a member of the local "singing band".

Present Illness

About nine months ago she became lean and coughing, complained of pains in her belly and head and wept often. Her illness so closely resembled that of her mother, who had spontaneously declared herself a witch, that it was assumed by everyone that the mother had given an *obayi* to the patient, who was similarly "caught" for it. She was brought to the shrine, where the *obosom* asked her whether she had anything to confess. She was too shy to say anything in public so was sent to the clerk, who wrote down her confessions. These were of the stereotyped kind—that the name of her *obayi* was Atufa, that she inherited it from her dead mother, that it was conveyed in red and white waist-beads, and that she used these for night-flying.

Interview

She was extremely wasted, pale, ill and miserable. Lanky but immature. There were no signs of puberty. E.S.R. 103 mm. first half-hour; 131 mm. second half-hour. She was almost mute with shyness and misery and could answer no questions about her illness or her troubles, but when led on to other topics, e.g., the singing band, she showed some interest and talked a little.

Her guardians seemed unaccountably anxious about her "confession", which they said would be useless because they were convinced that it was incomplete. They said it would be futile either to waste a sacrificial cow or to take her to hospital, till she had told all. They were not angry or bullying, only worried and concerned, so they asked me to endeavour privately to help her to talk. Under amytal and methedrine she said that her mother had given her something bad which she didn't want though she had not done anything bad with it. However, she then repeated her former fantasies and added a few extra ones, and also said she had made up her mind to kill one Abena and had been instantly "caught" for this resolve. Asked whether she had any other troubles or wrong-doings on her mind, she said, "No", and also denied that people ever worried her by thinking unjustly that she had. Asked about her dreams, she said that she dreamt she was going somewhere with her mother and they reached a river. The mother crossed the river and left her, telling her to remain.

Progress

The guardians completed the purification ritual, though still unaccountably convinced that the patient had more to confess. They resisted all urging to take her to hospital, saying that whatever was done for her by the hospital or by anyone else, the *obosom* would kill her if she did not confess all. They seemed genuinely fond of her and thought the whole business very sad, but I never obtained the key to their convictions of her further guilt.

The patient died about five months later.

COMMENTARY

A physical illness (almost certainly tuberculosis) without mental symptoms and with only conventional affirmations of guilt delivered without conviction.

Although this case involves the persisting influence of one self-declared witch on the next generation, the mother's influence would probably not have been invoked but for the striking similarity between the two physical illnesses. The dream seems to be yet another clear allegory. In this culture, as in many others—including our own—death is symbolised by the crossing of a river.

VII

INVOLUTIONAL PSYCHOSES

The majority of psychoses beginning at the involutional age are schizo-affective illnesses which gradually slide into chronic schizophrenia. I am discussing them elsewhere and reserving this present group for cases which are not predominantly, or not at all, depressive.

CASE 105. AFUA B. of Mpraaso, Kwahu. F. c. 50.

Shrine

Mframa at Mframaso.

Reason for referral

Patient complains of persecution by witches seeking to make her join their group.

Family History

Parents: Not cross-cousins. Illiterate non-Christian farmers—the father farming cocoa, the mother, foodstuffs. The father died in patient's infancy, the mother a few years ago of a broken leg.

Mother's elder brother: Patient's guardian. He is an old man now but he and the patient's elder brother arranged for the patient to come to Mframaso. They are very good to her, but live in Accra, trading, and want her to live in their Kwahu house.

Family mental history: Patient says many of her relatives have been "caught" by Tigari for witchcraft. Some talked "*basa-basa*" and some died. The patient's daughter was "caught" ten years ago when her youngest child was in early infancy. She was restless and disturbed for one month and rolled about on the ground "like someone in a fit". She has not succeeded in complete cleansing for she has had four rolling attacks since and has become very lean. This daughter confessed that her spirit was given to flying away at night and having sexual intercourse with all sorts of men spirits and that she had often brought these spirits home to have intercourse with her mother—without the latter's knowledge. These spirits, the patient says, have in this way given her

374

five different kinds of *babaso* (gonorrhea). The disease is not a visible disease and the patient did not know she had it till the daughter confessed.

Siblings: One sister, four brothers. Latter are two store-keepers, one trader and one farmer. Two have money, two have not. Patient was brought to Mframaso by a younger brother and his wife, briefed by elder brother.

Personal History

Childhood: The patient never saw her father. Household contained the patient's mother and her siblings and belonged to the mother's elder brother.

Schooling: Nil. Non-Christian.

Work: Trader in foodstuffs. She trades the produce grown by her sister as well as her own. Her own earnings supported two children at school.

Marriage: Four times married. The first time when very young. All except the last husband died. The patient went to Tafo trading with her first husband and lived there with him and was very happy. The present husband is a tinsmith (mends hurricane-lamps and makes cooking-pots out of sheet tin). He has no farm. The patient's family opposed this marriage but the husband has a strong will. The marriage was happy till witchcraft took away the patient's womb (i.e., till menopause), when husband began to plan another marriage to have children. Recently he has spoken of divorcing the patient.

Children: Seven born, two died, all by the first marriage. Three daughters are married and have children. The sons are literate. One has had some secondary education. Both are store-keepers in Accra and are unmarried.

Katamenia: Menopause abrupt about one and a half years ago. Patient's troubles date from this time. She is quite sure that once she gets rid of witchcraft, menstruation will return.

Household: Large house belonging to uncle and elder brother: they built it for the patient's mother, who lived in it with her siblings and children till envious witches caused her to break her leg and die. The patient was there with her own siblings, their children and her own, until she declared herself a witch, when they all departed, leaving her entirely alone.

Present Illness (Patient's account)

The onset coincided with the menopause. One day the patient's sister —previously "caught" for witchcraft by Tigari and subsequently cured —gave the patient some food she had prepared. Shortly after this the patient knew that the sister had given her an *obayi* that made her one of a company of witches. The members of this company persecuted her day and night. She often heard their voices calling her name and saying urgently, "Let us go" (to the witch meeting), but she never answered and never obeyed. At night as soon as she had entered her room she would hear their voices outside her window and door and see them bringing a light to look for her. When she made no answer they often brought "something like a lorry-handle" and wound up the outside of the door as a lorry-engine is wound up, and then they came in. She always became stiff with fear and then they carried her away. This has continued ever since. She insists that she is not asleep when she sees and hears these people. If she fastens all the doors and windows they get in through chinks and crevices, "like the wind": she hears a sound, "Tu-tu-tu", and in a moment they are all in the room. At first she saw them but could not identify them, but after a medicine-man gave her an ointment she was able to recognise among them two daughters and one son.

Last night a lot of these people tied her eyes and took her away: she was not asleep; she says she saw them. If she does go to sleep they take her spirit away in her sleep, and in her dreams she always finds herself "in some far-off place" which she does not recognise, wandering lost in thick bush or struggling through water which is trying to wash her away.

In the daytime she is afraid to go to her farm or anywhere else because she hears their voices and their footsteps following her. The *obayi* which they have given her takes various animal forms—cow and goat, but chiefly dog and bird. She hears the dog barking and the birds crying to her. Before her illness, when she went to her farm she never noticed birds, but now the witches have sent flocks of birds which follow her to her farm, urging her to come and be a witch. One night when she was afraid to sleep alone she went to another woman's house and on the way a big dog knocked her down. She lay quite stiff and powerless with fright, but after a time was able to reach her friend's house.

Since this trouble began she has cried nearly all the time. She is restless, can't sit still, but can't do any work. The witches have put a web over her eyes so that she cannot see clearly. She hears an unceasing sound, "Tim, tim, tim", in her belly and head and knows that this is a part of her witchcraft. She has consulted Tigari and various soothsayers. After each consultation she improves for a day or two, but then the witches all come back. Her distress and weeping moved her brother to send her to Mframaso.

First interview: 4.4.57

Correctly orientated, pleasant and co-operative. Thin, anxious, lined face. She is frightened, distressed and agitated. Very voluble and indignant at the persecution. Expresses no guilt or self-reproach. She says the witches want her to kill her grandchild but she is determined not to. She also says her own witchcraft destroyed her womb but this was not her fault as the witchcraft was given to her against her will. In telling her story she became excited and kept getting up to demonstrate how the witches wound the lorry-handle, what sort of crevices they traversed and what sort of cries and calls they made.

6.4.57. Last night on her way to the latrine, she says, she saw the sister who gave her the *obayi* standing with her mouth open. Later in a dream she saw this sister urging her to go and "hunt". In the morning, being frightened, she recounted this to the *obosom's* bath-water dispenser, but he reassured her that the *obosom* would drive these things away. She already feels safer in Mframaso. Yesterday she went to the river to wash clothes but saw and heard no frightening dogs or birds. The witches, however, still call her name. They come in the wind, and when she hears the wind she knows that they are about. They have many ways of calling her: she hears them whistle, sniff, and blow their noses. When she demonstrated the way they snuffled, bystanders laughed at her excellent comic performance. She herself joined in the laughter. Her laughter is warm and infectious. Her face in repose is worried and anxious.

7.4.57. Less voluble and excited, but quietly anxious.

11.4.57. Says she is better in that the witches now stand outside the town and daren't approach at night, but they send sheep and fowls who come and shine lights through the chinks in her room and call her to go and join the witches. They took her spirit away to Akim Tafo where she lived with her first husband and was happy. She looks extremely worried when she talks of the witches, but in other conversation can be merrily animated.

16.4.57. She came to tell me very happily that she is much better and sleeps quietly. The witches are afraid to annoy her now that she is being gradually strengthened by Mframa's protective baths.

24.4.57. Admits that the witches still send sheep to stand outside her room at night with lights, but they don't come in and she sleeps well. She looks worried when she talks of the witches, but otherwise seems a merry little soul.

25.5.57. Slight relapse. She appeared before the *obosom* to-day complaining of hearing her name called wherever she went. Affect warm: the congregation all laughed delightedly at her spirited narrative. The *obosom* ordered her special baths. She told me later that "they" chased her on the way to the river and she heard their feet pattering behind her. At night she hears their voices in the roof.

31.5.57. She has been busy, industriously making pottery, having noticed some suitable clay near the river. She is cheered by a dream she had in which all the relatives who wanted to do her harm had locked her in a room, but she fought and broke the door and got out.

15.6.57. Commotion in her landlord's house because last night she was terrified, came out into the yard, woke everybody, and they had to stay with her till morning. She looks exceedingly anxious and unhappy today. Her landlord (the *obosom's okyeame*), because *he* had had no sleep, asked me to give her a sleeping medicine the next night, "so that she would sleep so soundly she would not hear them calling".

20.6.57. Voices and dreams completely controlled by general sedatives by day and hypnotics by night. Sedatives were cut down yesterday and dreams returned, but she did not wake the household. She dreamt that an entirely *new* witch-company took her to a new place. There they asked her to pound *fu-fu*, after which they offered her some to eat, but she found that some of the meat in the accompanying stew was human flesh so she refused to eat. She woke and lay sleepless and frightened till morning.

24.7.57. She has had several ups and downs, but now says that though the witches' voices still call her to come with them she is strong in the power of the *obosom*, defies them and says she will never go. She is unmistakably hypomanic in her delight in her defiance. She claps her hands, laughs, sings and gives a comic performance of how she shoos them away like chickens. Everyone else laughs too and comments that "she isn't ashamed of her witchcraft", i.e., is not self-reproachful and retarded.

10.10.57. She has had several ups and downs. When depressed, the voices have power over her and the witches take her away. When elated, she still hears the voices but defies them and drives them off like thieving domestic animals. She similarly triumphs in her dreams. The audience laugh with her in her triumphs and she claps her hands with joy and joins in the general mirth.

29.1.58. After much fluctuation she suddenly took a decided turn for the better. She became blacker, fatter and ceased to look worried. She is very happy and planning to go home.

COMMENTARY

This is a paranoid schizophrenia with full preservation of the personality, setting in at the menopause and superimposed on a manic-depressive disposition. The attitude to hallucinations is coloured by the prevailing mood.

CASE 106. ABENA A. of Offinso district, Ashanti (Cocoa-"village".) F. *c.* 50.

Shrine

Akuaduosia (a new *obosom* of Awurawa).

Reason for referral

Self-accusations of witchcraft.

Family History

Parents: Dead. Not cross-cousins. Illiterate, non-Christian cocoa-farmers.

Siblings: Ten born. All died except the patient, two sisters and one brother. All illiterate, non-Christian cocoa-farmers.

Personal History

Childhood: Mother died in patient's infancy. Brought up by mother's sister in a maternal uncle's house.

Schooling: Nil, but she is a Christian.

Work: Farmer.

Marriage: She has never wanted to marry, but has consorted with many men.

Home: She lives in a cocoa-"village", in the household in which she was brought up, now owned by her brother.

Children: Nine, born of nine different fathers. Six died. One son and one daughter are grown up and are farmers. The son is a Christian. The youngest child, a son of about twelve, is at school, supported by the patient.

Previous Illnesses: Neither she nor any of her relatives have ever been "caught" by any *obosom* before. Patient has had "*kokoram*" (scrofula?) for many years, but it is not obvious or disfiguring.

Katamenia: Menopause not yet passed.

Present Illness (from elder brother)

Onset about two weeks ago. No complaint of headache, fever or malaise. Illness began with a bad dream. Patient dreamt that someone had given her a handkerchief and woke certain that an *obayi* had been given to her in it. She became more agitated and had no sleep because witches stood around her room at night calling her to come out and fly with them. She knew that an *obosom* had "caught" her because she saw one who stood before her at night and spat upon her. She then became terrified, quite wild and talked "*basa-basa*". She disappeared from home and search-parties failed to find her. Then the family received a message from Awurawa saying that she had turned up at the shrine there (some eighty miles from her home) saying that she was "caught" by the *obosom* for attempting to kill, by witchcraft, her son who had drunk at the shrine six months previously because he was not prospering.

First interview: 25.9.57

Seen at the shrine, where, because this was the first person "caught" by the new *obosom*, there was a great din of drumming, an excited crowd and a possessed *okomfo* dancing. The patient consented to come aside and talk for a little but was impatient to begin her "confession".

She was lean and ill-nourished, with the deeply lined face of the habitually anxious. She was restless, worried and apprehensive, and though not very attentive to questions was quite accessible, correctly orientated and—according to her lights—rational. She said she had had no fever or headache before the onset, but was frightened because witches came and stood round her room at night and called her name. She was emphatic that she was not asleep when she heard them, because they were preventing her from sleeping. (See also Afua B., Case No. 105). She said they had not troubled her since she arrived in Aworawa because they knew that the *obosom* was going to drive them away.

27.9.57. Quite controlled, and not depressed. Shallowly optimistic, over-talkative and fidgety. She was sitting preparing food for herself, her brother and her two sons. She smiled appropriately, was friendly, and said she had slept well since coming to the shrine. Yesterday she travelled to her home and back to fetch the articles—beads and a head-kerchief—which she thought might be harbouring the *obayi*. The head-kerchief was given to her several years ago by a sister who had always disliked her and, she thinks, may have maliciously put an *obayi* into it.

To-day she insisted that she was a long-standing Christian and chattered a good deal in Christian idiom saying that she was praying God to help her to overcome the devils (*abonsam*) who were troubling her.

6.10.57. A few days after ritual purification she said she could not sleep because she had another cloth at home that she thought might also contain an *obayi*, so she must travel home and fetch it to be cleansed. This she did. (I did not see her to-day as she had gone to wash clothes in the river. House-mates said she was well.)

30.10.57. After an apparently good recovery she began—according to witnesses—to talk very "*basa-basa*" and then became "very mad indeed" and was taken home. She said she was a leopard, went on all fours, snarled and attacked people.

COMMENTARY

This is not a typical witch, in that she regards herself as a victim of the malice of others. Her history of sexual promiscuity suggests feeble-mindedness, but her capable resolution in setting off alone on long journeys is against this. My impression was of a psychotic illness of an involutional type.

Involutional Psychoses

CASE 107. YAA. P. of Wenchi district, Ashanti. F. *c.* 50.

Shrine

Mframa and others.

Reason for referral

Relatives think she is becoming mad.

Family History

Parents: Not cross-cousins. Non-Christian, illiterate cocoa and yam farmers. Father is still alive, mother died shortly after patient's marriage.

Siblings: Eight born, two died. One brother is the priest of an *obosom*, about five generations old but occasionally used by its present priest in the modern money-making manner. Most of the siblings are known to me. They are strapping, handsome, happy, prolific people. One sister has a "village" a mile or so from my quarters. She is comely, smiling, intelligent, kindly and popular, indefatigable at both work and play. She is happily married, her husband has no other wives and she has ten good-looking, healthy, intelligent children and several grandchildren. She confidently expects still more children. All her sons have been, or are still going, to school. She herself paid for their schooling out of her own prosperous cocoa-farms where she employs labourers. She is, in short, everything the patient would like to be.

Personal History

Childhood: N.a.d.

Schooling: Nil. Non-Christian.

Work: Farmer and market-gardener. Admitted by everyone to be hard-working and successful.

Marriage: Married her cross-cousin. He has three younger wives, each of whom has children.

Children: Only one born. It died at about one year.

Home: Husband has built his own house in which he has all his wives and their children.

Present Illness

Onset about three months ago with physical illness, fever, headache, sweating, etc. Afterwards she could neither work, sit still, nor sleep, and often wept. She had "*basa-basa*" dreams. She once dreamt that two men seized her and flung her over a roof. She has eaten very little lately and has had "burnings all over", palpitations and some diarrhoea (sub-clinical mild pellagra precipitated by anorexia ?). She felt that she was a witch, knew that she had done other wrong things but felt that something was making her "dumb" (on this topic) so that she could not confess it. She went from one *obosom* to another, by herself, saying that she was sick and giving each *obosom* a free-will sheep but confessing nothing. She squandered nine sheep in this way to the disapproval of her relatives. This was the main reason for their thinking her to be going mad. They admitted that her talk was never "*basa-basa*", but thought her behaviour was.

At Mframa's shrine she was told to go to an old shrine at Krobo, which had some ancestral family connections. She went and was there able to talk about herself. She volunteered that she was a witch, had killed various children, had prevented her niece from bearing more than two, and had planned to kill her happy fortunate sister of whom she confessed herself jealous. She also confessed that she had procured a bad *suman* and put it in her husband's farm to kill his cocoa because he neglected her for the younger wives. She also stole a piece of cloth from the *obosom* Timani, and intended to make out of it a bad medicine to prevent Timani from getting fee-paying suppliants. She further said she had cursed her husband to a river.

First interview: 16.4.57

Seen at the Krobo priest's house about a week after her arrival. Well favoured. Thin, but otherwise healthy-looking. Her confessions had greatly eased her mind and she was eating and sleeping well. She said she wanted to end her days in Krobo because there she felt at peace, whereas in her own home she felt unceasingly disturbed. She looked as if this was true: she was contentedly cooking, smiled in friendly fashion, and gave a straightforward account of herself tallying with witnesses' testimony. She seemed neither anxious nor depressed, but cool, casual and surprisingly unconcerned.

20.4.57. Her relatives have been trying to persuade her to return home mainly because her food-farms are neglected. She says it is not their business and she is quite happy where she is.

10.5.57. She has gone home, seems quite well and serene, and is working hard.

1.8.57. She looks physically well and is outwardly contented, but I hear that she has not left off going to shrines and giving away sheep.

20.1.58. Within the past few months I have overtaken her several times on the road to other shrines where she presents sheep with only vague reasons for doing so. Not in the least depressed, she is brisk and incongruously cheerful, and her relatives may well be right that she is "getting mad".

14.2.58. I overtook her on the road to a new shrine near Badu, more than a dozen miles away. She was in a state of high indignation, and said people envied her and wanted to kill her because she was clever. They also wanted to make her into a witch so that an *obosom* would "catch" her and kill her. She said they had sent some swarms of lice which she felt crawling all over her, and by lamplight was able to see. She denied any other hallucinations. She said she had spent over £100 on her illness. This is probably not exaggerated. She looked physically well and said she slept soundly.

COMMENTARY

This case has probably not yet finished developing. It is possible that the patient's unending visits to shrine after shrine, taking a sheep to each for purification, are of an obsessive-compulsive nature. This is supported by her new delusion of a *concrete* infestation—usually the mark of the obsessive. In view of the rarity of obsessive-compulsive psychosis among Africans I do not wish to stress this, and would be in expectation of further development of the paranoid features. The *suman* and bad-medicine making are prognostically bad signs.

CASE 108. DEDE K. of Odumase district, Manya Krobo (Adangme Tribe). F. *c.* 55.

Shrine

Amfemfri, at Asueyi.

Reason for referral

Strange behaviour. (No suggestion of witchcraft, this institution being foreign to the Gã–Adangme tribes.)

Family History

Parents: No information, but the Adangme seldom practise cross-cousin marriage.

Personal History

Childhood: No information.

Marriage: Her husband has been dead ten years. The daughter says the couple quarrelled a lot, always on the provocation of the patient, the husband being a peaceable man.

Children: Six born, four survive and are all grown-up with children. She has thirteen grandchildren. The daughter is a fat, vigorous Krobo woman, strikingly different from the lean, ill-fed Ashanti.

Work: Hard-working, successful trader and farmer. She never quarrelled with anyone but her husband.

Katamenia: The daughter does not know when the menopause occurred.

Present Illness

The onset was sudden, two years ago. She opened her box of trinkets and other valued possessions, gave some of them away and threw away the rest. She shouted, quarrelled, fought, stripped herself naked. She was frightened, but no one knew of what: she kept running away to the bush in fear. Then she quietened down, wept a great deal and then became mute and motionless except during attacks of fear, when she ran away and talked "*basa-basa*". She remained in this state till the relatives heard of the shrine at Asueyi and brought her.

At the shrine the relatives had to tell her tale for her. The *obosomfo* told her that it was her husband's ghost troubling her and making her mad. She then became able to speak and said that she had been on bad terms with her husband and had misappropriated some trinkets left by him for the children.

First Interview: 9.8.56

I did not see her till two weeks after her *abisa*, during which two weeks she had been receiving daily ritual baths. They said she had improved during that time. She was thin by Krobo standards, but adequately nourished and healthy, in much better physical condition than most Ashantis. She sat mute, immobile and dejected, but not limp and not agitated. There was no inappropriate affect, no apparent hallucination or preoccupation, but there was something subtly wilful about her immobility which stamped it as not wholly depressive.

Provisional Diagnosis

I thought this a schizo-affective illness with an element of rationally based guilt-feelings, and, according to her lights, rationally based fear of revenge by her husband's ghost.

15.8.56. To-day she was able to speak and was quite accessible. She smiled appropriately though faintly on being greeted. She was correctly orientated for time and place, though vague about the length of her illness. She answered all questions about home and family correctly though reluctantly and almost inaudibly. Asked how her illness was getting on, she said she had been bathing in the *obosom's* medicines but did not feel any better.

On this interview alone I would have taken her for an uncomplicated depression.

20.8.56. Still sitting in the same place, but to-day she would not speak or shake hands and looked away smiling inappropriately.

30.8.56. To-day she was accessible and talked a little, though reluctantly. Her daughter thought she had improved since confessing at the shrine as she had not run away to the bush or talked "*basa-basa*". The daughter says she still does not rest quietly at night but walks about and stands in the yard.

4.9.56. She answered questions rather more readily. Asked how she was, she said, "Just the same", but her daughter said she had much improved and had begun to sleep quietly at night and to do jobs such as sweeping the yard and fetching water.

20.9.56. She has relapsed and has run away to the bush several times. The daughter is vexed because search-parties have to be paid. At interview she was reluctant to speak, questions had to be repeated and there was always a long wait for a reply, though replies were to the point and always depressive. "How are you?"—"Not at all well." "Do you like this place?"—"No, I don't like anywhere." When left alone she looked preoccupied.

28.9.56. She is brisker and smiled quite warmly when greeted and talked rationally though reluctantly. The daughter, however, says that when she sees any food she goes and eats it whether it belongs to her or not. She has also had several attacks of fright and run away to the bush.

12.10.56. She is now very solitary, will not come out of her room and sits shut up in the dark. She eats her meals alone in her room. She would not emerge to talk to me, but did speak. Witnesses say, however, that she has not run away to the bush and has helped a good deal with the work—cutting firewood, preparing meals, etc.

23.10.56. Distinctly improved. She chatted quite freely and said she was better. Witnesses say there have been no more disturbed episodes and that she is gardening and doing a good deal of work.

10.11.56. Improvement maintained. For the first time she greeted me spontaneously and smiled warmly as I entered the yard. Asked how she was, she said a lot better. Her daughter, encouraged by the improvement, had gone home but the landlady said the patient was working hard, gardening, cooking, washing clothes and fetching firewood and water.

20.11.56. A few days after the last note she rose early in the morning and went to the stream for water. She did not return, so the landlady went to look for her. She found her sitting in the stream, soaked and weeping and smeared with faeces. She was helped home and lay down and slept for the rest of the day. The following morning she was completely normal. She said that while she was dipping her water-pot in the stream she saw a ghost. She asked it to help her lift the water-pot on to her head. It did this, but as she turned to go it knocked her down and left her weeping in the stream.

Witnesses said her recovery was perfect with no sign of weakness of limbs or defect of speech. She immediately started working hard again —cooking, washing, gardening, etc. The landlady, however, sent for the daughter, saying she could not look after such an unpredictable lodger. The daughter said she could not spare any more time from home, so took the patient away at once.

COMMENTARY

Probably post-involutional psychosis, but the last episode raises the possibility of epilepsy.

VIII

POST-INFLUENZAL PSYCHOSES

A point that arises from time to time throughout these pages is that the person who seems particularly vulnerable to the transient acute psychosis is the latent schizophrenic. It will be noticed that two of the four post-influenzal psychoses now to be described were associated with socially unacceptable personalities whom one might have expected to develop frank schizophrenia at any time. Another exhibited schizoid aggression in the shape of bad *suman*-making. The fourth passed straight into that florid schizophrenia for which he seemed genetically destined.

CASE 109. AKOSUA A. of Bekwai district, Ashanti. F. *c.* 25.

Shrine
   Dimankoma, Akrofrom.

Reason for referral
   "Caught", presumably for witchcraft.

Family History
   Parents: Not cross-cousins. Illiterate, non-Christian cocoa-farmers. Mother seen, a good, pleasant personality.
   Siblings: Ten born, seven survivors. Youngest goes to school.
   Mother's mother: Had an illness with mutism but recovered.

Personal History
   Childhood: N.a.d.
   Schooling: Nil.
   Marriage. Separated from her first husband. Married present one about a year ago. He is away in North Ashanti trading and seldom sees the patient, who lives with her mother. He has two other wives, the patient being the youngest.
   Children: Three born, two survive: youngest, five weeks.

Present Illness

About three weeks ago when the patient's child was a fortnight old, she, with all the rest of the household, took influenza. When convalescent she one day made a great pile of chairs and oddments and asked people to help her carry them because she wanted to go to her husband. She then talked *"basa-basa"*, saying repeatedly, "If you do this, is it right?" Then she stopped speaking but cried all the time. At night she walked about restlessly, crying loudly, by day was quieter but still cried at intervals. Lactation failed, since when the patient's mother has fed the child by bottle. It was assumed that an *obosom* had "caught" the patient, though she uttered no self-accusations.

First interview: 20.10.57

Well-built, well-nourished woman, not looking physically ill. Quite mute but not inaccessible, shakes hands slowly. She sits inertly, looking miserable. At intervals she gets up and, standing, cries like a child, loudly howling and blubbering in a liturgical sing-song (as African children do). Sometimes she cried, *"M'agya, m'agya"* (My father). She sheds copious tears, stops crying suddenly and blows her nose. At the shrine she was unable to speak.

22.10.57. She has not yet spoken but has eaten and has stopped crying and howling. Looks better. She was taken to the shrine again. Her movements were slow and uncertain. While waiting her turn she sat mute, but turning her head with some degree of interest in her surroundings. When called to come and give her statement she obediently rose and went forward but could say nothing, though the *obosom's okyeame* spoke to her kindly and coaxingly. At one point her breathing quickened, into little gasps as if she was about to throw another paroxysm of blubbering, but she did not. She was told to go home and return when she could talk. She then became resistive and had to be dragged.

27.10.57. It was decided that the husband's *obosom* at Awisa, not Dimankoma, had caught her, so she was taken there. When seen at Awisa she was asleep, but her mother said she was much better and had been talking and eating normally. She had made no confession but was talking adequately about everyday affairs.

31.10.57. She is mute and retarded. She looks bewildered but not hallucinated. She shakes hands reluctantly. Her mother says she speaks a little, but mutteringly, and is not clear. She has not confessed anything.

1.11.57. She was taken to the shrine. She was dragged there as she was resistive. She said nothing.

I.V. Amytal and Methedrine

At first the patient shed tears and cried loudly like a child. Gradually she began to introduce speech into her howling but would not open her eyes. The content of her speech was depressive but she did not accuse herself of witchcraft. "If I died I should be glad. . . . My lot is very wretched . . . I shall never recover. . . . My intestines are decayed. . . . It would be better if I had never borne children. . . . I can't open my mouth and talk. . . . I am dying of jealousy. . . . I am tied up. . . . Let me cry and die. . . . I was asleep and my husband and his wife came and put some medicine into my eyes to kill me. . . . (To husband): Can you go and cut off a person's flesh and put it in the fire? . . . I shall never be well again. . . . I am worried about the debt my husband will run into because of me. . . . My children have all gone away to bush. . . . People say I am a witch. . . . It was my husband who took me to drink the medicine. . . . You should take my photo before I die. . . . There are knives all over my body. . . . They say I have chewed, but I have not chewed. . . ."

Asked point-blank whether she had done any wrong, she said, "No".

Husband seen

He says the patient stayed with him only twenty days and then left, taking all the things he had given her. There was no question of co-wife jealousy—the other wife was absent. He would have let her go completely but she was pregnant with his child.

He was reticent but seemed definitely resentful against both the woman and her family as though they had palmed off on him a bad personality.

4.11.57. Mother seen. She says patient bathed, talked and ate well after I had left on 1.11.57. She has slept well since except one night which she spent in crying, wailing and complaining that her room was full of lice. She insisted on another room, but no one else noticed lice. Her mother says she has talked *basa-basa* "a little", but the mother is a poor witness and cannot give instances. Concerning marriage, the mother and husband do not agree. Mother says the patient wanted the marriage but her father did not. Concerning the patient's first marriage the mother says patient's husband terminated the marriage because the patient was always quarrelling. Mother says the patient is in general a difficult and quarrelsome person.

First interview: 4.11.57

Mute. Movements slow. Will shake hands reluctantly. Does not seem inaccessible but looks bewildered, looks around in a puzzled way as if hallucinated.

13.11.57. Distinctly better. Speaks—in response—in a low reluctant voice, but rationally. Eating. Has a sore on her buttock,* so lies down.

18.11.57. Greatly improved, they say. She has gone home.

* Most buttock sores are due to illicit injections given by renegade dispensers.

20.12.57. I heard that she had since become "very wild and mad", that the sore on her buttock was worse and that she had been taken to Hwediem Mission Hospital. I wrote to the Medical Officer, who replied that she had been admitted in a disturbed psychotic state, had responded well to sedatives and to treatment for avitaminosis and had been discharged still depressed but not psychotic.

COMMENTARY

This seems to have been a brief, psychotic episode with severe depression, precipitated by a combination of influenza and childbirth. The previous personality appears to have been unsatisfactory.

CASE 110. AKOSUA M. N. of Kwaso district, Ashanti. F. 30.

Preface

When I first saw this patient she was already mute and there were no first-hand witnesses of the early part of the illness, which occurred when she was in Tamale with her husband.

Shrine

Mframa at Mframaso.

Reason for referral

"Caught" for wrong-doing.

Family History

Parents: Cross-cousins. Non-Christian, illiterate cocoa-farmers. Father died when the patient was about eight. Mother a few years ago.

Siblings: Nine born, only four, sisters, remain. One at school, others grown-up with children. No other relatives have ever been "caught".

Personal History

Childhood: N.a.d. Lived in mother's family house.

School: Nil. Non-Christian.

Work: Petty trader in Kumasi.

Marriage: No recognised marriage with customary ceremonial. She has been concubine to five different men who have supported her during the attachments. Family say "she only marries thieves and rogues". The present husband, however, is a respectable Christian literate carpenter, working in Tamale in the Northern Territories. He has been supporting her with a view to regularised marriage should her behaviour remain satisfactory for a reasonable period.

Children: Four born, all living. Eldest about ten, youngest four. None by present partner.

Previous Personality: She has always made quarrelsome scenes with her sisters and is regarded as an unsteady personality.

Present Illness (No first-hand testimony)

The onset was about two weeks ago. The patient was in Tamale with her husband when she, with other members of the household, had influenza. Instead of making a normal recovery as did the others, she became disturbed and frightened and confessed to recent sexual intercourse with two men other than her husband. (As he was supporting her, this ranks as adultery although she was not fully married.) She then talked "*basa-basa*" and was restless and noisy at night. The husband took her to hospital where she was given brief treatment, after which the doctor told her husband that there was nothing physically wrong and no more could be done for her. The husband brought her to her family in Ashanti and then went back to Tamale saying that she was adulterous, was caught for her sins and that he had finished with her. Asked whether she had more to confess she became mute, though for a few days she ate and drank; then she stopped eating and drinking and was brought to Mframa, at whose shrine her uncle had drunk on behalf of all his younger relatives.

First interview: 20.10.57

When seen she had been four days without food or drink and was dehydrated. She was lying in a windowless, dark room and was difficult to observe. The eyes moved and turned evasively away when she was addressed and seemed quite aware, but she made no response to any other stimuli, even painful ones, except a very slight wincing when the cornea was touched. The reflexes, including the pupils, were intact. All joints were excessively flaccid: when pulled into a sitting position she let her head flop heavily forward on to her chest; when the head was pushed up she let it fall equally far backwards. The relatives remarked that although she was like a dying person she did not breathe like one—i.e., respirations quite normal. My impression was of an hysterical state. 21.10.57. *Intravenous amytal and methedrine.* For an hour there was no response whatsoever. (This was what the relatives expected: "If the *obosom* is determined to kill you he won't let you talk and confess." They declined, fatalistically, further treatment.) At the end of an hour I went away to visit a distant shrine and did not return for several days. 24.10.57. The relatives said that shortly after I left, the patient started talking and talked for the rest of the day, saying only that she was going to die, and crying and groaning. She consented to drink but would not eat. When the talking stopped she sank into coma and died.

COMMENTARY

Post-influenzal affective psychosis with fear and some hysterical features in an unstable personality.

CASE 111. AFUA K. of Akwapim, cocoa-farming in Akim. F. *c.* 35.

Shrine

Mframa at Mframaso.

Reason for referral

Self-accusations of possessing bad *suman* and of being a witch.

Family History

Parents: Illiterate, non-Christian cocoa-farmers. Not cross-cousins. Both alive. Mother (seen) is a good personality. She left the father about four years ago. He had no other wife.

Personal History

Childhood: N.a.d. Parents and children in father's cocoa-village in Akim.

Schooling: Nil. Non-Christian.

Work: Since her early teens she has been an *okomfo* of the *obosom* Konode.

Marriage: The husband is an Akwapim man living on his cocoa-farm about ten miles away from the patient, who lives with her mother. They visit one another. The husband has five wives in all, but they all live in their own homes.

Children: Six born, eldest died. Eldest survivor is now about twelve. Youngest is three months, and was about six weeks at the onset of the illness.

Previous Personality: Said to have been lively and smiling.

Present Illness

Febrile illness while influenza was rife. The patient talked "*basa-basa*". Sudden onset with fever and "*basa-basa*" talk when the youngest child was about six weeks old. This cleared up but the patient said she felt "something like a cobweb" all over her and her joints were stiff. She was restless and miserable so she went to a Kramu medicine-man and bought a therapeutic medicine for herself. This included a pot wrapped in white calico. She did not improve but began to feel that the pot was a bad *suman* and that she was harming others with it. She became unable to sleep, walked about shouting all night and sometimes ran away in fear to the bush. She wept, repeatedly said she had done wrong and beat herself with a stick. As she had previously drunk at the shrine of Mframa, whose rules forbid the use of bad *suman*, it was believed that Mframa had laid hold of her, so she was brought to his shrine. Shortly before coming, lactation failed and the patient's mother has since fed the infant on tinned milk.

First Interview: 13.8.57

Short, thick-set, obese. Sitting miserably, dejected and mute. She shed tears when addressed, shook hands very reluctantly, but made no other response. After a few minutes when addressed again and asked her name she gave it in a whisper. Asked why she had come, she said because she shouted at night. After a long, mute interval she rose slowly to her feet and began slowly moving about the yard. Gradually her movements quickened and she livened up till she was dancing, singing and shouting, looking extremely anxious and distraught but with an occasional inappropriate smile. The content of her shouting was exclusive depressive. "I have done wrong. . . . I am in a sad way. . . . Alas, alas . . . I have died. . . . Oh, God, if I say it, it is no good. . . . Have I crossed a river? . . . I am going to sleep with a corpse. . . . I shall starve. . . . Am I lost? Am I lost? I was crucified last Friday. . . . It is no use doing good. . . . I deserve death."

Then she became more excited and ran out into the street shouting. Her landlord and his household followed and dragged her back. She became resistive and held on to the gatepost. Then she sank into apathy again and repeated the cycle throughout the day.

14.8.57. She spent a very noisy night but was mute, anxious and miserable in the morning. At the shrine she took her place voluntarily in the sinners' dock. When addressed by one of the shrine servants she managed to reply in a whisper, "I can't answer properly: my mind is "*basa-basa*". There were many suppliants and the patient waited all day for her turn. At first she was restless and kept walking out of the yard, but later settled into dejected lethargy and leant on the railing looking anxious and wretched but not disturbed. When the day's shrine-work closed she walked home and on the way became noisy and dancing again.

15.8.57. The household reports another noisy night. When seen in the morning she was pacing to and fro in mute agitation, looking deeply anxious and apprehensive but with an occasional inappropriate smile. When I entered, she knelt before me and touched my shoes—a gesture implying abject supplication for mercy.

16.8.57. She had a fairly quiet night and was mute but co-operative in the morning. At the shrine she waited apathetically for her turn, but when it came could say nothing. At the evening session, before the *obosomfo* became possessed, he came and talked to her very pleasantly and kindly but she could make no response. Later, when her turn came at *abisa*, she only giggled and smiled.

21.8.57. After several days of alternating noisy agitation and mute tearful depression her landlord, an *adunsini* who had unavailingly made various medicine to help her to speak at *abisa*, called in the neighbouring *obosomfo* of the ancient *obosom* Dzrobo. This friend implored the *obosom* Mframa for her, saying that she was an *okomfo* of the *obosom* Akonodi and that one *obosom* should forgive the servants of another. This plea was accepted. The *obosom* also agreed that she should not be shaven and publicly disgraced like other wrong-doers but cleansed in private. She was, however, to bring a cow.

25.8.57. The cow has not yet arrived, but since her absolution she has improved. She has been only slightly disturbed at night but is still much retarded in speech. Lactation has returned. She is suckling her child and doing jobs of cooking.

31.8.57. The cow has still not come but the patient has steadily improved and seems now quite well, though she says her dreams are still somewhat "*basa-basa*". She dreams that a crowd of people are trying to take her away and are shouting at her.

10.9.57. She is now quite happy, smiling and chatting.

COMMENTARY

Post-influenzal affective psychosis shortly after the puerperium.

CASE 112. ZUGU S. F. *c.* 30.

Lives in Bekwai district, Ashanti, but is a native of Zuarugu, Northern Territories.

Shrine

Kyinaman, Bredi.

Reason for referral

Self-accusations of witchcraft and bad-medicine making followed by "madness".

Family History

Parents: Cross-cousins. Non-Christian, illiterate grain-dealers.
Siblings: Eight born, six died.

Personal History

Childhood: In her native country. Non-Christian, illiterate.
Marriage: She is married to one of her own illiterate Northern Territory countrymen who is in the Government Forestry Ranger Force.

The husband has another wife—which the patient resents. He has recently become impotent, probably from fear of sorcery by the patient. He concealed from the patient that he had another wife at the time when he married her, and she has only just discovered it.

Children: Nil.

Present Illness

Onset one week ago with fever, headache, sweating and pains in the belly—probably influenza, which was then rife. She rapidly became frightened, said she dreamt that she was eating human meat, confessed that she had made bad magics and bought bad *suman*, and said that the *obosom* had "caught" her for these sins. She quickly grew worse, quite sleepless, and, according to the husband, "mad". She talked "*basa-basa*", screamed that she could see people coming after her with *nkotoba* (*obosom's* weapons), rushed about trying to flee and hide from them and clutched her husband crying in terror.

She was brought to the shrine together with several *suman* she had bought. These included a "tying medicine" (*siri*) made of a medicated cylinder to which was attached a length of twine: the operator of this winds the twine round the cylinder while speaking the victim's name. Another was a cow-tail switch (*bodua*), and a third was a white powder which if blown towards the victim should make him acquiescent in any demand, however unreasonable, or improbable, of the operator. On arrival the *suman* were surrendered at the shrine and the patient became instantly quiet.

First interview: 20.11.57

She is quite rational, but very thin, with a lined, anxious face. She is tremulous, miserable and on the verge of tears. She could say nothing except that she had done wrong. The husband was present: he is angry with her and she cringes before him.

2.12.57. The husband has gone and the patient's demeanour is now very different. She is agitated and frowning, but at the same time very talkative about her sins in a vivacious, shallow and uncontrite fashion. She says cheerfully that she has five lovers beside her husband, that she loves him but he does not love her, that she cannot sleep at night because something walks inside her head, that she dreams she hears witches calling, "Get up and come with us", that this is the second time an *obosom* has "caught" her, that she used a bad magic made of the hair of a dead man; that she went to a Kramu at dead of night and he told her to bring a red thread and a white thread to help her husband not to get the sack so that he would give her money.

16.12.57. To-day I thought her indubitably schizophrenic. I found her standing alone, upright in the middle of the yard, mute and shaking, and doing a sort of inhibited dance. However, she abandoned it to shake hands and began to talk. She said she had had nine proper husbands—she recited a string of names—and a great number of lovers. Then she took up a sardine tin of corn grains that she had been playing with and arranged the grains in patterns on the ground, saying that they were men she had married. Now and then she talked rationally: she said she dreamt she was giving yam to her husband's child, but the husband said, "Don't give witchcraft to my child", and gripped her by the throat.

COMMENTARY

This appeared at first to be a brief fear-psychosis, precipitated by a febrile illness, in an anxious, frustrated personality, guilty of acts of schizoid aggression. Later it seemed that this episode was ushering in a classical schizophrenia, but the ultimate outcome is not known. The *suman* are prognostically ominous.

CASE 113. KWAKU N. of Techiman district, Ashanti. M. *c.* 24.

Shrine

This patient was not at a shrine. I heard that a medicine-man who lived in a tiny forest "village" called Nyamabekyere had just had a madman referred to him, so I went to see.

Reason for referral

Madness.

Family History

Parents: Not cross-cousins. Illiterate cocoa-farmers. The mother is a Christian, the father and his people are not.

Siblings: Eight born, five survive. The youngest goes to school and is in Standard IV.

Paternal first cousin: The father's brother has a son who about a year ago, at the same age as the patient, became mad, attacked neighbours with a cutlass, was taken up by the police and sent to Accra Mental Hospital, where he still is.

Personal History

Childhood: N.a.d. No schooling. Non-Christian. Home in his father's house, where he still lives.

Work: Cocoa-farmer.

Marriage: He is happily married to a good type of young woman, and has one child.

Previous Personality: The neighbours say that he was pleasant and cheerful and hard-working. He especially enjoyed playing with children, who all adored him.

Present Illness

The onset was eight days ago. Influenza was rife and the patient fell sick complaining of influenzal symptoms. However, his behaviour was strange, he behaved angrily to people who tried to tend him, was assumed to have taken influenza with extra severity and was sent to hospital. He was admitted as an in-patient, but discharged himself after a day or two. He came home talking "*basa-basa*", said the police were after him and packed up all his goods to take flight. He also said that ghosts were chasing him. He left the house saying that he was going to the latrine, but wandered off, got lost and had to be sought. It was then decided to send him to Nyamebekyere.

First interview: 6.9.57

He was sitting on a log under a tree with several other people, who were coaxing him back when he wandered vaguely away. He was in good physical condition, afebrile with a normal pulse.

He was accessible, but greeted me with a fumbling, schizophrenic handshake. He answered a few simple questions, such as his name, but was inattentive to anything else. He looked bewildered, saying, "This is not my town. I want to go back to my town." He gave the name of his town when asked for it, but asked the name of his present habitat said it was a ghost town so he would not eat there. He was restless, kept rising to his feet and looking apprehensively around as if hallucinated. The medicine-man said he slept quietly at night.

7.11.57. I had not seen the patient for eight weeks as he had been round to a succession of medicine-men. His family said he had been sitting mute, but co-operative, ever since he left Nyamebekyere. His father thought he had something on his mind but could not speak, so asked me if I could help him to say it.

I found him mute but not inaccessible and he co-operated in an intravenous sodium amytal and methedrine abreaction. He began making clear replies to questions immediately.

Asked whether he was in trouble, he said, "Yes. I have been talking "*basa-basa*" ever since I had influenza." Asked whether he remembered Nyamebekyere, he said, "Yes. I remember that you came to see me there one day." Asked whether he had any worries concerning *suman*, he said he had bought two from a Kramu; one was for prosperity, but one was a bad medicine for "tying" people. He had never used either of them, but when he fell sick he thought they might be the cause so he threw them away. Asked whether he had done any other wrong things, he said, "No".

Asked whether he ever heard voices talking, he said, "Yes"—in the sky, in the roof, and on the way to the river and the latrine. He could not tell what the voices said. When asked whether his head felt quite well, he said that witches were putting something into it and spoiling his thoughts so that he heard his thoughts talking in his head. He could not describe what they said. Asked whether the witches did anything else, he said that they wanted to make him into a witch. In reply to a question about the police, he said they were still after him: sometimes he saw them, but more often he only heard them talking about him, but he was silent when asked what they said about him. To a question concerning *mmoetia* fairies, he said he never saw any but often heard them talking.

His father then asked him whether there was anything he resented. He said, "Yes", he had had a bad mind against his family ever since they refused a request. Asked whether anyone had a bad mind against him he gave the name of one individual. After about twenty minutes his replies were coming very reluctantly, and after a further ten minutes he was almost mute again.

16.12.57. I found him in poor physical condition, mute, inert, and refusing either to eat, drink or defaecate. His family readily accepted advice to send him to a Mission hospital to be tided over the period of danger of death. They were such well-disposed, sensible people that I felt that, apart from such physical treatment as tube-feeding, the mental prognosis was quite as good in his home as it would be in the country's overcrowded mental hospital.

COMMENTARY

Schizophrenia, attacking two young male first-cousins at the same age. This family-history supports the view that the rôle of a precipitating stress—in this case influenza—is more apparent than real.

IX

OBSESSIVE-COMPULSIVE DISORDER

In no illness known to psychiatry is the morbid manifestation so clearly of a piece with the pre-morbid personality as in that of the obsessive.

There is nothing in the everyday personality of West Africans to lead any psychiatrist to expect obsessive-compulsive illness. By and large these people are tolerant, adaptable, happy-go-lucky, impulsive, readier to observe the spirit of the law than the letter and more horrified by "a bad mind" than a bad medicine. Personal cleanliness is practised because bathing is enjoyable in a hot climate and unwashed people are unattractive.

The rarity of the obsessive personality is reflected in all social activities and institutions. Among indigenous magical procedures, the spell (defined as a recitation which must be meticulously word-perfect in order to work) is nowhere found. Nor, in African social organisation, are there any traces of that mental rigidity which could conceive and sustain so fantastic a social fabric as the Indian caste system. Long before the abolition of indigenous slavery there was always a continuous process of absorption of slaves into every rank of the freeborn. Inheritance and succession has always been by award and election, by merit and decency, rather than by codified rule. The position of women has never been rigidly defined or artificially circumscribed. Outstandingly able women have never been denied either opportunity or deference. There have been women Omanhenes and military generals. One of the new and flourishing Christian sects has a woman "Pope". Open-mindedness, flexibility and adaptability are everywhere apparent.

It was therefore surprising to find even two major cases of obsessive-compulsive illness—both young illiterate rural women—presenting themselves at a shrine, and it was not surprising to find the priest himself nonplussed. There were several others, but these left some room for doubt. These were older patients with the delusion that they were disseminating plagues of lice: they strongly recalled those English obsessives who, when in depression and self-denigration, postulate *concrete* agents—disease-germs and vermin—rather than defects of character, as constituting their menace to others.

CASE 114. EKWIA K. F. *c.* 70.

Native of Fanti country, far away in the Western Province by the sea, but she was staying with a sister who married into the Wenchi district, Ashanti.

Shrine

She was not brought to any shrine, having exhausted many shrines' treatments years ago, but was paying a one-day visit to a relative who had married into Mframaso. (I saw her only very briefly.)

Complaint

Invisible lice.

Family and Personal History

Scanty information. Her husband died years ago. She had four children who all died in infancy. She is said to have become very rich entirely through her own hard work and cleverness. Her senior siblings still work and she says she is not so old that she could not still work were it not for the lice.

Present Illness

About nine (?) years ago she started feeling lice crawling all over her at night. She went to various shrines and then to Kintampo hospital, where she had a course of injections. She says the lice receded a little, but came back and have since steadily increased. Now they walk both day and night. They come out of her eyes, ears, nose and mouth. When they come out of her eyes they impede her vision. She now fears that they may go and trouble other people. She never sees them, only feels them. She says she is restless and useless because of them and can do no work. There are no other symptoms except occasional occipital headache.

Among the shrines to which she was sent was Mframa's. There are no records except what people remember. The *obosom* was evidently baffled by this unusual affliction and said the lice must be witches' animal-associates and that she must therefore be a witch. This she stoutly denied and refused to confess to having harmed anybody by any invisible influence.

Interview

She seemed physically well preserved and walked some miles without effort. Intellectually she was alert and did arithmetical and other tests much better than most younger people. There were no visible skin lesions and no jaundice. She says the feeling is not of itching but of "walking".

Progress

About six months later I heard that she was dead.

COMMENTARY

This strikes me as an obsessive illness. The patient repudiates the ordinary depressive ideas of unworthiness and of harming people by mere influence, but insists that she is disgusting by reason of a *concrete* infestation. Later, when the illness gets worse, she is afraid she will do harm, but by means of her concrete agents.

CASE 115. YAA D. of Oda district, Akim. F. *c.* 15.

Shrine

Mframa at Mframaso.

Reason for referral

Self-accusations of witchcraft.

Family History

Parents: Not cross-cousins. Both alive. They are illiterate, Christian cocoa-farmers.

Siblings: One sister and two brothers, all married with children. The patient is the youngest. Illiterate cocoa-farmers. They are all Christians. One brother is a church leader. This brother drank at Mframa's shrine about eighteen months ago because he often felt sick and his cocoa was not flourishing. The patient was brought to the shrine by this brother and a maternal cousin.

Personal History

Childhood: N.a.d. disclosed.

Schooling: Nil.

Previous Illness: About three months ago the patient had a similar illness. She began by sitting about and weeping. Then she became agitated and said she was a witch and was "caught" for her sins by her brother's *obosom*. Then she started talking "*basa-basa*" and spent most of her time sweeping the yard over and over again. She was brought to Mframaso, cleansed at the shrine and immediately recovered.

Previous Personality: Energetic. She is not a member of the church but is a keen member of the church "singing band" and never misses dressing in her uniform and attending its meetings.

Present Illness

About a week ago she menstruated for the first time. The onset of her illness coincided with this. She arrived in Mframaso on a passenger-lorry late one evening. Everyone in the town heard her shouting as the lorry arrived and no one in her landlady's house had any sleep that night.

First interview: 5.4.56

The picture was that of a classical schizophrenia. She was on the ground wearing only drawers and covered with dirt. She slowly rolled around in the yard, writhing and twisting, and waving her arms and legs in strange, slow contortions, rolling her eyes and grimacing. At intervals she stopped and seemed to be both auditorily and visually hallucinated. Now and then she became momentarily accessible. Asked her name, she gave it but could not say where she lived. Asked why she came here, she said people envied her because she had in her belly the River Densu, some big trees and other valuables.

6.4.56. She was quiet and was sitting in the yard eating. When she saw me she said, "I implore you. I have done wrong. I am a witch. But it isn't my fault. Other witches are making me into a witch. Everybody in this town ought to bring forth children. Everybody ought to bring forth more children."

Throughout the day, though she shouted at intervals that the witchcraft was not her fault, she was reasonably quiet and manageable, though talking incoherently about angels helping her. The predominant facial expression was anxious.

In the evening she was taken to the shrine. She had flung off her clothes again and was resistive, crawling on the ground but saying nothing. She stood in the sinners' dock frowning, manneristic, giggling, posturing with her hands and occasionally looking visually hallucinated. Her brothers had to make her statement for her. She gave the household another disturbed night.

1.4.56. She was taken to the shrine, together with her sacrificial cow, for the cleansing ritual. She was restless but appeared to appreciate the nature of the occasion. When told to dance to the drums she charged furiously round the yard waving her shawl, but her performance was disciplined and rhythmical enough to be definitely a dance. When told to kneel before the *obrafohene's* pot she was resistive and had to be held there, but she sat in quiet co-operation while her head was shaved. In the house afterwards the other occupants had their first quiet night.

9.4.56. Dramatically improved. Clean, clothed, behaving quietly and normally. Correctly orientated for place but hazy about time. She answered questions sensibly about her home, but when asked about her friends she said they were witches and were making her into one and she did not like it. Asked about her parents, she said she liked her mother but disliked her father and his family. One brother confirmed that during her illness she had shown hostility to her father though never before. Later in the day, she became over-active, doing a great deal of unnecessary sweeping and tidying. Asked when she was going home, she said not until she had had enough baths to wash away the "abominable thing" that people were trying to put on her.

11.4.56. She is accessible but restless. Looks anxious and worried. She has done much unnecessary sweeping in the yard of the house and has also swept clean a huge area of the town outside. When asked to describe her own town, she said it was small, but nevertheless had a great many witches who troubled her and wanted her to become one of them. When the drumming started in the *obosom's* yard she went in voluntarily and danced and then placed herself in the dock looking perplexed and worried.

12.4.56. Over-active again, sweeping and re-sweeping the yard. Her house-mates say she shouted throughout the night that people were trying to put a "dirty thing" on her. In the evening she busily tidied up and scavenged the whole town, removing all bits of rubbish from the street to the rubbish-heaps. At intervals she stopped to scratch herself anxiously as if covered with lice, though she was, in fact, quite clean and had a shaven head.

13.4.56. Absorbed in sweeping. Her house-mates said she got up in the night and swept till they locked her up.

14.4.56. Still sweeping, striding about scavenging the town. She smiles appropriately if addressed and replies appropriately but perfunctorily. She will not concentrate on conversation for more than a few moments, but marches off and resumes the tidying of the town. Before shaking hands with me this morning she dusted and polished her hand on her clothes. At intervals she takes off her wrap and shakes it vigorously and disgustedly as if shaking insects out of it.

16.4.56. She has stopped sweeping but is fidgety and looks apprehensive. She giggles inappropriately.

18.4.56. Last appearance at the shrine.

Obosom (severely): Have you given up wanting to go with the witches at night?

Patient (giggling): Yes, Nana.

Obosom: When you feel them wanting to take you along, you mustn't get up.

Patient: Yes, Nana. I won't follow them again.

Obosom: You have given your brothers a lot of trouble and expense, buying cows and so on. If you persist in getting up when the witches call you, I shall kill you.

Patient (giggling): Yes, Nana.

19.4.56. Her brothers took her home to-day. She seemed imperfectly recovered and they looked extremely gloomy. They said that each of her two illnesses had cost them over £30, but they would not grudge it if she lived to have a child, for that would be worth more than £1,000 to them.

1.12.56. The patient and her two brothers returned to render thanks for her recovery. They said she had rejoined the singing band and was completely well.

Physically she looked extremely well and vigorous: had considerably developed and fattened. But her movements had an over-boisterous vigour, her affect was shallow and fatuous and her manner evasive.

COMMENTARY

Hebephrenia with obsessive features. Witchcraft delusions bound up with ideas of concrete pollution. She blames others, not herself.

That the menarche was the precipitating factor does not necessarily invoke endocrines. Young girls are usually married and become pregnant within a month or two of their first menstruation and the prospect may well be daunting.

CASE 116. ADWOWA T. of Bekwai district, Ashanti. F. *c.* 19.

Shrine

Mframa at Mframaso.

Reason for referral

Distressing impulse to attack her children with a farm-cutlass.

Family History

Father: A farmer. A non-Christian illiterate who died in the patient's early childhood.

Mother: Alive and well. A non-Christian illiterate. She separated from her second husband and has married a third, who is kind to the patient.

Siblings: Mother had nine children, of whom four (all daughters) survive. Two are older than the patient and have children, one has not yet reached puberty.

Personal History

Childhood: N.a.d. disclosed.

Schooling: She was four years at school and reached class III. She says the teachers all liked her because she was always top of the class. She left because her grandfather, who had been grudgingly financing her schooling, died. She was distressed at leaving.

Marriage: She married, three years ago, an illiterate, non-Christian farmer. He took the patient to live in his distant cocoa-"village" out of reach of her own family. Neither his family nor most of the patient's ever approved of the marriage, though her stepfather consented by drinking the "head-rum".

The husband was kind to the patient till about the beginning of her third pregnancy when he said that he no longer liked her and had taken another woman. She thinks this woman went to a Kramu medicine-man and "tied" the husband so that he would bow to all her own behests and no longer want to sleep with the patient. He sent the patient back to her mother early in pregnancy and she has not rejoined him. Formal separation has not yet taken place. (A pregnant woman may not be divorced.)

Children: She has three children, aged three, two, and three months. The last child was not wanted by the patient's husband because he wanted to speed up the divorce. Because of the husband's attitude the patient also did not want the third child, and says it has brought her much trouble.

Home: Since leaving the husband the patient has been in her mother's "village". The household consists of mother, the mother's brother, his wife and some of his grown-up children. All are farmers. The house is owned by the mother's sisters' sons, who are away working in the mines at Obuasi. The patient says her uncle and his wife are kind. That the patient came to Mframaso all by herself suggests that her mother and other relatives are out of sympathy with her.

Present Illness

The onset was on the day her last child was born. Labour was so long and difficult that there was talk of taking her to hospital. When it was over she suddenly felt that she wanted to kill the baby. Ever since, she has had almost daily urges to attack all her children with a farm-cutlass. The impulses come suddenly and terrify her. She often weeps because she "had always been good and liked children". She enjoyed helping her sisters to deliver and look after their children. These also are now included in her urge to kill.

She thinks she is being punished by the *obosom* Tigari (whose medicine she has drunk) because she once cursed her husband's relatives to God for spoiling her plantain-farm. (All cursing is against Tigari's rules.) She thought she ought to take her guilt to Tigari, but her mother, who had neglected some of her own Tigari observances, persuaded her to go to Mframa instead. As the patient has also swollen joints (secondary yaws) and a "stiff head", the mother thought that the "changed mind" was also a part of the same sickness. Mframa's *obosomfo* (who had clearly not met this type of witchcraft before) said that it was too wicked for him to deal with and the patient must go to Tigari.

Interview

A small young woman, well dressed and well nourished. Child well cared for.

She was anxious, frightened and tearful. She had suspicious misgivings after telling me her tale and came back and said that she had lied to me about her relatives' names and localities. She then invented new ones which did not tally with those she gave at the shrine. She went home at once and I do not know the outcome.

COMMENTARY

Obsessive-compulsive illness in a setting of reactive depression and anxiety. Onset of the compulsive symptoms was in the puerperium.

This illness has been said to be non-existent in rural Africa, and is certainly rare. This woman showed no appearance of racial admixture.

X

SCHIZO-AFFECTIVE PSYCHOSIS

This illness usually begins with self-reproach concerning offences which are often either wholly imaginary or trivial. Witchcraft is the commonest of the self-accusations.

CASE 117. ADWOWA K. of Techiman district, Ashanti. F. *c.* 35.

Shrine
Dimankoma at Akrofrom.

Reason for referral
Self-accusations of witchcraft.

Family History
  Parents: Cross-cousins. Illiterate, non-Christian cocoa-farmers. The father died many years ago, the mother when the patient was about twelve.
  Siblings: Seven born, four survived. All illiterate, non-Christian, cocoa-farmers.

Personal History
  Childhood: She has always been thin and sickly. As a child she had many ailments, including an illness which left her so deaf that shouting is necessary.
  Schooling: Nil. Non-Christian: illiterate.
  Work: Farming and trading in foodstuffs.
  Previous Personality: She belonged to the band of "Apo" singing women and "could smile sometimes" but has "never played and laughed". She kept herself apart and was shy. (Deafness probably partly responsible.)
  Marriage: Her husband is a cocoa-farmer of a nearby country-town. He has one other wife. He did not concern himself when the patient became ill: all this was left to her "father's" and mother's people and

her father's brother who is a rich cocoa-farmer. It is probably not a very happy marriage.

Household: The patient lives in her husband's home-town, but in her father's brother's household, a large and populous one containing his wives and a great many other relatives, including some young ones who go to school. The head of the house is one of the town elders, a good-natured, prosperous cocoa-farmer. All the people there seem happy and pleasant. The husband lives with his own relatives.

Children: Three born. The eldest died in infancy about sixteen years ago. The youngest is now about three.

Present Illness

The onset was about three weeks ago. First symptom: she "felt cold in the night" and had disturbing dreams. Since then she has hardly slept and has eaten very little. Shortly after the onset she realised that some beads that her grandmother left her contained an *obayi* and that she herself was a witch who had done a lot of harm, including the killing of her first child. When this realisation came to her she got up in the night and threw the beads, together with various other trinkets and clothes, into the public pit-latrine, thinking the *obayi* might have impregnated the lot. Witnesses say she weeps a good deal and says she is going to die. She is restless, will not lie down at night but stands in the courtyard, and has sometimes gone out into the bush and stood there till morning. She says that sometimes she finds herself in the bush not knowing how she got there and walking she knows not where. She also "sees bright lights". Witnesses said that on one occasion she said she was going to the latrine but was away for the greater part of the day, and was finally found by a search-party wandering vaguely and talking "*basa-basa*". She also often says that she sees a "*mpese-mpese*" standing over her and often hears voices which other people cannot hear.

Interview: 23.7.56

At the shrine she was anxious and agitated. She said she had killed three people, including her infant child, had planned to kill her uncle, and had made three women barren by stealing their wombs. Her *obayi's* name was "Menkomenya" (I alone have it). Apropos of her uncle, she said, "He has always liked me and given me everything I ask for, but we witches kill the people we love rather than the ones we don't." At interview she was depressed, agitated and full of self-reproach. The confusion featuring in the history was absent and she was correctly orientated, though too much agitated to concentrate.

Progress

30.7.56. Much improved. No more confusional wanderings or hallucinations. Sleeping fairly well. She was doing a little cooking but was very slow and bewildered. Agitation completely gone since confession. She could not do simple arithmetic, attention and memory tests.

7.8.56. Relatives say she is now quite well (which I doubt) and has gone away to some of her mother's people.

7.2.57. After repeated attempts I have contacted her again. She is now in another small country-town in the household of two maternal uncles—quiet, sensible, pleasant men. She is about seven months pregnant and must have been pregnant at the time of her illness. Since her illness her husband has failed to maintain her. Witnesses say that since her illness she has quarrelled with everyone and can hardly be civil, but she works hard on her uncles' farms, sleeps quietly and no longer wanders away.

When I saw her she was sitting outdoors on a stool by herself in a large open space in the sun. She came along rather sulkily to talk and seemed irritable. Asked how she was, she grumbled about her defaulting husband. To various verbal tests her responses indicated below-average general knowledge and intelligence, but attention and memory tests were satisfactory. Though not indubitably schizophrenic, she seemed a schizoid, ill-adjusted, unprepossessing person. (Several other women of the same district—e.g., Ekwia M., Case No. 14—after confessing witchcraft at the same shrines have *not* been cast off by their husbands, but regarded as the victims of strange misfortune.)

30.1.58. It was nearly a year before I had the opportunity of seeing her again, though I had heard that she had delivered her child. She was still in her uncles' household and everyone agreed that she had become quite mad, and that the madness set in a few weeks after the birth of the child. I found her standing motionless in the middle of the yard, her baby on her back, looking puzzled and hallucinated. She did not seem inaccessible but scowled and did not return my greeting. The house-people said she never did. They said she often talked in *"basa-basa"* fashion without ceasing for long stretches to invisible people and said she could see them. She sometimes seemed badly frightened, and shut herself up in a room, but never ran away to the bush. She had taken a dislike to her favourite uncle and often tried to beat him. She slept quietly at night, sold firewood, and was quite clean.

COMMENTARY

This is a schizoid personality in whom a febrile illness in early pregnancy produced confusional episodes, and ushered in an affective illness with self-reproach. In the ensuing puerperium a frank psychosis set in, settling down into unmistakable schizophrenia.

The friends' and relatives' comment is the usual one. "She was a witch so the *obosom* caught hold of her, but because she did not confess everything he made her mad."

CASE 118. YAW T. of Central Province. M. 50+.

Shrine
Mframa at Mframaso.

Reason for referral
Recurrence of self-accusations of witchcraft.

Family and Personal History
Scanty information. Patient is an illiterate, non-Christian cocoa-farmer. He came to the shrine alone. He has grown-up, married daughters, and some sons at school.

Previous Illness: He came to Mframaso three years ago accusing himself of witchcraft, was cured and went away.

Present Illness
Lately he has again felt that he was a witch and that his influence would kill his newborn grandchild and his own son. He said that Mframa had "caught" him for this sin.

First interview: 6.3.56
He is thin, but otherwise looks healthy and gives no history of physical indisposition. The face is lined and anxious. He is miserable and extremely agitated. He sits head-in-hands, but after a minute or so groans and sighs, gets up, walks about and sits again. He is correctly orientated and gives relevant replies when he consents to speak, but mostly he does not reply except to say irritably that he can't talk when his own thoughts are interrupting him so much.

At the shrine he placed himself in the penitent-dock but missed his turn several times by wandering restlessly out of his place. In his anxiety he chipped in several times out of his turn, interrupting and annoying the *obosom*. His landlord had to come and help him hand in his eggs at the right moment. He said he had done much wrong but could give little in the way of a witchcraft story except that his *obayi* was not thrust on him by anyone else but had been with him from his mother's womb. Asked the name of his *obayi*, he said it was "tsetse-fly" (a pursuing, persistent nuisance). He was co-operative in the ritual purification.

7.3.56. He looks rather brighter and less anxious. I met him on his way down to the river to bathe and wash his clothes. He was not willing to talk and said that if I was interested in his welfare I would give him the money to buy his two sheep for atonement.

15.3.56. He stayed only long enough for a short course of ritual baths and did not improve much after the first day.

This could be involutional depression, but in view of a three-year remission and his irritation at the way his thoughts are "interrupting" him, it may be a schizo-affective illness.

CASE 119. AKOSUA M. of Techiman district, Ashanti. F. *c.* 50.

Shrine
Abiri at Awuruwa.

Reason for referral
Self-accusations of witchcraft and numerous other sins. Weeping, walking about restlessly, inability to work, sleep or eat.

Family History
Parents: Cross-cousins. Illiterate, non-Christian cocoa-farmers.

Personal History
Childhood: N.a.d. disclosed.

Work: She has her own cocoa-farm and her own yam-farm, on which she worked hard till the onset of the present illness.

Marriage: Satisfactory. Her husband died four years ago. She has not married again.

Children: She has borne six, all alive. One daughter, five sons. The two youngest sons are at school. The two eldest are illiterate lorry-drivers.

Previous Personality: Well liked and respected. Hard-working: she says that the worst part of her present illness is that something stops her from doing work, and that is mainly why she weeps.

Katamenia: Menopause not yet reached.

Present Illness
The onset was two months ago. She could do no work but sat weeping or walked about aimlessly and restlessly. She was sleepless and lost her appetite. She said she often felt "suddenly hot". She said there was a fire in her head, noises, hummings and groanings and this meant that she had committed some offence. She had distressing dreams and often woke up weeping. She felt things crawling in her belly and in her head. She said that people ought to bring a gun and shoot her because she had done so many wrong things. Her family asked her if she was a witch: she replied that she was the worst witch that ever was.

She was taken to the shrine of the *obosom* whose medicine she drank ten years ago. I was not present on that occasion but I learnt that the confessions of witchcraft were the stereotyped ones and included the assertion that she had brought about the death of a sister who died seven years ago, though she had only lately realised that it was she who caused the death. She said that she did not want to do harm but had a bad mind.

Interview: 1.8.56

Grey-haired. Thin. (They say she was fat before her illness.) Dirty and unkempt.

Restless, agitated. She is disinclined to talk, but does so if pressed. She sometimes talks irritably. She answers questions sensibly and correctly unless they pertain to her present situation, when her talk becomes classically depressive.

Asked about her sleep, said she seldom slept but when she did had frightening dreams. Asked about the dreams, said recurring dreams are of a big, terrifying animal standing in front of her and of a *sasabonsam* raping her, she unable to shout for help. She also dreamt that she was walking in a crowd and gave *ampesi* (food) to a child. Then she saw someone in a black cloth who had come to arrest her. She fought with this person. She also dreamt that a crowd of men had caught one small boy and kept shouting, "Here is a small boy: he is lost: we are taking him to sell." She knew they wanted to "take him as a sheep to slaughter him" and she tried to rescue him.

She said she ought to be killed because she had done so much wrong, and wished that they would bring a gun and shoot her quickly. She added, "I know I am dead already: nothing can prevent me from dying." She said that there were humming and groaning noises in her head and "burnings" on her scalp and this meant that she had done wrong.

8.8.56. Wandering about the town chewing a chew-stick, looking dejected and worried. She speaks sensibly, amicably and rationally on everything but herself. "I may seem all right to you, but my mind is completely destroyed." But she described her inability to concentrate: "I can't set my mind to do my work as I used to. I used to set my mind to go to a place and do something and then I did it, but now I can't keep my mind to do it."

12.9.56. No change. "All the flesh of my belly is gone. My heart is destroyed."

29.9.56. She says she lies sleeplessly at night "counting all the things in the house." She says she eats her food but it does not taste and is useless. "I myself am useless. Everything is useless." She said irritably that she could not sleep and why didn't I bring her some medicine.

10.10.56. The household were celebrating the funeral of the patient's mother with wailing, bellowing and drinking. The patient was taking no part, but was walking around restlessly as usual.

2.11.56. I brought her some sleeping medicine a few days ago and explained to both daughter and son how to administer it, but she refuses to take it, saying that neither it nor anything could possibly do her any good.

26.11.56. No change. She was found sitting on the ground in the shade of an awning over a large bread-oven out-of-doors. Says she is miserable night and day, but night is the worse; she cannot sleep because her head is full of thoughts and burnings.

8.3.57. No change over the past few months. She still wanders around miserably or sits alone under any piece of shade in the town. She says she lies awake at night and hundreds of *asem* (matters, affairs) go through her head. She says she knows that eventually all her children will become as miserable and useless as she is and that it will be her fault.

1.10.57. Still unchanged. She sleeps outdoors under oven-awnings, etc., because, she says, she is not worthy to sleep in a house.

16.12.57. She now seldom comes into the town but wanders in the bush. There is an old firewood shelter under which she sleeps and where her relatives leave food for her. They say she does not talk *"basa-basa"*, but she shuns people, and they think she is going mad. (Africans are usually right on this point.)

2.2.58. I succeeded in seeing her once. She no longer seems oppressed but is inappropriately unconcerned. She says nothing irrational, but has a shallow, offhand manner and says she likes being in the bush. I think she is now schizophrenic.

COMMENTARY

Schizo-affective illness beginning as an involutional depression.

CASE 120. KOFI K. of Kwahu. M. *c.* 50.

Shrine

Kyinaman at Bredi.

Reason for referral

"Caught" for cursing his own soul (*kra*) to God.

Family History

Parents: Died 1933 and 1934. Not cross-cousins. Non-Christian, illiterate cocoa-farmers. Father had several wives.

Siblings: Seven whole siblings born, two survived. Patient came to the shrine with paternal half-brother, older than the patient. Pleasant, sensible person on very good terms with the patient.

Personal History

   Childhood: N.a.d.

   School: Patient reached Standard III, was a good scholar but had to leave because of money. Patient is a full church member but has drunk at Tigari's shrine as well as Kyinaman's.

   Marriage: Cross-cousin. Wife has not left him but has gone to live in another village. I felt that there was undisclosed marital anxiety but did not probe further at first interview. He complained that he was "not bringing forth children with his wife".

   Children: Eleven born, eight survived. Some are grown-up, some at school. One reached Standard VII and then went into the Army. One reached Standard VI and refused to go further. (This is usually ominous.)

   Home: Lives with several brothers, sons, daughters and daughters' children in a cocoa-village which consists of six houses.

   Previous Illness: 1944—"Caught" by Tigari. Illness similar to the present one. Duration—one year. 1954—Again "caught" by Tigari. Towards the end of the illness he came to Bredi, stayed two months and went home well.

Present Illness

Patient says that a few months ago he felt that all his affairs were going wrong—his cocoa was not flourishing, he was not begetting children, and the world seemed "*basa-basa*". One day he cursed his own soul to God. This being against *obosom* law, he was soon "caught". He dreamt that he was chased by cows and that witches gave him meat. He sometimes saw "fire" in his eyes (scotomata of migraine?). Then he became quite sleepless, wretched and weeping. He insists that his mind has "changed" and his thoughts do not do what he wants. When he talks to people he suddenly feels that they want to do him harm and he rounds on them angrily. One day he dreamt he saw a man who said he would recover if he came to Bredi, so he hastily did. His half-brother, another very good personality, corroborates his story. He says the patient is not restless but apathetic and despairing.

Interview: 20.6.57

I had only one brief interview as he was anxious to go quickly to the shrine. (I could not wait till after this as there was a rapidly rising river to ford.)

   Patient was a well-built, big-boned man, thin, and very miserable. No retardation. Good, straightforward account of himself. Friendly and pleasant. Intelligence tests exceptionally well done with good concentration. Smiles reluctantly but warmly. Good personality. Good insight. Not paranoid. He says he knows that people don't want to do him harm and is distressed by the sudden, irrational feeling that they do and thinks it is something that is being put into his head against his wish. He is also upset because, when he is thinking, something changes his thoughts.

23.6.57. Gone home to collect money. Expected back to complete his ritual.

30.8.57. He has still not returned.

COMMENTARY

Third episode of schizo-affective illness with good insight in a good personality.

CASE 121. AMA T. of Ahafo district, Ashanti. F. *c.* 45.

Shrine

Kyinaman, at Bredi.

Reason for referral

Suicidal attempt after self-accusations of witchcraft.

Family History

Parents: Not cross-cousins. Illiterate, non-Christian cocoa-farmers.

Siblings: Three full brothers, one full sister; three half-sisters (same mother). All are married, all have children, all are illiterate, non-Christian cocoa-farmers.

About two and a half years ago one brother (in the same household as the patient) went "mad". He was not fevered or physically ill but began by sitting inertly about, refusing to work or to speak. Then he became violent and attacked people. He has become inert again now. He has never talked irrationally but says he will kill anyone who annoys him. He has remained in the household throughout his illness and had only medicine-men's treatment. Married twice. One child.

Personal History

Childhood: N.a.d. disclosed. No schooling. Non-Christian.

Work: Farming.

Previous illnesses: Nil.

Marriage: Husband an illiterate, non-Christian cocoa-farmer. The marriage was happy till the present illness, when the husband left her.

Children: Only one child born. Alive and well. Aged eleven. When the husband left he took the child.

Katamenia: Menopause not yet reached.

Household: Patient, three half-sisters, three whole brothers (their wives and children are elsewhere), one whole sister and her children, three unspecified female relatives and their children, a young son-in-law of the elder brother. All are illiterate, non-Christian farmers.

Previous Personality: She is said to have been hard-working and amiable.

Present Illness

About ten months ago the patient and five of her relatives came to Bredi to drink the shrine-medicine, to ascertain whether any of them had by witchcraft caused the brother's madness (the implication being that they felt themselves innocent and wished for vindication). About six weeks later the patient began sitting about miserably, scratching her body and complaining of headache. She became unable either to work or sleep and was unwilling to speak. When her child approached her she drove it away. Her husband then left her and took the child, where-after she sat rocking herself, and moaning "My child, my child". Then she said she had been "caught" by the medicine for witchcraft. She said she had caused her brother's madness because he had refused to give her a due share of the family cocoa-farms. She also said she had by witch-craft damaged her own womb so that it had borne but one child. The name of her *obayi* was Huhuke. Then she went into the bush to hang herself but was seen trying to fling the rope round a branch. For about four months she has refused to drink water, saying that when she does she feels the water walking over her head. This is the only absurd thing she has said. She complained of "*basa-basa*" dreams but could not relate them. She always seemed frightened, but could not say of what.

Informants

One half-sister, one whole sister, senior brother, brother's young son-in-law. All well nourished, well dressed and adorned, well disposed and sensible, anxious to help the patient to be cleansed.

Interview: 10.10.56

A tall, well-built woman, very emaciated and dehydrated. Her hair was grey (unusual in Africans of her age). She was much retarded, speaking only a few whispered words and with difficulty. She was full of self-reproach. She would not shake hands or sit down: she said she was not worthy and was also afraid I was going to punish her. She fre-quently whispered "Ma ye boni" (I have sinned). She was agitated and apprehensive, twisting her hands and fidgeting.

At the shrine she was not able to make a coherent "confession". The priest accepted the relatives' statements and ordered the usual purifica-tion rites.

Progress

I did not see her again as she was taken home the next day. After a few weeks I heard that she had died.

COMMENTARY

The brother's illness does not suggest trypanosomiasis—the chief differential diagnosis from schizophrenia of abrupt onset. This makes it more probable that the patient's illness was the onset of a schizo-affective state, rather than an involutional depression, though I should not quarrel with a psychiatrist who insisted on the latter.

CASE 122. YAW F. of Prasu district, Kwahu. M. *c.* 50.

Shrine

Mframa at Mframaso.

Reason for referral

Voluntary confessions of stealing and planning to kill his sisters with bad *suman*.

Family History

Parents: Mother is dead but father still alive: an illiterate, non-Christian cocoa-farmer.

Siblings: The patient is the second of four, all illiterate, non-Christian farmers.

Personal History

Childhood: N.a.d.

Schooling: Nil. Non-Christian.

Marriage: He divorced his first wife, the second is alive.

Children: He has had about ten, of whom six survive. The eldest son is a palm-wine tapper, married with children; the second is a married daughter with children. The others are children.

Work: He spent twenty years in Oboase mines and retired to his cocoa-farm eight years ago.

Previous Illnesses: Nil.

Home: He lives with one full sister, one daughter of his mother's sister and an aged sister of the mother, who owns the house. The two younger women brought the patient to the shrine. The patient's wife lives elsewhere in the same town, as do the two husbands of the younger women.

Previous Personality: He was a strong, hard worker who "loved everybody", and often helped relatives in their financial and other troubles.

Present Illness

Six weeks ago the patient had an acute physical illness with confusion and delirium and "nearly died". (The two women who brought him to the shrine were poor witnesses and conveyed nothing indicating the nature of the illness.) He recovered sufficiently to walk about and behave rationally and was taken to a variety of medicine-men, a "Gospel Healer" at Tafo, a "Spirit Healer" at Koforidua, and the out-patient clinics of several hospitals where he was given injections. He did not improve, so it was decided that the *obosom* Mframa, at whose shrine he had drunk about six years ago, was implicated in the illness.

At the shrine he said Mframa had "caught" him and made him sick for his sins. He said he had stolen some of his father's cocoa from the farm and had also made up his mind to kill, with a bad *suman*, the two "sisters" with whom he lived. The sisters were astonished at both these statements.

Shrine appearance: 22.6.56

At the shrine he looked physically ill, thin and exhausted and was deeply miserable. He knelt abjectly and said he was wicked and a fool. The *obosom* told him that what he had done was "worse than witchcraft" and that he deserved to die; he concurred. The *obosom* told him he must pay a cow and three sheep, be baptised, given medicine and his life would be spared. This seemed to cheer him but little. As he was staying in the house of an elder who was at that time suspicious and unfriendly, I could not interview him personally, but I bribed his two sisters to come and tell me his story.

Progress

He stayed in Mframaso several weeks, improved, and went home apparently quite well.

8.8.56. He was brought back to Mframaso, this time by his "brother" (mother's sister's son), his wife, his wife's sister and his own sister's son. The "brother" has cocoa, but for eight and a half years also ran a general store which failed. The nephew is a goldsmith who has recently been in trouble with the police for buying stolen gold.

The brother said that shortly after the patient's return home he took him to an *obosom* in the Bekwai district whose medicine he had drunk some years earlier, and whose rules had been violated, no less than Mframa's, by his offences. There the patient added more to his confessions, said that he was a witch and had killed many people whom he named. Immediately he had finished the statement he fell down unconscious, stiff, foaming at the mouth and rattling in the throat. He came round after about ten minutes and the brother immediately hired a lorry and took him home. On reaching home he seemed so well and normal that the other relatives could not believe the story of the fit. But three days later he again said he was a witch and then began to talk "*basa-basa*", became wild and attacked people. He kept this up night and day. At night they locked him up, but he climbed over the wall into his brother's room (African rooms have no ceilings). He became at times "like an *okomfo*", and danced and sang.

They then decided to bring him back to Mframaso, and as they had already spent £200 (so they said) on his travelling expenses and various treatments they held a family meeting and resolved to sell his cocoa for further funds. In spite of his illness he could appreciate this seizure of his cocoa and much resented it. They bound him hand and foot to keep him in the lorry which brought him. This time he stayed in a different house in Mframaso and I was able to see him there on the evening of his arrival.

Interview: 8.8.56

He looked physically better than when he left but had a good many bruises and abrasions and was uncooperative and resistive. He displayed a mixture of self-reproach, fear and indignation, the latter directed at the relatives who had sold his cocoa. He sat groaning and rocking himself about in anguish and fear, crying, "Egyee, Egyee (Alas, alas). I have done evil. . . . They are coming with a gun to kill me for my wickedness. . . . The medicine is coming to kill me. . . ." At intervals he got up and tried to push away his brothers, who, he said, had taken his cocoa and were going to take his life.

14.8.56. To-day he was led to the shrine but could give no account of himself. He told his brothers that fellow-witches were squeezing his ribs and preventing him from telling his tale. He was then taken to the *obofohene*, who made medicine to induce him to talk, but without avail. The *obosomfo* then said that if he could not confess he could not be helped and would have to die. The brothers then asked me if I had any medicine that would make him talk. I said I would do what I could for him.

15.8.56: *Amytal and methedrine abreaction*

Q. "What is your trouble?"
A. "The world is no good."
Q. "Are you sick?"
A. "Yes."
Q. "How did the sickness begin?"
A. "In my belly."
Q. "When did it begin?"
A. "About six months ago."

Q. "Is it true you stole someone's cocoa?"

A. "Yes, my father's. About ten pounds' worth, and a police-magistrate wants to arrest me."

Q. "Have you done anything else wrong?"

A. "I have killed seven people, among them a nephew and a niece, and I made up my mind to kill Ama X.'s baby together with its grandmother."

Q. "What means do you use for killing?"

A. "I am an *obayifo*."

Q. "Has your *obayi* a name?"

A. "Yes—'Fa-me-ye'." (Make me your agent.—Lit. Take-me-do.)

Q. "What else do you do by means of this *obayi*?"

A. "Flying. I put *sahoma* leaves and *tofome* leaves on my *obayi* to make me fly."

Q. "Is it true that you have a special song to sing to it?"

A. "Yes."

Q. "Can you sing it now?"

After some hesitation and clapping his hands to make a rhythm he sang an entirely original and tuneful composition.

Kwesi Afra, Ee!	Kwesi Afra, Ee!
Bone a maye,	The evil I have done
Mesere Nyame	I will implore God
Ebi mma bio	Nothing will come again
Ma kyin-kyin	I have roamed, roamed about
Ma kyin	I have roamed.
Metu ko soro	I fly up to the sky
Tetwa wo, Tin!	I strike at you, Tin!

Q. "Have you any other songs?"

A. "Yes."

Me sen Yaa Ben.	I am greater than Yaa Ben.
Me sen Yaa Ben.	

Q. "Any more?"

A. "Yes."

Kokooko!	
Asofo Akwawa de	A.A. has brought the meat.
nam aba.	[Presumably human flesh for
Kokooko!	witches' feasting.]

Q. "Any more?"

A. "Yes."

Pepepe	Pepepe,
Mintie da	I will never listen again.
Pepepe	
Mintie da	

420

Q. "Any more?"
A. "Yes."

Aburumuru Ee!	Aburumuru Ee!
Bra ntem, ma yen ko agoro.	Come quickly and let us go and revel.

Repetitions and rhythm made these sentences into songs, and some of them he went on repeating, clapping his hands, till told to stop.

Q. "Have you done anything else wrong?"
A. "I determined to kill my brother B. and my nephew, but because they were kind to me I didn't."
Q. "What else did you do?"
A. "Sometimes my *obayi* runs away from me. I put a chameleon and palm-wine on it. When I put *abirumuru* leaves on it, everything is very nice."
Q. "Have you done anything else wrong?"
A. "My *obayi* caused my brother's store to fail, but it was not I who caused the police to arrest my other brother, but his aunts. It was I who spoilt [the wombs of] Abena P., Akua Q. and Yaa R. When I put a medicine on a porcupine it flies like an aeroplane. An Ayigbe man gave me some bad medicine."

16.8.56. The patient's "confession" was made on his behalf by his brother at the shrine, the patient assenting when asked if it was true. He was then "baptised" and his brothers went home to fetch money to buy a cow, leaving him with the two women.

17.8.56. Patient appeared much relieved and improved by his confession and baptism, was rational but irritable and restless. He stuffed himself with huge quantities of food and complained of constipation and sleeplessness. These yielded to purgatives and hypnotics.

18.8.56. He is still rational, but laconic and agitated.

19.8.56. Sharp deterioration. He became inaccessible. He sat moving his head slowly round, evidently following some visual hallucination, and saying, "Who are you?" to invisible people. Then he showed marked katatonic features with flexibilitas cerea, his limbs remaining stuck in the air if placed there, in the classic manner. He was laid on his mat, where he became quite stiff and then fell into a stupor.

20.8.56. Still in stupor. He did not respond to either intravenous amytal or intramuscular nikethamide. The relatives declined to let me take him to hospital.

21.8.56. Still unconscious. Incontinent of urine. Much dehydrated. Hypostatic pneumonia developing. (Penicillin given.)

22.8.56. Unconscious all day. Severely dehydrated. Sordes in mouth (Penicillin continued.) In the evening he opened his eyes and his mouth and when water was put in the latter he swallowed it. I stood over the relatives while they gave him several beer-bottles full of sugar and coloured water which I said was medicine. (Water is considered rather bad for sick people.)

23.8.56. This morning he was fully conscious, speaking a little and taking food and drink. Penicillin and coloured sugar-and-water were continued.

24.8.56. Chest better. Less dehydrated. More penicillin and fluids pressed.

25.8.56. Improving. Talks rationally. Eating and drinking very well. He won't sit up.

26.8.56. Physically improved. Rational and he speaks a little, but he is irritable, resistive and will not drink.

27.8.56. To-day he has sat up, eaten and drunk, but is quite mute.

28.8.56. He resists food and drink and is mute.

29.8.56. Relatives took him home.

24.9.56. His brother came to tell the *obosom* that the patient was dead. After leaving Mframaso he had continued to have alternate days of accepting and refusing food and drink.

COMMENTARY

Although there were marked schizo-affective features in this illness, I am not convinced that it was not of organic origin. The brother's description of a fit supports this. The hospital which he said he attended replied to my letter that they could not trace his records. Though the ultimate diagnosis thus remains in doubt, the *content* of his delusions and their social reception were traditional. That the delusions persisted under sodium amytal indicates that his witchcraft "confessions" were not made *pro forma*.

CASE 123. EKWIA D. of Kwaso district, Ashanti. F. 40+.

Shrine

1. Mframa at Mframaso.
2. Kwaku Firi, at Nwasi, near Wenchi.

Reason for referral

"Behaving like a mad person."

Family History

Parents: Cross-cousins. Non-Christian illiterates of Kwaso. Father, dead; mother alive and well; she came with the patient: a pleasant, sensible woman.

Siblings: At least six, all grown up, all Christian except one sister. One brother (main informant) was a teacher and says he left his post to look after his sick sister. However, he made an *abisa* before the shrine saying that he could not get employment.

Personal History

Childhood: N.a.d. disclosed.

Schooling: Nil, but Christian.

Marriage: She married her illiterate cross-cousin when they were both young. Her husband is a cocoa-farmer and store-keeper. He was a Christian when he married the patient but lapsed when he became sick and took his second wife, who now has three children. Formerly the patient's husband was a trader in Kwahu. He has a cocoa-farm in Kwahu and a new one in the Sunyani district, Ashanti. The patient left Kwaso with him and went to Kwahu where she ran the store and made it pay. About three years ago the husband, having become well-to-do, largely through the steady work of his wife, visited Kwaso leaving her in charge of the store. In Kwaso he married another wife and took her home to Kwahu. She arrived expensively dressed and the husband put her into the same house as the patient and lavished gifts upon her while withholding bare necessities from the patient. The patient several times took her complaint (neglect of marital obligations) to the elders of her husband's family under the presidency of her husband's uncle and each time he was reprimanded and ordered to make retribution, but did not. The patient therefore went one day to the riverside and cursed him to the river. (Every river is a deity.) Shortly after this the husband removed his store and his two wives to Kwaso where the patient continued to run the store. In Kwaso the husband installed his new wife in another house and continued to pamper her at the expense of the patient.

Children: Seven born, two died. Eldest survivor an illiterate daughter with one child. Three went to school: the eldest of these, a son aged about nineteen, came to Mframaso with the patient. He has just passed his Standard VII examination. Two younger children are at school. The youngest child is an infant.

Home: The patient lives in the Kwaso house in which she was brought up. It belongs to her mother's absent brother. Other occupants are the patient's mother, four of the patient's married brothers (their wives are elsewhere), the patient's sister and her children and the patient's husband (*sic*).

Previous Personality: She ran her husband's general store successfully and worked on his cocoa-farm and on her own farm. She paid for her children's schooling herself. She is a Methodist member and attends church with her children twice every Sunday, and during the week goes to Women's Fellowship, singing practice and bible-class.

Present Illness

Seven months ago she had a miscarriage (so her mother says) and has had amenorrhea and low spirits ever since. About six weeks ago she began singing Methodist hymns and praying aloud for mercy and forgiveness all day long. There was no indication of any febrile or other physical illness. She appeared to be possessed by some spirit (*honhom*), and as she was singing Christian hymns her friends thought the spirit must be the Holy Ghost, so they took her to a Presbyterian woman who had a harmonium and was famed for making prayers. This woman prayed with the patient and sang to the harmonium, but concluded that the patient had "something in her mind that she wanted to say and couldn't." She rapidly became worse till she was "like a mad person", crawling on the ground, tearing off all her clothes and eating faeces. At this stage she was mute. She was taken to four different medicine-men but could give no account of herself beyond saying that she had done wrong. As her uncle (the head of her family) had drunk at the shrine of the *obosom* Kwaku Firi on behalf of all his junior relatives, it was assumed that she had transgressed one of this *obosom's* rules was was "caught" by him. She was taken to the shrine of Kwaku Firi where she was able to confess that she had cursed her husband to a river because he treated her badly. After this confession she greatly improved, kept on her clothes and began to talk quietly, though with but little sense. The *obosom* told her that she had more to confess, and as she was unable to do so she was referred to Mframa's shrine where Mframa in turn referred her to the *obofohene* who was to make medicine to enable her to talk.

Interview

I had only one interview with her as she stayed in Mframaso only one day and then went back to Kwaku Firi, to whose shrine I had not access, but I saw her brother, mother, son and husband—the latter having been ordered by his own relatives to come with her. She was not noisy or unmanageable, was clean and clad and partly accessible. She was restless and her expression anxious and frightened with intermittent, inappropriate smiles. She could answer questions about her children's names and doings but was not correctly orientated and kept relapsing into rambling talk and getting up and wandering restlessly out of the house. Her mother said she gluttonously ate enormous quantities of food, after which her belly always swelled like a pregnancy but subsided after an enema. When I saw her the belly was enormously distended but resonant like a pseudo-cyesis. Apart from that, she looked physically well.

424

Progress

She was taken back to Kwaku Firi's shrine the following day, no one giving a hopeful prognosis because "she had more to confess but couldn't talk". I heard no more of her for about five months, when I sent a messenger to Kwaso to ask after her. She had stayed at Kwaku Firi's shrine for about three months, had made more confessions and a perfect recovery. On returning home, restitution of conjugal rights had occurred to the extent of her becoming pregnant.

COMMENTARY

Schizo-affective episode precipitated by guilt, fear, and much marital stress.

XI

MENTAL TROUBLES OF CHILDREN

Apart from epilepsy, backwardness in learning to talk, and so on, the majority of children who come to shrines with other than purely physical ailments, come because of feverish imaginings and terrifying dreams during febrile illness, most commonly malaria. More often than not the child, who has heard gossip about witchcraft, dreams that witches are carrying her away to make her one of themselves. One little girl of eight, deplorably thin and feeble (with hookworm, it was later established), one day found her limbs trembling as she was carrying home a four-gallon vessel of water from the river. The trembling was remarked upon and people thought "something had come to her and shaken her". She became frightened and dreamt that an *obosom* had flung its stick at her because she was a witch.

Sometimes a child's unwontedly wayward or startling behaviour will send the parents to a shrine, where the pronouncement may be made that the child is unwittingly a witch, either congenitally or by some older witch's secret and malicious contagion.

All these child witches are regarded as blameless victims—as indeed are most adult witches of obvious good-will—and are never unkindly treated. It is true that they are made to "confess their sins", which the shy ones dislike doing and the young exhibitionists thoroughly enjoy. The doctrine of congenital witchcraft is no worse than that of original sin, and the child's situation not so embarrassing as were the whipped-up "pi-jaws" inflicted on squirming children within my own memory in England. The young "witches" say everything conventionally expected of them, and know what kind of animals they are expected to say they ride upon as surely as our own children know that Santa Claus drives reindeer.

There is, however, one interesting feature about children's "confessions". They say they have planned to kill those whom they do *in fact* dislike, and their "confessions" are thus far illuminating.

CASE 124. AFUA M. of Sunyani district, Ashanti. F. 15.

Shrine

Dimankoma, Akrofrom.

Reason for referral

To be cleansed of witchcraft, presumed because of *"basa-basa"* talk about night-flying.

Family History

Parents: Both alive. Illiterate, non-Christian farmers. Both seen: sensible, quiet, pleasant people. They seem rather elderly. Father has one other wife. Mother drank at Dimankoma's shrine, three years ago, supplicating for more children.

Siblings: Patient is the only child of her mother, but has several half-siblings by her father's other wife.

Personal History

Childhood: N.a.d. disclosed.

Schooling: Left about a year ago because of illness. She liked school. Form I.

Previous Personality: She has always liked reading books at home, but "is a laughing girl" and helps her mother willingly.

Katamenia: Menarche not yet reached.

Household: Parents, father's parents, father's other wife and children.

Present Illness

Onset over a year ago. She has had three recoveries and relapses. Onset slow. Deafness. Photophobia. She could not see the blackboard in school. Headache, pains in the neck, stomach and bones. In the daytime she sits still and cries but is not prostrated. At night she dreams that big, mad cows chase her, but more often she cannot sleep at all and roams restlessly about the house. When she is falling asleep she feels something take her from her bed and make her fly. The mother says that at night she talks *"basa-basa"* and says she has seen mad cows, bad snakes and *mpese-mpese* men.

Interview: 4.9.56

(I could see the parents and the patient only very briefly as they were hurrying to get home the same day.)

Well-grown, tall girl. Conjunctivae well coloured, sclerotics not yellow. Looks less than fifteen (breasts undeveloped).*

---

* Illiterate Africans very seldom know their children's ages. The rare exceptions point to the conclusion that the puberty of rural children is later than that of over-nourished European children.

She was brought to the shrine during an interval of freedom from the illness. She was upset and slightly tearful at the nature of the occasion, but was co-operative and sensible. She did various scholastic tests very well. She said she was quite well at the time of interview but corroborated all her mother had said about her three illnesses. The parents said they would take her to hospital if the illness recurred after ruling out her own fear that she is being made into a witch.

10.1.57. I sent a messenger to the patient's home to enquire whether she was still well and, if not, whether any hospital investigation had been carried out. The messenger saw the household and was most impressed by its opulence. The patient's father is a very wealthy cocoa-farmer and has built a large two-storey house, the ground-floor of which is let to a big trading firm. The upper storey is surrounded by wide verandahs and is occupied by the patient's father and his relatives, his two wives and their children.

The patient has not had any recurrence of the illness. Her father has bought her an expensive sewing-machine, has apprenticed her to a seamstress, and she is enjoying her new work. There has been no more eyesight trouble.

COMMENTARY

There is little doubt that this is an organic reaction, the recurrent nature of the illness suggesting cerebral malaria.

CASE 125. AKOSUA P. of Kwahu district. F. *c.* 12.

Shrine

Mframa at Mframaso.

Reason for referral

Patient complained that people tried to carry her away at night to join witches.

Family History

Parents: Non-Christian, illiterate cocoa-farmers. Mother is an invalid with a disabled foot. Father has several wives in different houses. One of these quarrels with the patient's mother, and also reviles the patient.

Siblings: Five born, two died, including the last-born. The patient is the fourth. The elder brother and his wife brought the patient to the shrine. One brother goes to school.

Personal History

Childhood: N.a.d. disclosed. The house belongs to the father, who built it. The occupants are the patient's parents and their children and a Krobo farmer lodger.

Schooling: Nil. Non-Christian.

Present Illness

About ten weeks ago patient was feverish, unhappy and weeping. She slept very little and dreamt that people were trying to lift her up and carry her away. She has been poorly ever since. About three weeks ago she became suddenly worse and felt an urge to run out of the house. She ran away to the bush, not shouting but crying and weeping. She was pursued and brought back. The next day her hand and arm became "useless". She was taken to a local shrine where they said Mframa had laid hold of her for witchcraft.

First Interview

At the shrine she said someone unknown had made her into a witch, that she had killed her elder sister's baby and was planning to reduce her elder brother to poverty before killing him. (He had drunk at the shrine because he was not prospering.)

Patient was anaemic, excessively thin and complained of intermittent fever and headache. The affected arm showed wrist-drop and exaggerated tendon reflexes, paresis and wasting. She was a friendly, intelligent, good personality and not depressed, helpful and unselfish in the household, sustaining her obvious physical discomforts with fortitude. She said she remembered the episode of running to the bush and felt that something forced her to do it.

Progress

She was taken home a day or two after the interview.

COMMENTARY

Febrile fluctuating illness, probably malaria with malarial embolus to brain giving paresis.

CASE 126. ADWOWA B. of Kwahu district. F. *c.* 10.

Shrine

Amfemfi at Asueyi.

Reason for referral

Uncontrollable excitement and violence.

Family History

Parents: Not cross-cousins. Both illiterate, non-Christian traders with no cocoa. The father has one other wife. The wives are on good terms with one another, but the patient's mother always quarrelled with the husband, separated from him two years ago and married her cross-cousin, also a trader.

Siblings: The patient is the only live child. One later pregnancy miscarried at six months. The mother has been to several *abosom* supplicating for another child.

Personal History

Home: The patient lived first with her parents in Accra where they were trading. After the divorce the mother went back to her Kwahu home. On her second marriage she went to live in Nsawam where her new husband trades, leaving the patient in Kwahu with the maternal grandmother and great-aunts. The patient hates Kwahu and is always disobedient and argumentative there. She refuses to go to farm or to school and says she wants to go to her mother.

Schooling: She was put to school in Kwahu but always escaped and ran home before the first two or three lessons of the day were over. Later she refused to go at all, saying that something inside her wouldn't let her.

Present Illness (Patient's own account)

"My mother had come to Kwahu for a few days and we all had *kokonte* to eat in the morning. Afterwards my grandmother made me go with her to the latrine and carry for her a chamber-pot with medicine in it, and an enema syringe. When we got to the latrine she syringed herself behind, and then she wanted to syringe me. I didn't want it and I fought her but she forced me and I was very angry. I don't mind my mother syringing me but I didn't want my grandmother to do it. I was fighting all the way home and when we got home I found that I wanted to bite everybody except my mother. I couldn't stop biting and when I heard the sound of lorries I had to run out after them. I knocked over everybody's soup except my mother's. I couldn't help doing all this, so I knew that some bad thing had come to me and I was frightened. Then my mother took me to Tigari and made a prayer and promised Tigari a fowl if the biting stopped, but I couldn't stop. Then my mother took me with her to Nsawam, but when my aunt wanted to take me back to Kwahu without my mother I kept jumping out of the train and fighting and biting again and I couldn't stop. So I knew that something bad was given to me when I was syringed."

The patient said that she remembered clearly everything that had happened, but the mother and other witnesses, while corroborating the story, said that the child had been more violent than she had described and had talked "*basa-basa*". She was so wild that it was difficult to keep her in the lorry on the journey to the shrine, but she became quiet as soon as her head had been ritually shaven, and the "bad thing" taken away from her. I was not present when she made her confession at the shrine, but was told that she said her grandmother had given her an *obayi* in the syringe, that her band of witches played ball with a human head, that they met at a place where there were three mountains and she was their leader. She said it was she who had taken the babies out of her mother's womb and that she had planned to kill her grandmother.

First Interview

The patient is an exceedingly intelligent, lively, friendly child, not at all shy. She gave a ready and clear account of herself, at first quite calmly, but gathering heat as the tale proceeded and becoming anxious and restless and twisting her hands.

Asked how she slept at night, she said that she dreamt she was laughing and having fun with her father, playing ball with a lime-fruit. In another dream her father gave her a new dress and she put it under her pillow. She also dreamt that she and other children were sweeping out a yard in the dark.

When released from talking she began to play with a *wurri*-board by herself with tremendous speed and over-activity.

COMMENTARY

This behaviour disorder in an exceptionally intelligent, over-active child is an undoubted protest at separation from her mother. Her dreams seem to indicate that she also misses her divorced father. The episode of violence over which the patient felt herself to have no control, though possessing insight and consequent fear, was precipitated by an aggressive act on the part of the mother-substitute to whom the patient is hostile.

CASE 127. AMA P. of Nkyiraa, Ashanti. F. *c.* 6.

Shrine
Kotokro at Nkyiraa.

Reason for referral
Mentally disturbed at night.

Family History
Parents: Cross-cousins. Non-Christian, illiterate cocoa-farmers. No marital disharmony.

Siblings: Patient is the youngest of four, of whom two died. The other survivor is a boy about ten.

Personal History
Previous Health: Never ill before. She was fat and sturdy.

Household: Large household belonging to mother's maternal uncle. Both parents are there and various other married people and their children. Father's sister seems to be the patient's principal "mother". The owner of the house—an old man—gives the impression of a sour, selfish old tyrant, impatient with children.

Present Illness

About three months ago the patient had "strong fever" with "bitings" in the belly, loss of appetite, constipation, and some respiratory distress at first (worm pneumonia ?). She cried all night, shouted "*basabasa*" talk, and refused to lie down. The illness came and went many times. The patient was taken to various medicine-men, who eventually said that the *obosom* had laid hold of her. She was taken to the shrine, where the *obosom* confirmed that he had laid hold of her for witchcraft. Asked whether this was true, she said, "Yes". Asked the name of her *obayi*, she said she didn't know. Asked whether she had ever killed anyone, she said, "No", but added that she wanted to kill her elder brother and her mother's old uncle.

On examination

Very thin, feverish and peevish. Distended belly. Probably malaria and worms. Terrified of me (probably her first European), hid her face and shrieked.

Progress

The family were advised to take the patient to hospital—a procedure which people will resort to only after the supernatural causes of illness have been explored. Two months later, the patient was quite well and plump.

COMMENTARY

Febrile illness with delirium at night. The "confessions" are interesting in that the patient probably did entertain a childish "death-wish" towards the surly old great-uncle and the elder brother. The latter probably teased her, and both probably secured food which the patient coveted. Children's main grudge against their elders seems to be because of the much superior food which the latter eat.

CASE 128. AMA N. of Asamankese district, Akim. F. *c.* 11.

Shrine

Mframa at Mframaso.

Reason for Referral

Self-accusation of witchcraft.

Family History

Father: An illiterate, non-Christian cocoa-farmer.

Mother: An illiterate trader in enamel basins. She is a Christian.

Siblings: Four sisters, three brothers. The brothers are grown-up and are literate lorry-driver, agricultural foreman and farmer respectively. The eldest sister is eighteen and is pregnant. The younger sisters are eight and three.

Personal History

Home: The household consists of the mother, three small sisters, and two brothers. One brother lives elsewhere with his father. The parents and brothers drink at Mframa's shrine annually, though one is a Roman Catholic and the other a Methodist. The patient is washed with Mframa's holy water when they bring some home.

The patient says her father's three sisters do not like her and have worried her a lot. She says they also quarrel with her mother. (No grown-up would make such indiscreet revelations.)

Present Illness

About a month ago she felt pains all over her, but did not cry. At night when she lay down she felt people flinging her up into the air and dropping her down. She dreamt she saw people coming to kill her with a knife. She thought people were trying to make her into a witch and that she was responsible for her driver-brother's lorry accident at Christmas.

She was brought to Mframaso by her mother. The *obosom* confirmed that he had "caught" her for witchcraft, the *obayi* having been given her by malicious people. She was duly cleansed at the shrine.

Interview: 1.3.56

A wiry, lively, pleasant little girl, looking healthy and happy. She herself gave me the above account.

Commentary

I only saw her once, and that briefly, as she left Mframaso the day after I arrived. Her mother, when I talked to the child, had gone to Wenchi marketing. The patient no doubt had a short febrile illness (probably malaria) with some light-headed talk which alarmed the relatives, who communicated their alarm to the child.

CASE 129. YAA G. of Bekwai district, Ashanti. F. *c.* 10.

Shrine

Kyinaman, Bredi.

Reason for referral

Shouting in fear at night and crying by day, because witches are enticing her to become a witch.

Family History

Father: Non-Christian, illiterate cocoa-farmer. Well disposed.

Mother: Died about a year ago.

Siblings: There was only one other child, a year old when the mother died. It then went to the mother's sister and died four months later.

Personal History

While the mother was alive the patient lived with her, the father and another wife in the father's house and was happy. When the mother died the two children were sent to the mother's sister. (This is customary.) The patient missed her mother and says her aunt disliked her, scolding her all the time and making her often to cry. When the baby sister died the father visited the aunt and accused her, he says only of neglect, but probably also of killing the child by witchcraft. There were bitter recriminations and the father took the patient away to live with his other wife and her children. The patient says this woman likes her and is kind.

Present Illness

The father says that eight months ago, shortly after re-joining his household, the patient was often hot and feverish and shouted in fear at night, saying that witches were carrying her off. The patient says she often dreamt she was chased by cows and by people and found herself swimming in a big river. Often at night she dreamt that a woman stood over her calling her name and urging her, "Get up, and let's go." Sometimes when people chased her they caught her, tied her (as a baby is tied) on someone's back and took her away to the bush where they made a big fire and flung her in. At that point she always woke screaming in terror. She was taken to a medicine-man and recovered but about a week ago the trouble returned. The patient says she thinks the aunt who allowed the baby sister to die is a witch and has also made her (the patient) into one. (The aunt's traditional defence would be that the mother was killed in punishment for witchcraft, and that she bequeathed the witchcraft to the patient, who used it to kill the baby.) The patient says that all her playmates think the same and are afraid of her. When she wants to play with them they run away and leave her. Grown-ups are also afraid of her and shun her. The stepmother is kind and knows it is all the aunt's fault. Before this happened everybody else liked her.

Interview

Intelligent little girl. Shy and unhappy, but quite composed and a good, straightforward witness. Physically she seems in good condition with no active fever now.

COMMENTARY

Probably recurrent malaria whipping up fears implanted by traumatic events. The dreams and ideas are traditional in content.

Interview

XII

STABLE PERSONALITIES

We have already had occasion to suspect, in examining reactions to fear, that only people made especially vulnerable by dormant schizophrenia, temporary toxaemia or fever are likely to be spectacularly affected. For the edification of those inclined to suppose that all Africans are of equal instability, I append here a group of stable personalities, all with reason to believe themselves smitten by an outraged deity, yet preserving astonishing self-command.

CASE 130. AMA T. of Ahafo district, Ashanti. F. *c.* 50.

Shrine
   Kotokro at Nkyiraa.

Reason for referral
   Self-accusations of witchcraft.

Family and personal history
   No information except that she has ten grown-up children and numerous grandchildren, a husband still alive, and all kinsmen non-Christian, illiterate cocoa-farmers.

Present Illness
   Onset four months ago when she began to get thin and to sleep badly because of coughing and palpitations. Her feet swelled, she had pains all over and "burnings" in the belly and was unable to walk for weakness. She has been to several hospitals. At the last one she was an in-patient for a short time but was told that no more could be done for her. Only a few days ago she said she was a witch and dreamt that an *obosom* was standing over her.

Interview
   At the shrine she said she had made one of her sons a drunkard and another a pauper, had killed three of her kinsmen and resolved to kill

another, and had put a sickness into her brother's head and spoilt his crops by encouraging her fellow-witches to dance in his farm. She travelled to meetings on a crocodile. Her *obayi* abode in her belly, was covered with a net and looked like red clay. The *obosom* told her that he had "killed her already", but as she had confessed would do his best to restore her.

In her landlord's house she seemed far removed from the typical witch. She was not depressed and talked freely and pleasantly. Indeed, she seemed the nearest thing to a "spes phthisica" that I have ever seen. She was plainly extremely ill, grossly emaciated and dehydrated. Two surly sons—I think the drunkard and the pauper—broke up the interview by saying that the Europeans had had their chance to cure her and had failed and that the *obosom* had laid hold of her and would deal with her as she deserved.

COMMENTARY

Advanced pulmonary tuberculosis (checked up at Techiman Hospital). The key-personality in this case is the drunken son. The only people who openly accuse others of witchcraft are drunkards in their cups and a few other aggressive or paranoid ne'er-do-wells. The patient is a stable personality, quite willing to be of service in saving the face of her drunken son.

CASE 131. ABENA S. of Nkyiraa. F. *c.* 48.

Shrine

Kotokro, Nkyiraa.

Reason for referral

Physical illness resistant to physical treatment: presumed to be punishment for undisclosed sin.

Family History

Parents: Not cross-cousins. Non-Christian, illiterate cocoa-farmers. Mother died when the patient was a young woman.

Personal History

Childhood: N.a.d.

Marriage: Not cross-cousins. Husband a non-Christian, illiterate cocoa-farmer who died about seven years ago.

Work: Yam-farmer.

Children: Seven born, four survive. Some of these have their own children, one being about ten.

Household: Patient has lived in the same house all her life. The house is owned by the patient's grandmother (*sic*), a charming and vigorous old lady with perfect teeth, looking considerably younger than the patient. Of the grandmother's eight children, only four sons now survive. Most of her descendants live in her house and seem very happy under her wise and capable rule. She and the patient seemed on very happy terms.

Present Illness

Onset more than eight years ago, but she was able to do light work till three months ago. About two years ago she was an in-patient of a Mission hospital.

Interview

At the shrine she was told that she had done wrong and would die if she did not confess. She said she would go home and think about her wrong-doing. At interview she presented as an exceedingly sick woman, wasted, pale and weak, but, with cheerful fortitude, had not taken to her bed. She said she always slept well and had no bad dreams. She was not in the least depressed or frightened and accepted the *obosom's* dictum with casual composure and even humour. When I asked whether she had done anything wrong she said not that she knew of, but very likely the *obosom* knew of something that she did not: she gave a little laughing shrug and said she might have killed a few people without knowing it. When she next went to the *obosom*, she said, she would name all the dead kinsmen she could remember.

COMMENTARY

This case is recorded because of its unlikeness to the general run of witchcraft cases. The patient is not depressed, has no conviction of sin and does not come forward with voluntary self-accusations. The *obosom's* diagnosis that the illness was in punishment for sin implied that the sin was witchcraft on the grounds that everything else had been eliminated.

CASE 132. ABENA E. of Kwahu. F. *c.* 55.

Shrine
   Kyinaman at Bredi.

Reason for referral
   "Caught" by a physical illness, presumed punishment for witchcraft.

Family History

Parents: Not cross-cousins. Both long dead. They were non-Christian, illiterate farmers.

Siblings: Seven born, all grew up, but only two still survive.

Personal History

Childhood: N.a.d. Illiterate, non-Christian.

Marriage: Her first husband left her eight years ago after neglecting her for a number of younger wives. Her second husband left her forty days ago when she fell sick. He has two other wives.

Children: Two born, one son survives: he is a literate cocoa-grader and is under the protection of the *obosom*.

Katamenia: Menopause five years ago. Uneventful.

Present Illness

Onset four months ago. The patient's belly swelled up and she also found that a large hard thing had in some way been introduced into it. She went to *abisa* in her town and was told that the hard object was an *obayi* by virtue of which she had become an *obayifo*. The *obosom* had smitten her with illness for possessing this.

Interview

She was extremely ill and wasted, with a gross ascites. The "hard thing" in her belly was a much enlarged hard liver. Mentally she was in excellent condition, and clearly a very good personality. She was lying quietly smoking her pipe, she smiled pleasantly and talked freely without any depression. She said she had no idea how the *obayi* got into her belly and that she had never done any harm with it.

COMMENTARY

This is a stable personality, who refuses to be thrown into self-reproach by suggestions—indeed by, to her, concrete evidence—that she is guilty of witchcraft.

CASE 133. KWESI F. of Kwahu. M. *c.* 40.

Shrine

Mframa at Mframaso.

Reason for referral

"Caught" for wrong-doing.

Family and Personal History

No information except that the patient is a non-Christian, illiterate cocoa-farmer under the protection of Mframa.

Present Illness

A year ago the patient took a gift of rum to the chief of his town and asked approval for his proposal to implore a local *obosom* in Kwahu to kill a man who was unjustly attempting to deprive him of some land. The chief assented.

As the patient was under Mframa it was wrong to contrive another's death in any manner. No sooner had he made his resolve than he began to cough small amounts of blood. He postponed the aggressive act against his adversary but did not, in spite of the clear warning, abandon the idea. A few days ago he "vomited" a quantity of bright, frothy blood. He was startled and came straight to Mframa. Mframa fined him two cows and a sheep and he went home the next day.

Interview

This man was extremely ill, very gaunt and wasted with tachycardia and severe dyspnoea—undoubtedly in advanced tuberculosis. But he was cheerful and composed, had kept going and proposed to go back to work at once now that he had retrieved his error.

Commentary

This stable personality is described for contrast with those in frenzied guilt-and-fear psychosis. He had committed a grave offence against the *obosom*: he had dramatic evidence that he was mortally smitten for it, but he was not perturbed. He quietly set about putting matters right. Observe also that there was nothing schizoid in his manner of setting about the destruction of his adversary. He quite openly went to the chief and asked approval.

CASE 134. KWAME C. D. of Akim Aboakwa. M. *c.* 36.

Shrine

Mframa at Mframaso.

Reason for referral

"Caught" with a physical illness.

Family History

Parents: Not cross-cousins. Non-Christian, illiterate cocoa-farmers.
Mother's sister: Was "caught" by Tigari, vomited blood, became "*basa-basa*" but recovered.
Siblings: Two born, both alive and well.

Personal History

Schooling: Nil. Non-Christian.
Marriage: First wife died four years ago. Present wife is very young

Children: Five born, one died. Eldest is sixteen.
Home: He built the house himself. It contains only his wife.

Present Illness

The patient had a wounded and swollen foot and went to a Kramu. About a week ago he became ill with pains in his throat and jaws. He could not talk, swallow or sleep. He then remembered that he had promised Mframa a cow if he successfully avoided the acceptance of a family stool and its irksome responsibilities. He was duly successful but accepted a share in the associated stool land. On recalling this he came forthwith to confess to Mframa and make amends.

At the shrine he told his tale succinctly. The *obosom* told him that the Kramu had not given him the right medicine but had given him an evil *obayi* for which the *obosom* had caught hold of him.

On Examination

The patient was lying down looking extremely ill though quite rational. He seemed a very good personality. He could not open his jaw, his head was retracted and at short intervals his arms and legs stiffened and then relaxed. There was some respiratory distress. He had a septic wound in the foot.

Progress

Shrine ritual was performed promptly and the patient went home immediately. I urged him to go to hospital quickly: he probably did so, as no subsequent message arrived reporting his death.

COMMENTARY

This is a case of severe physical illness (almost certainly tetanus, of which I have seen several cases presenting similarly) interpreted as punishment for sin. The patient is an example of a good personality who did not become the prey of panic but, though extremely ill, handled the situation with cool-headed promptitude.

CASE 135. YAA B. of Bekwai district, Ashanti. F. *c.* 35.

Shrine

Mframa at Mframaso.

Reason for referral

Physical illness, attributed to offence against *obosom* law.

Family History

Sibling of Adwowa P. (See Adwowa P., Case No. 100.)

Personal History

Childhood: N.a.d. (See Adwowa P., Case No. 100.)

Marriage: Marriage broke up six years ago. Since then patient has consorted with many men.

Children: Six born, four survive. Youngest survivor less than one year old. Eldest about to finish school.

Present Illness

Began at the birth of her fourth child. She had pains all over and became thin and weak. Two years ago she came to the shrine complaining of feeling ill. The *obosom* told her that she was associating with too many men and should stick to one. She was given ritual treatment, felt better and went home. She failed to pay her shrine dues and did not return within a year to render thanks. When reminded of this by her mother she spoke slightingly of the *obosom*. A month ago she was "caught" with pains all over and "knockings" in her chest.

Interview: 17.7.57

Well built and plump, but looks grossly anaemic, pale and languid and is dyspnoeic. She said she often vomited worms. Not depressed or agitated: seems a self-confident, matter-of-fact, stable personality. No morbid self-accusations. Coolly admits her offence against the *obosom* and bases her belief in his displeasure on concrete evidence.

Progress

20.8.57. Declined European treatment. Looks no better. When she had been about a week in Mframaso with her mother, another sister brought Adwawo P. and various children.

COMMENTARY

Physical ill-health attributed to wrong-doing. No accompanying mental manifestations. This patient is in sharp contrast to many transgressors of *obosom* law in that she calmly kept her head and developed no fear-reactions. Not even her sister's death, taken by everyone as an example of the *obosom's* method of dealing with offenders, threw her off her perch.

CASE 136. YAA E. of Techiman district, Ashanti. F. *c.* 30.

Shrine

Mframa at Mframaso.

Reason for referral

Physical illness believed to be the result of wrong-doing.

Family History

Parents: Not cross-cousins. Non-Christian, illiterate cocoa-farmers.

Siblings: Ten born, two died. No one in the family has ever been "caught" by an *obosom* before. The sister who accompanied the patient was fat and healthy, but a suspicious, reticent witness.

Personal History

Childhood: N.a.d. The home was the father's house, built with cocoa-money.

Schooling: Nil. Non-Christian.

Marriage: She was married ten years ago to her cross-cousin. The husband is a store-keeper. The patient works with him in the store. He drinks, beats her and does not fulfil his maintenance obligations. He has recently taken a second and younger wife whom he supports mainly on the patient's earnings in the store.

Home: The patient lives with her husband at the store. The new wife is elsewhere.

Children: Eight born, three died, the youngest now two years old. The patient is now six months pregnant.

Present Illness

Onset three weeks ago with pain in ribs, coughing and fever. She went to hospital but refused to be an in-patient. After seven attendances as an out-patient she felt no better so concluded that the illness was punitive and began to have "*basa-basa*" dreams and sleeplessness.

Interview: 14.6.57

At the shrine she confessed that she had a bad mind against her husband, had cursed him to God, had resolved to leave him and had stolen from him money and cloth because he had failed to supply this. She was frail, pigeon-toed, and undersized. Pale, ill and in respiratory distress. Though frightened and anxious, she was not depressed, deluded or irrationally guilt-ridden, and retained a very good self-command.

Progress

No information. The patient gave a propitiatory sheep and left on the day of *abisa*.

COMMENTARY

Physical illness attributed to misdeeds which had in fact been committed. Mental state less disturbed than the circumstances would excuse.

XIII

CHRONIC SCHIZOPHRENIA

Introduction

It was no part of my plan when I first went to Ashanti to concern myself with chronic schizophrenia. I went to study the pilgrims at shrines. However, during the last few months of my stay the shrines suffered a slack spell. A drought had impoverished both cocoa-crops and food-crops and made money scarce. Also lorry fares had suddenly risen. For a time the stream of pilgrims almost dried up, so I decided to kill time in taking a look at these chronic schizophrenics who dwelt in the countryside around.

That these were numerous was obvious to the most casual tourist. Every time I drove to the post-office I drew up under a shade-tree beneath which sat a mute shaggy-haired madman, clad in ragged sacking and hatted with an enamel basin, beating a sardine tin rhythmically by the hour with a piece of iron. After some months he disappeared and later another madman took his place under the same tree, this one noisy, excited and often in some danger from traffic. Once he tried to wrench off my driving-mirror, but, failing, spat on it till his saliva gave out. In the market-place of the same town I often saw an unkempt woman, with a baby on her back, dancing, singing, laughing and shouting. A few miles away by the roadside was a bizarre house bristling with long spars of timber sticking out at all angles. I commented that it looked as if built by a madman and was told that this was indeed so and that the builder lived in it all alone. I called on him: he was friendly and gave me a gift of maize, but most of his maize-crop was lying in heaps of ashes inside his house, partially charred or consumed by innumerable fires which had been lit on every inch of the floor and poured their smoke through haphazard holes in the walls. Again, while taking an evening walk along bush paths around Mframaso I came upon a "village" consisting of one household and on entering it found a man and wife each preparing food. The man greeted me warmly, the woman sat with her face turned away and seemed to be a deaf-mute. I moved into

444

her line of vision and extended my hand. She took no notice: she was mad. Her husband told me later that he had taken her home to be cared for by her kinsfolk but she always ran away and returned to the village, where he had resigned himself to living alone with her. He said she had been a good wife before her illness, and as she was not a witch but mad "from God" it would have become him ill to abandon her.

It was clear that madness was common—commoner, most people thought, than in other districts. To find out exactly how common I sought the help of the chiefs and headmen of the various villages and country towns: these in turn put me in touch with those elders who were the heads of local kinship groups. To work in this way it was necessary not only that the chief should be friendly but that he should be in good accord with his elders. In towns with any uncooperative elders, I saw all the patients the other elders showed me and included them in figures relating to such matters as cross-cousin marriage, but I excluded them, and excluded their towns, from the figures pertaining to the number of patients per head of the population. I also excluded "strangers" such as the man in the crazy-looking house who was thought to be from the Northern Territories, the singing woman in the market who, they said, came from Mo on the distant Volta bank, and the two men outside the post-office who came from none knew where. The woman whom I found mutely preparing supper in her village was also excluded from the numerical survey, for she belonged to a disunited town, sections of which disregarded the chief's request for cooperation. Those who finally qualified for inclusion in my numerical survey were all, save one, so inconspicuous that I should not have found them without help.

A type of patient sometimes introduced to me by the kinsmen as "mad" was the epileptic. There were also two cases of late-treated trypanosomiasis, one of which I should certainly have taken for a schizophrenic had I not been told that she had been treated by the Trypanosomiasis Field Unit: she was in complete mental disintegration, rolling stark-naked in the dust. The other whom the Unit had treated was a youth—a peevish thief with a markedly paranoid attitude, but also with some stigmata of cranial nerve damage.

Excluded also from the survey were those patients who presented any possibility of differential diagnosis. Among illiterate people, schizophrenia simplex may simulate mental defect, though this difficulty arose less often than might be supposed. When it did arise it could usually be solved from the history. If the parents said, "He was a clever obedient boy till he became a youth and then he got indolent and heedless", one could infer schizophrenia, but if the mother said, "I took him to an *obosom* when he was about eight because he had not learned to talk", there was little doubt of mental defect. But there was one youth in Mframaso who baffled me. He had been sent to school, rather unsuitably in distant Accra, and also with a very late start. He made no progress and gave up. He came home, but though he did little or no work this may have been from a sense of superiority, for he wore scholarly shirts, was clean and had a knowing haircut. When he said he wanted to marry, his parents gave him £2 to "knock at the door" of the suggested bride's parents, but he frittered away the money and lost interest in the girl. When I had known him about a year he joined a gang of timber-workers. How long he would have stuck to this work none can tell, for he came to me after a week or two with a tendon-sheath infection and a distended palmar-space. Now, all sensible Africans know that an infected finger "can spoil your hand quicker than anything". The boy's mother fully appreciated this: she co-operated briskly when I said the youth needed in-patient hospital treatment and she sent him off. After three days he turned up again with a vague story, no evidence that he had ever been to hospital and his hand in a terrible state. This time I took him to hospital myself. There he made a good physical recovery, but the nursing-nuns thought him "a queer sort of boy". As I myself never felt quite certain of the nature of his queerness I did not include him in my schizophrenic survey. But whether schizophrenic or defective, he is an example of a personality who "gets by" in an illiterate society which has enough kinship solidarity to carry passengers, but would conspicuously fail in a society whose members must be self-reliant. His father was very much like him, but was notorious, not only for stupidity and indolence, but also for palm-wine addiction. His capacity for drink was poor and a thimbleful made him quarrelsome. His wife was a very good personality, endured him for years, but left him a few weeks before my departure from Ashanti. How father and son fared without her I do not know.

Another youth whom I could never assess lived in the same village with his mother but ate with and battened on his uncle. He was a strapping handsome youth of about twenty, seemingly intelligent, quite sociable, pleasant and obliging. He spent much time arranging his hair in front of a hand-mirror, and he sometimes painted his finger-nails with red varnish. He was said to have had quite normal illicit love-affairs but had no desire for a wife or any other responsibility. He started various jobs—

timber labourer, lorry-driver's mate, assistant to a prosperous medicine-man—but stuck at none for more than a few weeks. Everyone said he was lazy and useless, but he was unashamed and, without being vague or withdrawn, was quite unconcerned. He had not the limp self-pity of the usual "inadequate personality" nor the hardihood of the psychopath; neither was he probably a schizophrenic, but he was an incorrigible passenger.

It must be expected that universal literacy, when it comes to Ghana, will show up many simple schizophrenics of the kind hitherto concealed by the capacity of the traditional rural family to carry passengers. In our own society there has always been a proportion of good-for-nothings—tramps, work-shy, slum-makers, poachers and (abroad) beachcombers and "poor whites", unemotionally resisting all redemptive effort or, if they accept it, always shambling back to their old ways. It is now recognised that most of them are either mentally defective or schizophrenic. In the East (I do not know the East) I suppose their counterparts become beggars. In West Africa they stay with their kinsmen, drink palm-wine and trap "bush-meat".

Assessment of the Circumstances of Onset of Chronic Schizophrenia

The age of an illiterate African always brings in guesswork and inference drawn from such facts as the number and size of his children, grandchildren or siblings. It is more difficult still to decide how old he was at the time of an illness an unknown number of years past, unless one is given some such clue as "His eldest daughter was then beginning to toddle and has now just reached the menarche".

Nor is it always easy to assess the pre-morbid personality, for people dislike speaking ill of others. But often a single remark gives a picture in bold relief. "He never played with other boys but used to trap rats and eat them by himself." "He always liked to go and stay for a long time in a forest hut all alone and no one knew what he ate." "He never did any work and never listened when you talked to him." "She was always so shy that she dared not look at your face and then suddenly she became bold and hit her mother."

Most difficult of all is to glean from the relatives' history whether the onset described by them as sudden was really so, though occasionally they give a clear picture of suddenness. For instance, "She liked to play and loved everyone and was going to be married. She worked hard and earned money and bought a sewing-machine and then one day she went to farm and didn't come back and when we went to look for her we found her mad." More often, however, further questioning elicits clear evidence that a reputedly acute onset was insidious. A man who had been "very clever" came out of the Army in his twenties and married shortly after. He had learnt lorry-driving in the Army and wanted his father to buy him a lorry. His discharge gratuity, however, was not forthcoming, for he had lost his "discharge book". He then decided to be a teacher and went to a training course, but after four months was dismissed as unsatisfactory. It was not till he had completed a long spell of loafing and drinking that he became "suddenly mad" and was sent to the Trypanosomiasis Unit and, after negative findings there, to Kumasi for further physical investigations, presumably to check up on syphilis.

Again, a young man whose parents said his illness began suddenly had a history of attending school in boyhood. There he had never cared for football or mixing with other boys, and in his penultimate school year said he did not want to continue school. He obtained a job as Native Court Bailiff, but dropped it and reverted to farming. He never married, nor desired to marry. In his thirties he became frankly mad and "*basa-basa*", accused people of poisoning his drinking-water and stealing his money and was found to have made secret bad medicines against his supposed enemies. He still does some farm-work but has episodes of standing motionless and mute under a tree and phases of refusing food. I found him in a highly indignant, incoherent mood. There can be no doubt that though his friends say he became mad four years ago as the result of making bad medicines, his illness would, in our own society, have been regarded as setting in gradually before he left school, and it is unlikely that he would ever have been regarded as employable.

A further example of an assessment different from our own was provided by the kinsfolk of a mad woman who regarded her as the victim of bad medicine. At the age of puberty she became sexually promiscuous but never remembered what sleeping appointments she had made. Indignant customers who had paid in advance came and complained to her family that she had accepted their money but failed in her commitments. When taxed with this she always giggled fatuously. She was duly given in marriage to a palm-wine tapper—a singularly lowly marriage for an elder's daughter—but he complained that she never did any work. After a year's marriage she became suddenly worse, talked "*basa-basa*" and committed various bizarre acts. Her family concluded that bad medicine had been made—very reasonably, they thought—

against her by some resentful man whose money she had fraudulently accepted.

Incidence of Chronic Schizophrenia

Omitting uncooperative towns and the patients in them (though these patients appear in other connections), I found forty-one chronic schizophrenics in twelve Ashanti country-towns and villages, representing a population estimated by the 1948 census at 4,283.*

Male Chronic Schizophrenics: Summary

Total number in Survey	26
Cross-cousin parents	8
Schizophrenic near-relative (sibling, parent or first cousin)	8
Patient married to cross-cousin or inherited partner	3
Pre-morbid personality regarded as unsatisfactory (never worked, etc.)	10
Literate (completed school)	2
Semi-literate (abandoned school against kinsmen's wishes)	4
Christian	11
Farmers	22
Other occupations (teacher, illiterate contractor, weaver, storekeeper)	4
Paranoid features	12
Bad medicine-making confirmed at onset	4

Situation at onset

Insidious onset in teens (one had acute exacerbation in thirties, one in fifties)	9
Acute onset about twenty	9
Acute onset in twenties (one after Army)	2
Insidious onset in twenties (one after Army)	2
Gradual onset in thirties	2
Sudden onset in thirties	1
Sudden onset about sixty	1

Marital situation

Never married	11
Married and fertile before illness	15
Marriage continued after illness	4
Widowed or separated before illness	0

* In Europe and America the expectation of schizophrenia in the general population is usually estimated at about 0.8%.

Ages at Present

About 20	6
20–30	6
30–40	9
40–50	2
50–60	1
60–65	2

Female Chronic Schizophrenics: Summary

Total number in Survey	24
Cross-cousin parents	10
Schizophrenic near relative (sibling, parent, or first cousin)	5
Patient married to cross-cousin	5
Pre-morbid personality regarded as unsatisfactory (indolent, solitary, shy, silent, promiscuous, quarrelsome)	8
Literate	Nil
Christian	3
Depressive onset with weeping and self-accusations of witchcraft	11
Paranoid features now	4
Bad-medicine making confirmed at onset	3

Situation at onset

Teens (including two at menarche precisely)	5
Puerperium	8
Twenties	2
Thirties	2
Involutional	7

Marital Situation

Never married	3
Married and fertile before onset	17
Marriage ended at onset	15
Promiscuously fertile	6
Children all died	1
"One-child sterility"	1
Not fertile though married	1
Widowed or separated before onset	6

Ages at Present

Below 20	2
About 20	1
20–30	4
30–40	4
40–50	3
50–60	10

Differences between Men and Women Chronic Schizophrenics

Though it would be unsound to generalise from fifty Ashanti cases, one is struck by several marked differences between the male and female groups.

Though pre-morbid schizoid personalities seem to exist equally in the two groups, a noticeable type among the males is the young man who appears quite normal till the age of about twenty. He is industrious, sociable and married: then suddenly he becomes floridly schizophrenic. There is no clear-cut female counterpart of this group, nor does it appear to be masked by a puerperal onset, for the puerperium, whatever its endocrine significance, often seems to be the precipitating stress upon young women plainly destined for schizophrenia. Out of the eight puerperal cases recorded, two had cross-cousin parents, one a family history of schizophrenia, one had always been loudly quarrelsome, abusive and antisocial, while three were markedly schizoid and withdrawn.

Most striking of all is the delayed onset, shown by almost one-third of the women, till the involutional years: among the males, all but four out of the total twenty-five cases had developed before the age of thirty.

Among the girls there were two cases of sudden onset precisely at the first menstrual period. I incline to regard such an onset as precipitated by social rather than endocrine stress. (I had already met such a case among the acute schizophrenics: the girl babbled a good deal about giving birth to babies.) There is always social fuss and excitement at the menarche and plans are immediately discussed for the girl's marriage. There is feasting in the household, and the new-created woman, clad in grand clothes and borrowed gold ornaments, is led through the town in procession with drumming and singing. I once saw a little girl of about six, with her hair studded with wild flowers, sailing haughtily along the street followed by a band of other little girls: on inquiry I learnt that they were playing make-believe that the flower-decked child had begun to menstruate. That the social stress of marriage can precipitate frank schizophrenia I had already learnt at a shrine where I saw a girl of the lumpish, sluggish type recovering from an illness of three years' duration. She was well into the twenties, but had always expressed distaste for marriage: this was at last overruled and she was given to a suitable partner. She at once became *"basa-basa"*, wild and shouting, ran to bush and was mad for three years.

Not only do the male and female age-groups differ in size, but they have different tendencies in clinical features. More than half the males are markedly paranoid and complain that the police are after them, that people have stolen their money, are trying to kill them, have poisoned their drinking-water or prevented them from becoming rich and great. Out of eleven Christians, one thought that he was Jesus Christ and two that God had called them to be great preachers. Among the women, on the other hand, the illness is most often schizo-affective and strongly depressive and is ushered in by delusions of guilt and unworthiness and self-accusations of witchcraft. In general terms, the women are prone to think themselves the source of their own and the world's hapless plight, the men to think themselves the virtuous victims of external evil. The men project: the women introject. It is furthermore my impression that until the disease has destroyed all mental organisation the patient's psychotic delusions are all of a piece with his pre-morbid personality.*

Relation between Literacy and Chronic Schizophrenia

It would be wholly unsound to seek any relationship between literacy and chronic schizophrenia in the small rural area which I studied. I have no literacy figures for the general population *in that area*. Most of the schools were new and most of the older patients had had no opportunity of literacy.

Of the total of five male literate patients, two had cross-cousin parents and one of these had also a schizophrenic family history. These two were thus probably predestined for schizophrenia, literate or not. Two other literates had always been schizoid, had never taken a normal part in school life and failed to complete their schooling: they also would probably have become schizophrenic in any circumstances.

Among women patients there were no literates at all: in only a few places could any of their *contemporary* townswomen have been literate either. Only one woman patient had been married to a literate (a store-keeper) but she had never lived anywhere but with her own kinsmen in a traditional household.

It seems therefore that my figure for chronic schizophrenia may with reasonable fairness be regarded as applying to an *illiterate* rural Ashanti population practising cross-cousin marriage. How far this applies to other parts of Ashanti I do not know. As for non-Ashanti parts of

---

* I should not be surprised to find that among the Trans-Volta Ewe tribes the distribution of paranoid and depressive traits reverses the Ashanti distribution, for the Ewes are a very different breed. The typical rural Ewe male, unlike the Akan, has a long, bony, melancholy, reflective face and a slow, but tenacious disposition. The women tend to be of the complementary type—quick, resourceful and unabashed.

Ghana, it is likely that the situation is much less gloomy. I think I could count on one hand the number of madmen I have met over the years elsewhere, with the exception of a group of grossly dilapidated schizophrenics in a medicine-man's village on the Ankobra River in the Western Province.

As has been said in connection with acute schizophrenia, literate schizophrenics are more conspicuous than illiterate, but not necessarily more numerous. From all directions this impression is reinforced. For instance, I know two schizophrenic brothers, one an illiterate farmer and trapper, the other a literate teacher. The first is withdrawing, gradually and unobtrusively, into mental disintegration. The active literate is fighting off, with courage, insight and suffering, repeated acute attacks, apparently precipitated by the stresses of his literate circumstances. Whether the ultimate state of the one will differ much from that of the other can as yet only be guessed.

Home Background at the Onset of Illness

Of the male patients, all except the teacher, who was with his wife in another country-town, and a youth who was with a group of other youths working as seasonal cocoa-labourers away from home, were living, at the onset of illness, with their own kinsmen in the traditional type of compound. The women similarly were all in their ancestral homes, except one who was with her trader-husband and his other wives in a distant town.

Occupation at the Onset of Illness

With the exception of one teacher, one illiterate contractor, one literate store-keeper and one bailiff at the Chief's Court, all the patients were doing traditional jobs at the time when they fell sick, except one who had been in the Army and was doing nothing. Another who had been in the Army had returned to farming. Both these ex-soldiers had "learnt to drink" in the Army, and the literate non-farmer had certainly undergone additional deterioration before his discharge.

Rural Care of Chronic Schizophrenics

The majority of chronic schizophrenics in rural districts are treated with such patient and sustained kindness by their relatives and tolerance by their neighbours that the prognosis for their recovery is probably better than it would be were they herded with other patients in under-staffed mental hospitals. If they have phases of destructive violence or of wandering off into the bush they are usually either locked up or fettered to a log during these phases but are released at the earliest moment. It is only when they refuse food and drink that hospital could do anything for them that is not better done at home.*

The younger schizophrenics are always cared for by their parents, the mothers especially displaying impressively uncomplaining devotion. After the parents' death the brothers and sisters take over. The husbands of schizophrenic women usually abandon the marriage early, generally in the belief that the illness is retribution for witchcraft. The wife of a schizophrenic husband is more often inclined to stay with and care for him, an impulse encouraged by his family but not by hers.

Case Recording

Though I recorded all the histories in equal detail I have space here for only a few sample cases.

CASE 137. KWAME M. of Wenchi district. M. *c*. 60.

Family History

Parents: The parents were not cross-cousins. Both are long dead and were non-Christian, illiterate cocoa-farmers.

Siblings: The patient is one of nine siblings, of whom four survived infancy. All grow cocoa except the patient, are non-Christian illiterates, and are sensible.

Personal History

During his teens he became restless and disobedient and would not go to farm. He has never done any work except for a very short time in the Escort Police, from which job he was soon dismissed. He has spent most of his life wandering to distant places such as the Northern Territories and Manya Krobo, taking short jobs as a sawyer, trader, labourer. He never married in the normal way. A brother's widow was assigned to him, by family council, but he took little notice of her and had no children. He came home a few years ago, but except for failing eyesight he seemed to his kinsmen not to have changed.

History of Illness

Two years ago he suddenly sent for the brother in whose house he was living and who was temporarily absent in a neighbouring town. The brother found him sick and his eyesight much worse. He recovered physically, though his eyesight did not improve and he became quickly mad. He shouted all night that he had killed all sorts of people and would

* There is no insulin unit in Ghana (1957).

kill more, and accused his brother of arranging for a gang to come and kill him.

He went to various shrines without avail and then came home again, since when he has refused to emerge from his room, and if approached or addressed shouts abuse, though he never offers physical violence.

Interview

He was in the dark in his room but was persuaded to come out, where he sat interrupting everyone's conversation with indignant shouting, "You're lying! You all hate me. All the people beat me and tread on me...." At intervals he consented to converse and revealed himself as not demented. He did arithmetical, geographical and general knowledge tests very well and gave a good account of his work and travels except that it was embellished with such grandiose boasts as that of taking all his meals with the paramount chief. He was particularly offended with his brother—who has in fact looked after him with great patience and kindness. "My elder brother has killed all my children and thrown them away. I am the *omanhene* [paramount chief] but my brother has ordered everyone to kill my children and take out my eyes and come and kill me. They want to take my eyes to make bad medicine. They are all saying things against me because I am head of this town." Though his talk is threatening in content it is often accompanied by a smiling, genial manner.

COMMENTARY

Senile exacerbation of a lifelong sub-clinical schizophrenia. In an advanced community this man could probably never have been acceptable.

CASE 138. KWESI S. of Techiman district. M. *c.* 25.

Family History

Parents are not cross-cousins. They are both alive and are non-Christian, illiterate cocoa-farmers. The father left the mother ten years ago. The latter is a good personality. The patient is the eldest of eight, of whom three died in infancy.

Personal History

A non-Christian, illiterate cocoa-farmer. The cocoa died and he took to yam market-gardening. He is still a good farmer. He has never married or shown any interest in women.

History of Illness

The onset was in his teens. He began weeping and wandering about, sometimes hitting people, saying that they were putting things into his head and making him sick. He was taken to hospital, whence he was referred to the trypanosomiasis unit, with a negative result.

He still insists that people are making him sick, that they want to kill him, have made him blind, broken all his bones and committed various other outrages. He says he had a lot of money till people stole it. Sometimes he shouts abuse at people, but witnesses do not think he is ever hallucinated. He will never eat except in solitude. He never washes or tidies himself, but is not dirty in the matter of excretions. He is very solitary, often going off to a forest camp alone. He drinks sometimes and becomes very disorderly on a very small amount. He does some farming and palm-wine tapping erratically but with fair competence.

Interview

Though I visited his home several times, he had always gone off alone, but I did once get within greeting distance of him on the way to his farm. He was ragged, dirty and unbarbered, and did not respond to my greeting.

COMMENTARY

Schizophrenia with a slight paranoid colouring, beginning at adolescence and, in the primitive rural circumstances, permitting some degree of social usefulness.

CASE 139. KODZO D. of Techiman district. M. *c.* 25.

Family History

Parents: Cross-cousins, alive and well. They are non-Christian, illiterate cocoa-farmers.

Siblings: Six siblings were born, four survived, the patient being the only son.

Personal History

He had no schooling but was clever and learnt to read the vernacular. He became a devout Roman Catholic. He disliked farming, but became a weaver and was a skilled hard worker. He has never shown any interest in women or marriage.

History of Illness

No one noticed anything wrong with him till one day two years ago when he became feverish and ill. He was taken to hospital and treated, but after he was discharged became "very wild" and tried to run to the bush. He recovered from the wildness and settled down into good behaviour, but has done no work since. He spends whole days praying under a tree and reading his vernacular Bible aloud, or he takes his flute to Techiman, saying that he is going to play in a football match. He spends much time beautifying and tending his room, which he has fitted up as a chapel.

Interview

The patient looked physically very well. He was a well-favoured, slight, gentle-mannered, smiling person, pleased to talk and exhibit his room. He wore a neat little beard and was dressed in a topi to which he had given an ecclesiastical aspect by covering it neatly in black paper with silver decorations. He carried a prayer-book and several rosaries. He was meticulously clean. His shirt had a teacup-sized round hole, neatly edged with button-hole stitching, in both back and front, which he said was to let in the air. A green lace curtain with a crucifix device was hung in front of the door of his room. When asked if he would show me his room he unlocked it and took me in. It was spotlessly neat, containing his own sleeping-mat as the only everyday chattel, but four crucifixes set around with elaborate embellishments and jars of fresh flowers.

I asked him whether he ever heard voices which other people could not hear: he replied yes, and said that they always told him that he was Jesus Christ.

COMMENTARY

Schizophrenia with delusions of grandeur in a thwarted would-be literate, socially tolerable and even agreeable, but not able to earn any part of his keep.

CASE 140. KWAME K. of Techiman district. M. *c.* 45.

Family History

Parents: Cross-cousins. Illiterate, non-Christian cocoa-farmers.

Many women relatives have been "caught", with misery, weeping and inability to work, have confessed to witchcraft and been cured by the *obosom*.

Nine siblings were born, four died. The patient is the only son.

Personal History

He had no schooling, but became a Christian.

He has two wives, neither a cross-cousin. Thirteen children were born, of whom nine died.

His work is farming and he is a town elder.

History of Illness (from patient and other relations)

The onset was sudden, about thirteen years ago. The patient heard shoutings in his ears, "Hoo hoo!" and heard people saying, "Let's go and kill him! To-day we have caught him." The voices prevented him from sleeping and he ran to the bush in fear. He was brought back talking "*basa-basa*" and after a few months recovered.

Since then he has had several more attacks, but none so severe as the first, as he has learnt that the voices only threaten but no harm comes to him. He has never seen the owners of the voices. He is always to some extent hallucinated at night but has become accustomed to it. When acute attacks are imminent he sits huddled and mostly silent, but sometimes asks his friends to give him protection. Between attacks he does his work, lives a normal life and is respected.

Interview

A pleasant, friendly man of good insight on the whole. He refers to his condition as "this sickness". He told me that he was hearing voices on the day of the interview, but he knew they were not real and they were not interfering with his work. The voices invariably utter threats. When asked what he thought was the cause of the illness he said that some of his kinsmen must have sent it because they envied him and resented his possession of cocoa, his position as an elder and his success in life. He uttered these sentiments in a pleasant, casual and unaggressive fashion.

COMMENTARY

Schizophrenia of paranoid colouring, arising in middle life, in a good personality who handles the disability with insight and courage.

CASE 141. AMA E. of Techiman district. F. *c.* 27.

Family History

Parents: Cross-cousins. Non-Christian, illiterate cocoa-farmers. The mother is dead. The father is alive and is a town elder, though blind.

Siblings: Nine born, five died in early childhood. The survivors are all normal.

Personal History

No schooling. She was hard-working and well liked before her illness. She married at the normal age but her husband left her when she became mad.

History of Illness

Six years ago the patient bore her first and only child. The birth was difficult; she was six days in labour and she started to talk "*basa-basa*" as soon as it was over.

She has not changed since. She is never violent, abusive or unmanageable, but she walks from town to town and stays away from home for periods lasting from two weeks to six months. She weeps and laughs without cause, is heard talking to non-existent people and seems to hear them talking. Sometimes she sits for days without moving or speaking and sometimes goes for as long as twenty days without washing.

Interview

I never had an interview with this patient, though I saw her several times walking the roads and recognised from her unkempt appearance and heedless manner that she was mad. On the occasions when I called on her family no one knew where she had gone.

COMMENTARY

Schizophrenia of onset in the puerperium in a previously good personality.

CASE 142. ADWOWA J. of Techiman district. F. *c.* 27.

Family History

Parents: Not cross-cousins. Non-Christian, illiterate cocoa-farmers.

Siblings: The patient is the youngest of six, of whom three died in childhood. One older brother is an elder, another a headman; both are very good personalities.

Personal History

The patient is a non-Christian illiterate. She has never married, but has had three children by unknown fathers. The youngest is three weeks, the eldest seven years: one died.

History of Illness

The onset was during the patient's first menstrual period. She had gone to the stream to fetch water, and on the way back flung it down and ran away to the bush. She was brought back, wept a great deal and never recovered, though the illness has exacerbations from time to time. She laughs and cries without cause, reviles people and hits them. Sometimes she refuses either to speak or eat or wash for several days. She defaecates anywhere, indoors or out. She talks and listens to invisible people. Sometimes she does a little work on the farm and in the home.

Interview

She was sitting over an empty fireplace, doing nothing. She shook hands, but would not speak, and then fell into smiling, posturing and scowling.

COMMENTARY

Schizophrenia setting in at puberty accompanied by affective symptoms.

CASE 143. EKWIA J. of Techiman district. F. *c.* 17.

Family History

The parents are not cross-cousins and are non-Christian, illiterate cocoa-farmers. The mother was seen: a very good personality caring for the patient assiduously and kindly.

Siblings: The patient is one of three, of whom an older brother, a literate who reached Standard III, died "of the same sickness" about two years ago. He had been ill about a year, and so far as I can discover was about twenty when the illness attacked him.

First cousin: The mother has a brother whose son (whom I saw) became mad at the age of about twenty.

History of Illness

The patient became ill four days after her brother's death. She had been a good worker and well liked. She had joined a Christian Church, had just become apprenticed to sewing-machine work, and was going to be married. The onset was sudden: she took off all her clothes and ran off to the bush and had to be sought.

Since then she has been alternately violent and mutely inert. When unmanageable she is locked up. At times she cries and sings, laughs and smiles, and talks to invisible people.

Interview

She was fat and lumpy, but clean and very well cared for. She was sitting on a stool in the yard, with her feet shackled together so that she could shuffle around but not run off to the bush. She was mute, but transiently accessible and would then carry out simple orders. She got up at intervals and moved vaguely round with an inappropriate smile.

COMMENTARY

The interest of this case is the family history and the fact that the young brother died. Probably many such patients die who with skilled care would live and raise the chronic schizophrenia figures to yet higher levels.

CASE 144. KWABENA N. of Tainso district. M. *c.* 65.

Family History

Parents: Cross-cousins. Non-Christian, illiterate cocoa-farmers.

Siblings: The patient is one of five siblings, of whom two survive.

The patient's elder brother is a good personality and still works hard on his farm.

Personal History

The patient is a non-Christian, illiterate. Before his illness he was a cocoa-farmer. He was hard-working and was a town elder. He married his cross-cousin and had ten children, of whom five died.

History of Illness

The onset was sudden, six years ago, without any fever or other physical illness. One morning he got up and knocked a door off its hinges with a stick, and then drove his wife off, saying that she was an adulteress. He also said that people had "caught" one of his daughters and killed her.

Since then his behaviour has fluctuated but has never been normal and he has done no work. When at his best his intelligence is good and keen, with no signs of failing memory, absent-mindedness or other senile deterioration. He never talks "*basa-basa*" but says things that are untrue and unreasonable and is much preoccupied with adultery. He accuses his brother of adultery with his wife and with a great many other people. At times he does not sleep at night but walks about shouting that people want to kill him because they covet the big house he has built. Sometimes he has indignant conversations with non-existent people and accuses them of seducing his wife.

Since the illness started he has run away to the bush four times and on one occasion stayed there three days. About a year ago he seized a cutlass and attacked his nephew and various people who went to the latter's help and was taken to court, where he appeared mentally responsible and was sent to prison for three weeks. Three weeks ago he ran away to another village and when brought home said he was being treated like a slave.

Interview

He was suspicious and surly and asked his brother why he was bringing a stranger into his house. He consented to answer a few questions, though reluctantly. I did not get any impression of general dementia.

COMMENTARY

Though arteriosclerosis has to be considered, the florid and fluctuating nature of the behaviour and the absence of general dementia point to an involutional paranoid schizophrenia.

CASE 145. ABENA O. of Wenchi district. F. *c.* 55.

Family History

Parents: Cross-cousins. They have been dead a long time. Nothing much is remembered about them except that they were illiterate, non-Christian rubber-farmers.

Siblings: There were seven siblings, who all grew up and are all normal so far as I could discover, but my informant, the patient's younger brother, was very reticent.

Personal History

The patient was an illiterate, non-Christian yam-farmer. She went with the man she married for eight years to the French Ivory Coast. He is still there, but has two other wives in Wa in the Northern Territories. There were six children, all alive, the youngest about fifteen. The sons are all literate. The patient's previous personality is said to have been pleasant and "playful", but very bustling, with much sweeping, cleaning and washing which still persists.

History of Illness

The onset was about three years ago. The informant is reticent, but it is clear that the patient was quarrelsome and violent, and though still quarrelsome is considerably quieter. She occasionally beats her younger brother, abuses everyone loudly and walks out of the house, planting herself in some other relative's house. She never stays anywhere very long, but while there she vigorously cleans and sweeps the house and berates the occupants. She takes dislikes to people and will not speak to them: she stayed with her brother recently for a month without addressing him a word, but told another relative that he was the one who was killing her and had taken all her property. She says she is a friend of the District Commissioner and would be a very big woman if people had not deprived her of her rights.

Interview

She was thin but looked healthy and was full of physical activity. She talked volubly and indignantly, saying that people always stole from her and had left her nothing. People, she said, were all jealous of her because she had had so many lovers. Her enemies, she declared, tampered with her drinking water, putting into it poison, ink, urine and all sorts of dirty things so that she had to throw it away.

She was correctly orientated and fully accessible but lacked the well-preserved personality that characterises many paranoid schizophrenics. She rambled off into a long, disorganised story about stolen property and other grievances, all told with inappropriate smiling and giggling and sometimes a little clapping and singing. "People have taken all my land. One day when I was in the French Ivory Coast I was sitting down and a big lizard fell on me, and someone gave me some *kenkey* to eat and that put something bad into my head, and now I have something like a heavy load on my head, and burnings like fire and something like a rope tied round my head."

I met her on several other occasions by chance. Though her talk always suggested that she was in a high dudgeon, her behaviour was mostly kindly. She looked after children, carried them round the town on her back and treated them affectionately. Her relations were waiting for her to take umbrage, as was her wont, and march off to some other kinsman.

COMMENTARY

This is one of the rare cases of paranoid schizophrenia in an Ashanti woman.

CASE 146. YAA S. of Techiman district. F. *c.* 55.

Family History

Parents: Cross-cousins. Non-Christian, illiterate kola-nut growers.
Siblings: "Many" siblings were born, but all died except the patient.

Personal History

Non-Christian, illiterate market-gardener—ground-nuts, etc. She has always been a good worker. Marriage was normal. Her husband died "a long time ago" and she did not remarry. She bore seven children, of whom five survived and have children of their own.

History of Illness

Onset eight years ago at the menopause. She said that the *obosom* Senyon Kupo had "caught" her for witchcraft. She cried a great deal and said she had done all sorts of wrong and killed innumerable people. She could not sleep, was restless and ran to the bush. Her agitation increased till she became impulsive and aggressive and was locked up. After some months she settled down into her present condition, which is one of social adequacy with episodes of "*basa-basa*" talk and withdrawn unsociability, when she goes off and sleeps in the bush.

Interview

She was in a good phase and had just come back from her farm. She was over-talkative, shallow, laughing, bustling and clattering. When asked how she was, she replied airily that she was *mad*. Asked why she thought so, she said, "It comes and goes, and people tell me afterwards I have been *"basa-basa"*. It occurred to me that she might be amanic-depressive, but her affect was shallow without any warmth.

COMMENTARY

Pre-senile schizophrenia beginning as an affective illness at the menopause.

INDEX

(A) *General,* (B) *Reference to Case Histories*

(A) *General*

Aaron, 81n

Abenase, 89

Abihu, 81n

Abijan, 52

Abisa, term explained, 17; analysis or routine, 105–6; miscellaneous, 132–133; priest's induction of dissociation before routine, 59; mentions of (*not including those in case histories*), 28, 50, 67, 68, 70, 72, 74, 80, 93, 95, 96, 100, 101, 102, 103, 105, 131

Abodo (fairies), 44

Aboetia (plural *Mmoetia*—fairies), 17, 44, 44n, 45, 46; *see Mmoetia*

Abonsam (devils), 380

Abreactive techniques, 11, 14; *see Amytal*

Accra, 32, 33, 48, 125, 199, 255, 257, 333, 338, 374, 375, 430, 446; 1937 food survey in, 33n; Mental Hospital at, 212, 358, 396

Acharontica Spiritus ("Sixth and Seventh Book of Moses"), 42

Achimota, 33n

Adangme, 24, 25; cocoa-farming of, 29; fairy lore from, 44; good-quality food of, 34. *See also* Ga

Addae festivals, 103

Adope (fairies), 44

Adunsini (medicine-man), 41, 93, 363, 394

Afahye festivals, 330

Ageing, depression associated with, 187–200

Agogo: district, 221, 301, 357; Mission Hospital, 15

Ahafo district, 216, 415, 436

Ahulu (fairies), 44

Akan, 14 seqq.; definition of, 17; matrilineal rule of, 24

Akim (people and district), 17, 33, 60, 65, 91, 214, 289, 304, 312, 392, 401; Akim Aboakwa, 198, 289,

440; Akim Kade, 291, *see* Kade; Akim Kotoku, 75n, 89; cocoa virus - disease affecting, 110; Adangme and Akwapim ousting of, 24n, 29, *see also* Akwapim

Akom (dancing), 60, 72, 222; *akom* work, 97; *akomfo, see Okomfo*

Akonodi (an *obosom*), 394

Akotia (fairies), 44

Akpeteshi (illicitly distilled spirit), 74, 165

Akrofrom district, 170, 234, 243

Akropong, 254

Akrowa, akura (village) 23

Akuroma river, 184

Akwapim (migrant farmers, with Adangme), 17, 24, 24n, 29, 33, 34, 90, 112, 125, 171, 172, 189, 248, 254, 259, 288, 293, 307, 321, 322, 324, 335, 336, 337, 338, 340, 363, 364, 392 (people and district)

Akwatia, 261

Akyeame (spokesmen at shrine), 94

Akyima ceremony, 70, 100

Alcohol: dissociation induced by, 60; alcoholism, 165; *and see* Drunkards

Alvarez: *The Little Strokes,* 360n, 370

Amenorrhoea, and "pregnancy not growing" complaint, 106, 126, 150

Amnesia, in "possession", 57

Amoma village, 228

Amytal and methedrine abreactions, 184, 256, 270, 339, 372, 388, 391, 397, 419–21

Anatomy of Villainy, The (Balchin), 39n

Ancestral households, three systems of, 24–5

Animal totemism, possible origin of, 317–18

Anituel, Ariel, Aziel ("Sixth and Seventh Book of Moses"), 42

Ankobra river, 453

Anoch ("Sixth and Seventh Book of Moses"), 41

465

Index

Nyamabekyere, 396, 397
Nyongmo Tsaweh—Jahweh connection, 48
Nzima, 208; people of, 17

Obayi (evil entity inhabiting obayifo), 18, 35, 36, 37, 117, 130, 158, 159, 178, 182, 184, 185, 187, 193, 194, 213, 215, 225, 227, 230, 239, 240, 288, 289, 290, 323, 346, 367, 372, 375, 376, 377, 379, 380, 431, 432, 433, 437, 439, 441; Kyim as vehicle of, 132; named, 161, 238, 262, 342, 372, 408, 410, 416; obayifo (witch), 18, 35, 236
Obo (ancient deity), 64n; Obo Kofi: spirit on a rock, 64
Obofohene, 18, 69, 72, 73, 92, 93, 419, 424
Obosom (deity, son and deputy of Onyame), 18, 41, 46, 51, 52, 59, 60, 63, 74, 92, 93, 96, 99, 104, 114, 117, and in case histories, 149 seqq., passim; stern ethical demands of, compared with Christian leniency, 50
Obosom-brafo, 18, 63, 66, 71, 88, 89, 90, 91, 103, 104, 364
Obosomfo, 17, 53, 63, 64, 73, 102, 183 191
Obrafohene (chief executive officer at shrine), 17, 69, 72, 96, 97, 99, 100, 101, 120, 208, 232, 241, 355
Obrafoso (grove), 62, 67, 95
Obsessive-compulsive illness, 19; cases 114 to 116, 399–406; rarity of among Africans, 383, 399
Obuasi mines, 405, 417
Oda district, Akim, 401
Odikro (headman), 24n, 93
Odumase district, Manya Krobe (Adangme), 383
Odunsini at funeral, 122
Offinso district, 378
Offuman district, 15, 150, 228, 247, 320
Oil-shale, Sinai: rôle of, in Moses story, 81n
Okomfo ("possessed" person), 17, 18, 59, 61, 62, 70, 74, 92, 104
Okra ("cat" or "soul"), 314
Okuampah, Emmanuel, 15, 50
Okumaga (deity), 48
Okyeame, 18, 48, 99, 102, 129, 311

Oman, omanhene, 18, 23, 23n
Onyame (supreme god), 18, 47–8
Oracular utterances, explanation of frequent wisdom of, 57–8
Organic illness, as abisa complaint, 117–19
Osani (natural death, no witchcraft involved), 228
Osudoku (Shai Plain), fairy cults of, 44

"Pains all over" symptom, 107, 111, 113, 114, 129, 159, 165, 178, 190, 197, 282, 294, 442
Palm-wine tapping, as occupation, 94
Palpitations, anxiety causing, 113, 114, 115, 128
Paranoid attitudes, universality of, 87, 111; "normal" and "morbid", 296–7; paranoid reaction, (cases 72 to 79), 296–314
Paranoid schizophrenia, a rare case of (Ashanti woman), 463
Paranormal faculties, possessed persons, 57, 58
Patients, absent, abisa on behalf of, 127
Patrilineal systems, Adangme and Ga, 25
Paul, the Apostle, on "gibberish" of alleged prophets, 58
Peace-making day, unknown in Ashanti, 113
Persecution feelings, suggested basis of, 28
Philip, baptism of eunuch by (dissociation episode), 85
Photographing at shrines, 104
Physical illness, mental disorders following (cases 94 to 104), 353–73
"Pneuma", spirit (New Testament), significance of, 79
Possession: and early Christianity, 78 seqq., 84, 85; "fit" of described, 56–7; by woman auxiliaries to priest (in Ghana, outside Ashanti), 88. See Spirits
Prasu district (Kwahu), 417
"Pregnancy doesn't grow", (post-menopause abisa), 106, 126, 150; pregnancy hazards as complaint, 121-2
Priest-charlatan, example of, 74–6
"Primitive people" defined, 148n

472

Index